W9-CRV-273

SPECTROMETRIC TECHNIQUES

VOLUME IV

Contributors

W. R. HUNTER

EDMOND MURAD

JAMES J. VALENTINI

SPECTROMETRIC TECHNIQUES

Edited by GEORGE A. VANASSE

Optical Physics Division
Air Force Geophysics Laboratory
Hanscom Air Force Base
Bedford, Massachusetts

VOLUME IV

ACADEMIC PRESS, INC. 1985

(*Harcourt Brace Jovanovich, Publishers*)

Orlando San Diego New York London
Toronto Montreal Sydney Tokyo

ACADEMIC PRESS, INC.
Orlando, Florida 32887

United Kingdom Edition published by
ACADEMIC PRESS INC. (LONDON) LTD.
24–28 Oval Road, London NW1 7DX

Library of Congress Cataloging in Publication Data
(Revised for vol. 4)
Main entry under title:

Spectrometric techniques.

Includes bibliographies and indexes.
1. Spectrum analysis–Collected works. 2. Spectrum analysis–Instruments–Collected works. I. Vanasse, George A. II. Baker, Doran J.
QC450 535.8'4 76-13949
ISBN 0–12–710404–6 (v. 4)

PRINTED IN THE UNITED STATES OF AMERICA

85 86 87 88 9 8 7 6 5 4 3 2 1

Contents

CONTRIBUTORS vii

PREFACE ix

CONTENTS OF PREVIOUS VOLUMES xi

Chapter 1 **Coherent Anti-Stokes Raman Spectroscopy**

James J. Valentini

1.1 Introduction 2
1.2 Phenomenology of CARS 7
1.3 The Practice and Application of CARS 25
1.4 Conclusion 59
References 59

Chapter 2 **Diffraction Gratings and Mountings for the Vacuum Ultraviolet Spectral Region**

W. R. Hunter

2.1 Introduction 63
2.2 Diffraction Gratings 65
2.3 Grating Mountings 146
References 175

Chapter 3 **Mass Spectrometric Techniques**

Edmond Murad

List of Abbreviations 182
3.1 Introduction 182
3.2 Ion Sources 183
3.3 Major Types of Mass Spectrometers 197
3.4 Detectors 209
3.5 Uses of Mass Spectrometry 216
References 240

INDEX 253

Contributors

Numbers in parentheses indicate the pages on which the authors' contributions begin.

W. R. HUNTER* (63), Naval Research Laboratory, Washington, D.C. 20375-5000

EDMOND MURAD (181), Air Force Geophysics Laboratory, Hanscom Air Force Base, Bedford, Massachusetts 01731

JAMES J. VALENTINI† (1), Chemistry Division, University of California, Los Alamos National Laboratory, Los Alamos, New Mexico 87545

* Present address: Sachs/Freeman Associates, Inc., Bowie, Maryland 20715.

† Present address: Department of Chemistry, University of California, Irvine, California 92717.

Preface

The present volume covers three widely diversified fields of spectrometric techniques. We decided to include a chapter on coherent anti-Stokes Raman spectroscopy (CARS) since this area is expanding very rapidly and also because of its similarity in optical implementation to the phase conjugation technique using degenerate four-wave mixing. It is true that the literature abounds with articles and monographs on grating spectrometers. However, we felt that there was a lot of material on UV and soft x-ray grating spectrometers that should be pulled together, particularly in the synchrotron radiation field; therefore a chapter on grating spectrometers was deemed appropriate. The chapter on mass spectrometry departs from all other articles in this and previous volumes by dealing with a spectrometric technique which does not involve "light." This chapter covers in detail sources, types of spectrometers, detectors, and uses of mass spectrometry. It was the editor's intention to follow this chapter with one on Fourier transform mass spectrometry (FTMS); however, time precluded including the latter topic in the present volume.

Contents of Previous Volumes

Volume I

Hajime Sakai, High Resolving Power Fourier Spectroscopy

Doran Baker, Field-Widened Interferometers for Fourier Spectroscopy

Robert J. Bell, Applications of Fourier Transform Spectroscopy

E. Ray Huppi, Cryogenic Instrumentation

John A. Decker, Jr., Hadamard-Transform Spectroscopy

Randall E. Murphy, Measurements of Infrared Transient Phenomena

Thomas P. Condron, Calibration Techniques

D. J. Lovell, Performance and Characteristics of Commercially Available Instruments

Volume II

Guy Guelachvili, Distortions in Fourier Spectra and Diagnosis

James B. Breckinridge and Rudolf A. Schindler, First-Order Optical Design for Fourier Spectrometers

Alexander S. Zachor, Isaiah Coleman, and William G. Mankin, Effects of Drive Nonlinearities in Fourier Spectroscopy

H. R. Schlossberg and P. L. Kelley, Infrared Spectroscopy Using Tunable Lasers

Leon Heroux, Absolute Photon Counting in the Ultraviolet

Volume III

David G. Murcray and Frank J. Murcray, Experimental Atmospheric Spectroscopy

Rudolf A. Hanel, Planetary Exploration with Spaceborn Michelson Interferometers in the Thermal Infrared

F. W. Taylor, Pressure Modulator Radiometry

Jyrki K. Kauppinen, Fourier Self-Deconvolution in Spectroscopy

Samuel J. Howard, Improved Resolution of Spectral Lines Using Minimum Negativity and Other Constraints

Chapter **1**

Coherent Anti-Stokes Raman Spectroscopy*

JAMES J. VALENTINI†

CHEMISTRY DIVISION
UNIVERSITY OF CALIFORNIA
LOS ALAMOS NATIONAL LABORATORY
LOS ALAMOS, NEW MEXICO

1.1. Introduction 2
A. Nature of This Review 2
B. The Raman Effect 2
C. CARS 5
1.2. Phenomenology of CARS 7
A. Electric-Field-Induced Polarization 7
B. Generation of an Electromagnetic Wave 10
C. Raman Resonance in $\chi^{(3)}$ 12
D. Symmetry Properties of $\chi^{(3)}$ 17
E. Selection Rules 18
F. Signal Intensity 19
G. Spectral Line Shape 21
1.3. The Practice and Application of CARS 25
A. General Applicability 25
B. Experimental Apparatus 26
C. Background-Free Techniques 35
D. Resonance CARS 44
E. High-Resolution Spectroscopy 46
F. Combustion Diagnostics 50
G. Time-Resolved Spectroscopy 53
H. Other Applications 56
1.4. Conclusion 59
References 59

* This work was performed under the auspices of the U.S. Department of Energy.
† Present address: Department of Chemistry, University of California, Irvine, California.

ISBN 0-12-710404-6

1.1. Introduction

A. Nature of This Review

This chapter presents a brief review of the phenomenology and application of coherent anti-Stokes Raman spectroscopy (CARS), the most commonly used of several coherent, nonlinear, optical techniques that exploit the Raman effect. It is not our purpose to provide a fully detailed formulation of the theory of CARS or a complete review of the practice of the technique. It is beyond the scope of this review to completely develop the theoretical basis of coherent anti-Stokes Raman spectroscopy, and even a simple compilation of all the demonstrated applications of CARS would consume a major fraction of the space allocated for this chapter. Rather, we wish to provide an introduction to and overview of the field, with sufficient references to original work on the theory and use of CARS to afford the reader an opportunity to explore more fully all aspects of this useful spectroscopic method. We hope that this chapter will serve as a compact reference for current practitioners of the technique, as well as a guidebook for the uninitiated. The reader is advised to consult other reviews (Druet and Taran, 1981; Nibler and Knighten, 1977; Levenson and Song, 1980; Esherick and Owyoung, 1982) and monographs (Harvey, 1981; Eesley, 1981; Bloembergen, 1965) for a more comprehensive view of all coherent Raman spectroscopies. This chapter was completed in December, 1982, and reviews the literature published through that date.

B. The Raman Effect

In 1928 C. V. Raman observed that when dust-free liquids or gases were illuminated by light of a particular wavelength the scattered radiation had not only the wavelength of the incident light (Rayleigh scattering) but also light of different wavelengths (Raman, 1928). In the same year Landsberg and Mandelstam observed this phenomenon in transparent solids and reported the light scattering with change of frequency in quartz (Landsberg and Mandelstam, 1928). This Raman effect is an inelastic photon-scattering process, in which an atom or molecule absorbs one photon while simultaneously emitting another photon at a different frequency. The emitted photon is at a frequency ω_0, which can be greater or less than the frequency ω_1 of the absorbed photon:

$$\omega_0 = \omega_1 \pm \Delta\omega, \tag{1.1}$$

where $\Delta\omega > 0$.

The frequency shifts $\Delta\omega$ are characteristic of the material responsible for the light scattering and are found to correspond to the energy differences between rotational and vibrational levels in molecules (or, less frequently, electronic levels in atoms and molecules):

$$\Delta\omega = (E_r - E_g)/\hbar = \omega_{rg}, \tag{1.2}$$

where r and g identify the states with energies E_r and E_g. Figures 1.1 and 1.2 show energy-level diagrams for Raman scattering. When $\omega_0 = \omega_1 - \omega_{rg}$ (Fig. 1.1), the process is referred to as Stokes scattering, and when $\omega_0 = \omega_1 + \omega_{rg}$, it is termed anti-Stokes scattering.

Because the frequency shifts of the Raman-scattered light are the frequency differences between molecular states, the Raman effect can be used as a spectroscopic tool. This was immediately recognized by early investigators of the Raman effect, and for more than 50 years Raman spectroscopy has been an important method for the investigation of molecular structure (Long, 1977; Weber, 1979). It is particularly useful in that it allows observation of transitions between molecular states for which the dipole matrix element

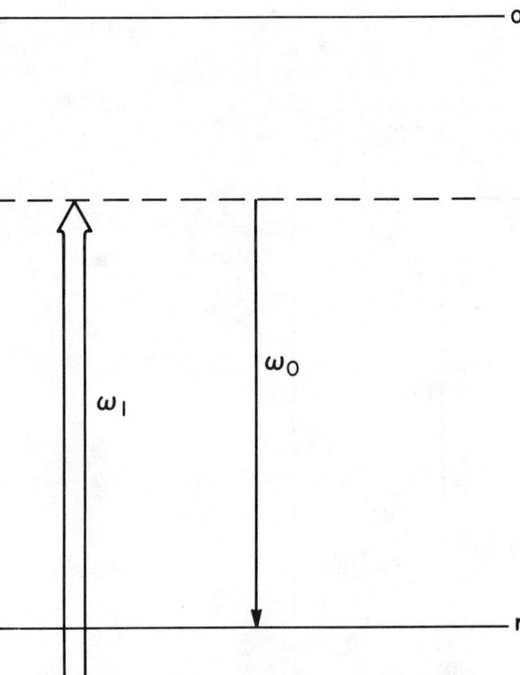

FIG. 1.1. Energy-level schematic for Stokes Raman scattering. Dashed line indicates a virtual electronic state.

vanishes, for example, transitions involving totally symmetric vibrations and rotational transitions in molecules having vanishing dipole moments. As a result, Raman spectroscopy has proved to be a valuable complement to infrared spectroscopy (Herzberg, 1945).

Unfortunately, the inelastic light scattering of the Raman effect is extremely inefficient, and low intensity has remained a problem in Raman spectroscopy, even with the use of laser sources for sample illumination. Raman cross sections are generally 10^{-30} to 10^{-31} cm^2 sr^{-1}, and for a typical Raman experiment with a gas at 1 torr pressure only about 1 incident photon in 10^{15} will be observed as an inelastically scatterred photon. Even with intense cw ion lasers having outputs of $\sim 10^{19}$ photons/s the Raman scattering would yield only $\sim 10^4$ photons/s. Using a 1-MW peak power, 10-ns pulse duration pulsed laser as the excitation source would produce only about 20 Raman-scattered photons per pulse. This low conversion efficiency means that sample luminescence and laser-induced fluorescence can often mask the

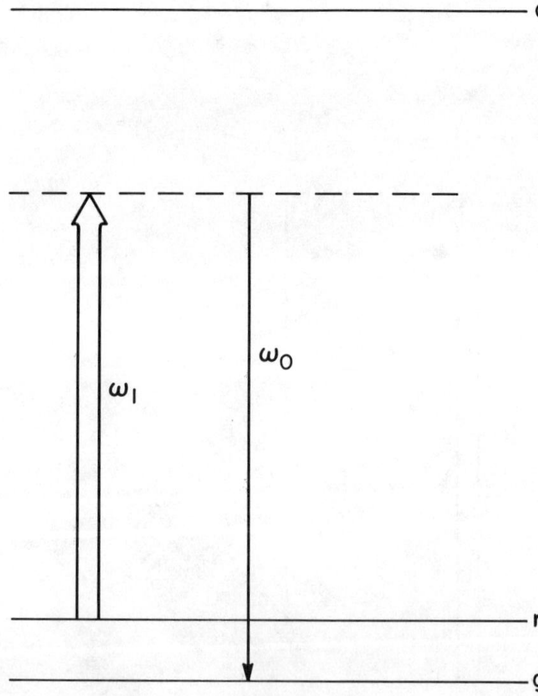

FIG. 1.2. Energy-level schematic for anti-Stokes Raman scattering. Dashed line indicates a virtual electronic state.

Raman spectra, and Raman investigation of transient phenomena is particularly difficfilt.

C. CARS

Coherent anti-Stokes Raman spectroscopy (CARS)† is a relatively new technique that overcomes many of the problems connected with the low efficiency of spontaneous Raman scattering and has expanded the range of application of Raman spectroscopy in physics, chemistry, and biology. It is one of several coherent Raman spectroscopic techniques that are based on the existence of Raman resonances in three-wave mixing. In three-wave mixing electric fields at frequencies ω_1, ω_2, and ω_3 are mixed to produce a fourth field at frequency ω_0. The amplitude of the field at ω_0 is given by

$$\mathbf{E}(\omega_0) \propto \boldsymbol{\chi}^{(3)}\mathbf{E}(\omega_1)\mathbf{E}(\omega_2)\mathbf{E}(\omega_3), \tag{1.3}$$

where $\boldsymbol{\chi}^{(3)}$ depends on the frequencies ω_0, ω_1, ω_2, and ω_3, as well as on the material in which the mixing takes place. The mixing is coherent since the field at ω_0 is in phase with the fields at ω_1, ω_2, and ω_3. The mixing is nonlinear, specifically third-order, since $\mathbf{E}(\omega_0)$ is proportional to the product of three amplitudes. The electric fields at ω_1, ω_2, and ω_3 are produced by laser beams and hence the generated field at ω_0 is also a laser beam.

For the process known as CARS the frequencies are related by

$$\omega_0 = \omega_1 - \omega_2 + \omega_3, \tag{1.4}$$

where $\omega_1 > \omega_2$. When $\omega_1 - \omega_2 = \omega_{rg}$, where, as in Eq. (1.2), $\hbar\omega_{rg}$ is the energy difference between two molecular levels connected by a Raman transition, this nonlinear mixing is greatly enhanced. These Raman resonances constitute a CARS spectrum, which is scanned by varying ω_1 and/or ω_2 and is detected via the coherently generated signal at $\omega_0 = \omega_3 + \omega_{rg}$. In almost all CARS experiments $\omega_1 = \omega_3$ and ω_1 is held fixed in frequency while ω_2 is scanned. Equation (1.4) thus becomes

$$\omega_0 = 2\omega_1 - \omega_2, \tag{1.5}$$

and at a Raman resonance

$$\omega_0 = \omega_1 + \omega_{rg} \tag{1.6}$$

and

$$\omega_2 = \omega_1 - \omega_{rg}. \tag{1.7}$$

Therefore, ω_1 is often referred to as the pump or laser frequency, ω_2 the

† In this review we will use the term coherent anti-Stokes Raman *scattering* to describe the phenomenon that gives rise to the spectroscopic technique coherent anti-Stokes Raman *spectroscopy*. For convenience the acronym CARS will be used for both.

Stokes frequency, and ω_0 the anti-Stokes frequency. An energy-level schematic for the CARS process is shown in Fig. 1.3. Because the anti-Stokes signal beam at ω_0 is generated by a *coherent* mixing of ω_1 and ω_2, it is characterized by a high intensity, often several orders of magnitude greater than that of spontaneous Raman signals, and a small divergence; i.e., it is laserlike.

Coherent anti-Stokes Raman scattering was first observed by Terhune (1963) as a by-product of stimulated Raman scattering. The nonlinear mixing process responsible for the effect was explained (Bloembergen and Shen, 1964) and experimentally verified (Maker and Terhune, 1965; Yajima and Takatsuji, 1964) shortly thereafter. The early nonlinear Raman experiments were carried out with ruby lasers generating ω_1 and ruby-pumped stimulated Raman scattering in liquids producing ω_2. This arrangement precluded

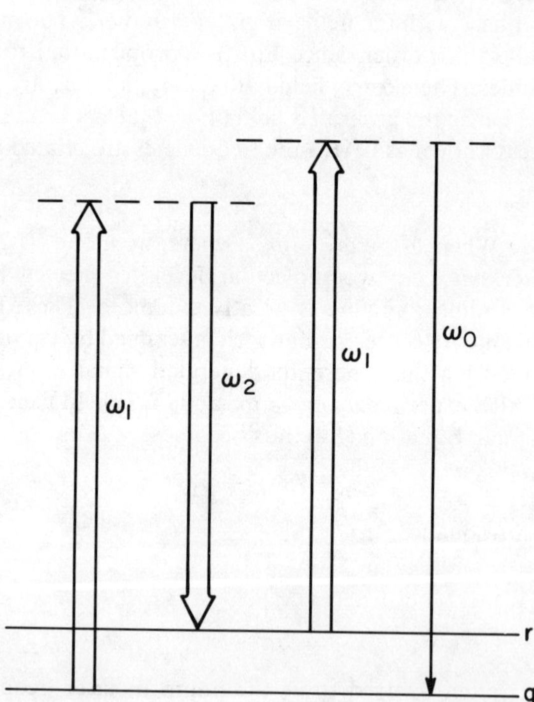

FIG. 1.3. Energy-level schematic for coherent anti-Stokes Raman scattering. Dashed lines indicate virtual electronic states.

the continuous variation of $\omega_1 - \omega_2$ necessary for coherent anti-Stokes Raman *spectroscopy*. Thus, although the phenomenon of coherent anti-Stokes Raman scattering was understood in the early 1960s, utilization of this coherent Raman effect for spectroscopy did not develop until reliable tunable lasers became available almost 10 years later. With the development of tunable laser sources came a rapid development of coherent anti-Stokes Raman scattering as a method for the spectroscopy of gases, liquids, solids, mixtures, and solutions. Coherent anti-Stokes Raman spectroscopy now has been applied to very high-resolution Raman spectroscopy, combustion, photochemistry, plasmas, biochemistry, kinetics, and molecular beams.

1.2. Phenomenology of CARS

A. Electric-Field-Induced Polarization

The electric dipole moment induced in a molecule or atom by an electric field $\mathbf{E}$ can be expanded in powers of the field

$$\boldsymbol{\mu} = \boldsymbol{\alpha}\mathbf{E} + \boldsymbol{\beta}\mathbf{E}^2 + \boldsymbol{\gamma}\mathbf{E}^3 + \cdots \tag{1.8}$$

(Bogaard and Orr, 1975). The coefficients $\boldsymbol{\alpha}$, $\boldsymbol{\beta}$, $\boldsymbol{\gamma}$, etc., are tensor quantities to account for the fact that the induced dipole vector may point in a direction different from that of the electric field vector. The polarizability $\boldsymbol{\alpha}$ is of rank 2, and the hyperpolarizabilities $\boldsymbol{\beta}, \boldsymbol{\gamma}, \ldots$ are of rank 3, 4, ..., respectively. As a consequence of the dipole moment induced in its constituent atoms or molecules, a medium displays a bulk polarization. The polarization $\mathbf{P}$ is given by

$$\mathbf{P} = \boldsymbol{\chi}^{(1)}\mathbf{E} + \boldsymbol{\chi}^{(2)}\mathbf{E}^2 + \boldsymbol{\chi}^{(3)}\mathbf{E}^3 + \cdots, \tag{1.9}$$

where $\boldsymbol{\chi}^{(1)}, \boldsymbol{\chi}^{(2)}, \boldsymbol{\chi}^{(3)}, \ldots$ are the first-order, second-order, third-order, ... dielectric susceptibility tensors.

The polarization $\mathbf{P}$ is related to the induced dipole $\boldsymbol{\mu}$ by

$$\mathbf{P} = N\zeta\boldsymbol{\mu}, \tag{1.10}$$

where N is the particle density and ζ a factor that relates the applied macroscopic field to the field acting on the individual particles (Armstrong *et al.*, 1962; Kittel, 1971; Pantell and Puthoff, 1969). For materials for which the optical index of refraction is near unity, such as gases, the macroscopic and microscopic fields are nearly identical, and

$$\mathbf{P} = N\boldsymbol{\mu}; \tag{1.11}$$

moreover,

$$\boldsymbol{\chi}^{(1)} = N\boldsymbol{\alpha}, \qquad \boldsymbol{\chi}^{(2)} = N\boldsymbol{\beta}, \qquad \text{and} \qquad \boldsymbol{\chi}^{(3)} = N\boldsymbol{\gamma}. \tag{1.12}$$

It is important to emphasize this connection between the macroscopic polarization and the induced dipole, and between the dielectric susceptibility tensors and the molecular polarizabilities, because a theoretical description of the effect of the applied fields deals with the molecular properties, while experimental measurements are of necessity macroscopic.

The susceptibility $\boldsymbol{\chi}^{(1)}$ is responsible for classical linear optical phenomena, including refraction, Rayleigh scattering, and normal Raman scattering. The susceptibility $\boldsymbol{\chi}^{(2)}$ gives rise to second-harmonic generation, sum and difference frequency generation, hyper-Rayleigh scattering, and other effects. In isotropic media, for example, a liquid or a gas, in which the macroscopic dielectric properties always exhibit inversion symmetry, $\boldsymbol{\chi}^{(2)} = 0$ (Bloembergen, 1965). It is $\boldsymbol{\chi}^{(3)}$ that concerns us here, for it is responsible for CARS as well as other effects such as third-harmonic generation. The susceptibility $\boldsymbol{\chi}^{(3)}$ is nonvanishing even for isotropic media. We limit our consideration then to the $\boldsymbol{\chi}^{(3)}$ term in Eq. (1.9) and write

$$\mathbf{P}^{(3)}(\mathbf{r}, t) = \boldsymbol{\chi}^{(3)}\mathbf{E}(\mathbf{r}, t)\mathbf{E}(\mathbf{r}, t)\mathbf{E}(\mathbf{r}, t), \tag{1.13}$$

where the spatial and temporal variation of the fields and induced polarization is made explicit.

We shall assume that the electric field is made up of harmonic components that are plane waves:

$$\mathbf{E}(\mathbf{r}, t) = \frac{1}{2}\sum_{j=1}^{3}[\mathbf{E}(\omega_j, \mathbf{r})\exp[i(\mathbf{k}_j \cdot \mathbf{r} - \omega_j t)] + \text{c.c.}], \tag{1.14}$$

where $k_j = |\mathbf{k}_j| = \omega_j n_j/c$, n_j is the index of refraction at ω_j, and c is the velocity of light. Coherent anti-Stokes Raman scattering and other three-wave mixing processes involve up to three distinct field frequencies j, so the summation in Eq. (1.14) is over $j = 1$ to 3. Equation (1.14) can be more conveniently written as

$$\mathbf{E}(\mathbf{r}, t) = \frac{1}{2}\sum_{\substack{j=-3 \\ j \neq 0}}^{3} \mathbf{E}(\omega_j, \mathbf{r})\exp[i(\mathbf{k}_j \cdot \mathbf{r} - \omega_j t)], \tag{1.15}$$

where $\omega_{-j} \equiv -\omega_j$, $k_{-j} \equiv -k_j$, and $\mathbf{E}(\omega_{-j}, \mathbf{r}) \equiv \mathbf{E}^*(\omega_j, \mathbf{r})$.† Combining Eqs.

† While this is a convenient formulation of the Fourier expansion of $\mathbf{E}(\mathbf{r}, t)$ and $\mathbf{P}(\mathbf{r}, t)$, it must be remembered that the real field $\mathbf{E}(\mathbf{r}, t)$ at frequency $|\omega_j|$ is given by $\mathbf{E}(\mathbf{r}, t) = \frac{1}{2}[\mathbf{E}(\omega_j, \mathbf{r})\exp[i(\mathbf{k}_j \cdot \mathbf{r} - \omega_j t)] + \mathbf{E}(\omega_{-j}, \mathbf{r})\exp[i(\mathbf{k}_{-j} \cdot \mathbf{r} - \omega_j t)]$, and similarly for the real polarization at $|\omega_j|$.

(1.13) and (1.15) we have

$$\mathbf{P}^{(3)}(\mathbf{r}, t) = \frac{1}{8} \sum_{\substack{i,j,k=-3 \\ i,j,k \neq 0}}^{3} \boldsymbol{\chi}^{(3)} \mathbf{E}(\omega_i, \mathbf{r}) \mathbf{E}(\omega_j, \mathbf{r}) \mathbf{E}(\omega_k, \mathbf{r}) \times \exp[i(\mathbf{k}_i + \mathbf{k}_j + \mathbf{k}_k) \cdot \mathbf{r}] \exp[-i(\omega_i + \omega_j + \omega_k)t]. \quad (1.16)$$

We see that the polarization $\mathbf{P}^{(3)}$ will have frequency components at

$$\omega_0 = \omega_i + \omega_j + \omega_k, \quad (1.17)$$

where ω_i, ω_j, and ω_k can be positive or negative. Thus $\mathbf{P}^{(3)}$ will have many frequency components, including $3\omega_1$, $3\omega_2$, and $3\omega_3$, which correspond to third-harmonic generation, $\omega_1 + \omega_2 + \omega_3$, giving frequency summation, as well as a CARS component at $\omega_1 - \omega_2 + \omega_3$, where $\omega_1 > \omega_2$. Note that $\boldsymbol{\chi}^{(3)}$ is a function of ω_0, ω_i, ω_j, and ω_k, and therefore cannot be removed from the summation in Eq. (1.16).

Expressing $\mathbf{P}^{(3)}(\mathbf{r}, t)$ in terms of its Fourier components we have

$$\mathbf{P}^{(3)}(\mathbf{r}, t) = \frac{1}{2} \sum_{\substack{i,j,k=-3 \\ i,j,k \neq 0}}^{3} \mathbf{P}^{(3)}(\omega_0, \mathbf{r}) \exp[-i(\omega_0 t)], \quad (1.18)$$

where ω_0 is given by Eq. (1.17). Combining Eqs. (1.16) and (1.18), we can relate the Fourier components of the polarization to those of the electric fields:

$$\mathbf{P}^{(3)}(\omega_0, \mathbf{r}) = \tfrac{1}{4} \boldsymbol{\chi}^{(3)} \mathbf{E}(\omega_i, \mathbf{r}) \mathbf{E}(\omega_j, \mathbf{r}) \mathbf{E}(\omega_k, \mathbf{r}) \times \exp[i(\mathbf{k}_i + \mathbf{k}_j + \mathbf{k}_k) \cdot \mathbf{r}]. \quad (1.19)$$

We can rewrite this expression in terms of the Cartesian components of the vectors $\mathbf{P}^{(3)}(\omega_0, \mathbf{r})$ and $\mathbf{E}(\omega_i, \mathbf{r})$ and the tensor $\boldsymbol{\chi}^{(3)}$ as

$$P_\rho^{(3)}(\omega_0, \mathbf{r}) = (6/n!) \tfrac{1}{4} \chi_{\rho\sigma\tau\nu}^{(3)}(-\omega_0, \omega_i, \omega_j, \omega_k) \times E_\sigma(\omega_i, \mathbf{r}) E_\tau(\omega_j, \mathbf{r}) E_\nu(\omega_k, \mathbf{r}) \exp[i(\mathbf{k}_i + \mathbf{k}_j + \mathbf{k}_k) \cdot \mathbf{r}], \quad (1.20)$$

where $\rho, \sigma, \tau, \nu = x, y$, or z. The $\boldsymbol{\chi}^{(3)}$ notation of Bloembergen (1965) is used such that $\boldsymbol{\chi}^{(3)}(-\omega_0, \omega_i, \omega_j, \omega_k)$ represents the susceptibility for the process in which a polarization is induced at $\omega_0 = \omega_i + \omega_j + \omega_k$. While the ordering of the frequencies ω_i, ω_j, ω_k or the Cartesian indices σ, τ, ν cannot be permuted without altering $\chi_{\rho\sigma\tau\nu}^{(3)}$, permutation of the pairs (i, σ), (j, τ), and (k, ν), which corresponds to permuting the order of the electric fields in Eq. (1.20), does leave $\chi_{\rho\sigma\tau\nu}^{(3)}$ unchanged. The factor $6/n!$, with n equal to the number of identical frequencies, accounts for the fact that each such distinct permutation contributes to the polarization $P_\rho^{(3)}(\omega_0, r)$.

For CARS we usually have $\omega_1 = \omega_3$ and $\omega_0 = 2\omega_1 - \omega_2$, in which case Eq. (1.20) becomes

$$P_\rho^{(3)}(\omega_0, \mathbf{r}) = \tfrac{3}{4}\chi_{\rho\sigma\tau\nu}^{(3)}(-\omega_0, \omega_1, -\omega_2, \omega_1) \times E_\sigma(\omega_1, \mathbf{r})E_\tau^*(\omega_2, \mathbf{r})E_\nu(\omega_1, \mathbf{r}) \exp[i(2\mathbf{k}_1 + \mathbf{k}_2)\cdot\mathbf{r}]. \quad (1.21)$$

Note that Eqs. (1.20) and (1.21) are in effect definitions of $\boldsymbol{\chi}^{(3)}$, and the reader is cautioned that there is no universally accepted definition of $\boldsymbol{\chi}^{(3)}$ in the nonlinear optics literature. Another formulation of Eq. (1.20) is (Maker and Terhune, 1965)

$$P_\rho^{(3)}(\omega_0, \mathbf{r}) = (6/n!)\chi_{\rho\sigma\tau\nu}^{(3)}(-\omega_0, \omega_i, \omega_j, \omega_k)\cdots, \quad (1.22)$$

which incorporates into $\chi^{(3)}$ the factor of $\frac{1}{4}$ in Eq. (1.20). Taran prefers yet another definition (Druet and Taran, 1981; Regnier *et al.*, 1974):

$$P_\rho^{(3)}(\omega_0, \mathbf{r}) = \tfrac{1}{4}\chi_{\rho\sigma\tau\nu}^{(3)}(-\omega_0, \omega_i, \omega_j, \omega_k)\cdots, \quad (1.23)$$

which incorporates the $6/n!$ factor in Eq. (1.20) into $\boldsymbol{\chi}^{(3)}$. These and other definitions of $\boldsymbol{\chi}^{(3)}$ have been discussed and reconciled by Orr *et al.* (Orr and Ward, 1971; Bogaard and Orr, 1975).

B. Generation of an Electromagnetic Wave

The nonlinear polarization $\mathbf{P}^{(3)}(\mathbf{r}, t)$ at frequency ω_0 acts as a source term in Maxwell's equations to produce an electromagnetic wave $\mathbf{E}(\mathbf{r}, t)$ at ω_0, where

$$\left[\nabla^2 - \frac{n^2}{c^2}\frac{\partial^2}{\partial t^2}\right]\mathbf{E}(\mathbf{r}, t) = \frac{4\pi}{c^2}\frac{\partial^2}{\partial t^2}\mathbf{P}^{(3)}(\mathbf{r}, t) \quad (1.24)$$

for a nonmagnetic, homogeneous, and isotropic medium (Druet and Taran, 1981). Here n is the index of refraction and c the velocity of light. Substitution of Eq. (1.16) into Eq. (1.24), with $\omega_0 = 2\omega_1 - \omega_2$, yields a relation for the field amplitude of the CARS signal beam ω_0 in terms of the field amplitudes of the pump ω_1 and Stokes ω_2 driving beams. In solving Eq. (1.24) we will take the driving fields to be plane light waves with parallel field vectors and with parallel propagation vectors aligned along the space-fixed z axis. In this case, as we shall see later in discussing the symmetry properties of $\boldsymbol{\chi}^{(3)}$, the vector direction of the source polarization $\mathbf{P}^{(3)}(\mathbf{r}, t)$, and thus of the generated field at ω_0, is also parallel to the vectors of the driving fields at ω_1 and ω_2. We can thus neglect the vector nature of tle electric fields, as well as the tensor nature of $\boldsymbol{\chi}^{(3)}$, and Eq. (1.21) becomes

$$P^{(3)}(\omega_0, z) = \tfrac{3}{4}\chi^{(3)}(-\omega_0, \omega_1, -\omega_2, \omega_1)E^2(\omega_1)E^*(\omega_2) \times \exp[i(2k_1 - k_2)z], \quad (1.25)$$

and the induced polarization at ω_0 becomes

$$P^{(3)}(z, t) = \tfrac{3}{8}\chi^{(3)}(-\omega_0, \omega_1, -\omega_2, \omega_1)E^2(\omega_1)E^*(\omega_2) \times \exp\{i[(2k_1 - k_2)z - \omega_0 t]\} + \text{c.c.} \tag{1.26}$$

Equations (1.26) and (1.24) lead to a solution for $\mathbf{E}(\mathbf{r}, t)$. Our boundary conditions are that our sample is a gas occupying the space $z = 0$ to $z = L$, and we neglect dispersion in our sample, so $n(\omega_1) = n(\omega_2) = n(\omega_0) = 1$. We find (Regnier *et al.*, 1974; Druet and Taran, 1981; Nibler and Knighten, 1977) that the generated wave at ω_0 is also a plane wave traveling in the z direction:

$$\mathbf{E}(\mathbf{r}, t) = E(z, t) = \tfrac{1}{2}\{E(\omega_0, z)\exp[i(k_0 z - \omega t)] + \text{c.c.}\}, \tag{1.27}$$

with

$$E(\omega_0, z) = \frac{-3i\pi\omega_0}{2c} E^2(\omega_1)E^*(\omega_2)\int_0^L \chi^{(3)} \exp(i\,\Delta k\, z)\, dz, \tag{1.28}$$

where $\Delta k = 2k_1 - k_2 - k_0$ and for simplicity we have dropped the ω notation in $\chi^{(3)}$. Since we have neglected dispersion in our gas sample $k_i = |\mathbf{k}_i| = \omega_i n_i/c = \omega_i/c$, and we have for the exponential

$$\Delta k = 2k_1 - k_2 - k_0 = 2\omega_1 - \omega_2 - \omega_0 = 0. \tag{1.29}$$

When $\Delta k = 0$ the beams are referred to as phase-matched. Therefore, we have

$$E(\omega_0, L) = (-3i\pi\omega_0/2c)E^2(\omega_1)E^*(\omega_2)\chi^{(3)}L. \tag{1.30}$$

Now, using the fact that the intensity (power per unit area) is related to the field amplitude,

$$I(\omega) = (c/8\pi)|E|^2, \tag{1.31}$$

we find

$$I_0(L) = (12\pi^2\omega_0/c^2)^2 I_1^2 I_2 |\chi^{(3)}|^2 L^2, \tag{1.32}$$

where I_i is the intensity of the beam at frequency ω_i.

This result illustrates the characteristic features of coherent anti-Stokes Raman scattering. The signal intensity scales as the product of the Stokes laser intensity I_2 and the square of the pump laser intensity I_1. Hence CARS signals are enhanced considerably by using pulsed lasers of high peak power, even though such lasers have much lower average power than many cw lasers. The intensity I_0 is proportional to $|\chi^{(3)}|^2$ and hence [cf. Eq. (1.12)] proportional to the square of the sample density.

Equation (1.32) also shows that the CARS signal intensity should grow as the square of the sample length indefinitely. This behavior is a consequence of our assumption that the dispersion of the (gas) sample is zero. If we

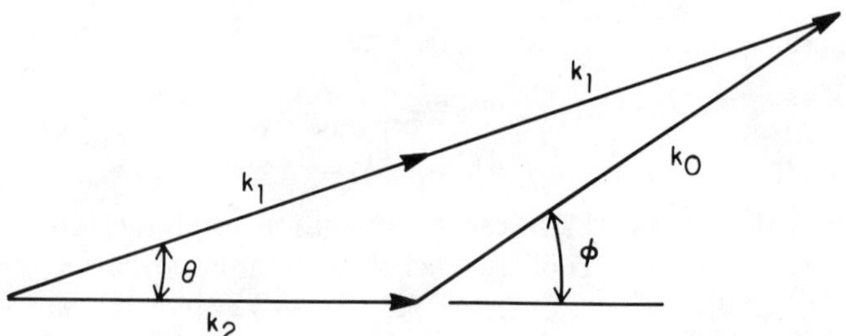

FIG. 1.4. Coherent anti-Stokes Raman scattering phase-matching diagram.

explicitly take account of the index of refraction variation in the medium we find that the integral in Eq. (1.28) is

$$\int_0^L \chi^{(3)} \exp(i\,\Delta k\, z)\,dz = \chi^{(3)} L \frac{\sin(\Delta k\, L/2)}{\Delta k\, L/2}. \tag{1.33}$$

Therefore we have

$$I_0(L) = \left(\frac{12\pi^2\omega_0}{c^2}\right)^2 I_1^2 I_2 |\chi^{(3)}|^2 L^2 \left[\frac{\sin(\Delta k\, L/2)}{\Delta k\, L/2}\right]^2, \tag{1.34}$$

and I_0 will vary sinusoidally with path length L. We can define a coherence L_c as the path length to reach maximum signal, i.e.,

$$L_c = \pi/\Delta k. \tag{1.35}$$

The quantity L_c is a function of the dispersion of the gas and is given by (Hauchecorne *et al.*, 1971)

$$L_c = \frac{\pi c}{(\omega_1 - \omega_2)^2}\left[2\frac{\partial n}{\partial \omega} + \omega_1 \frac{\partial^2 n}{\partial \omega^2}\right]^{-1}. \tag{1.36}$$

The coherence length for most gases is of the order of 100 cm at STP and is inversely proportional to density. Since the term in square brackets in Eq. (1.34) is nearly equal to 1 for $L < \sim L_c/3$, Eq. (1.32) is a good approximation to the signal intensity for almost all gas samples usually encountered.

Because of the much larger wavelength dispersion in condensed phases, L_c is of the order of millimeters, and the maximum CARS intensity allowed by Eq. (1.34) becomes coherence length limited. To increase L_c the ω_1 and ω_2 beams are crossed at an angle θ, as shown in Fig. 1.4, such that $\Delta k = 0$. This angle θ is called the phase-matching angle and is of the order of 1–3°. In condensed phases the CARS signal generation consequently becomes limited by the finite spatial overlap of the crossed ω_1 and ω_2 beams.

C. Raman Resonance in $\chi^{(3)}$

As discussed in Subsection 1.1.C and illustrated in Fig. 1.3, the coherent anti-Stokes Raman scattering process that generates the anti-Stokes signal beam at $\omega_0 = \omega_1 - \omega_2 + \omega_3$ is greatly enhanced when $\omega_1 - \omega_2 = \omega_{rg}$, the frequency of a Raman allowed transition between molecular energy states g and r. This resonance behavior, which makes coherent anti-Stokes Raman scattering a useful spectroscopic tool, arises from Raman resonances in $\boldsymbol{\chi}^{(3)}$. The source of these Raman resonances in $\boldsymbol{\chi}^{(3)}$ becomes clear when we consider the detailed molecular behavior of $\boldsymbol{\gamma}$, the third-order molecular hyperpolarizability, which, as discussed in Subsection 1.2.A, is the molecular-level equivalent of the macroscopic quantity $\boldsymbol{\chi}^{(3)}$.

The hyperpolarizability $\boldsymbol{\gamma}$ can be obtained by a quantum-mechanical time-dependent perturbation theory calculation. Such a calculation shows (Armstrong *et al.*, 1962) that each of the 81 Cartesian components of the fourth-rank tensor $\boldsymbol{\gamma}$ is given by the sum of 24 terms, each of which is itself a threefold sum over all molecular states, with each element of the threefold sum a product of dipole matrix elements divided by a product of frequency factors. For the CARS process, in which an electric field at frequency $\omega_0 = \omega_1 - \omega_2 + \omega_3$ is created by the interaction of fields at ω_1, ω_2, and ω_3, the components of $\boldsymbol{\gamma}$ are given by (Christie and Lockwood, 1971)

$$
\begin{aligned}
\gamma_{\rho\sigma\tau\nu} = \frac{1}{\hbar^3} \sum_{j,k,l} \Bigg[& \frac{\langle g|M_\rho|l\rangle\langle l|M_\tau|k\rangle\langle k|M_\nu|j\rangle\langle j|M_\sigma|g\rangle}{(\omega_{jg} - \omega_1)(\omega_{kg} - \omega_1 - \omega_3)(\omega_{lg} - \omega_0)} + \frac{\langle g|M_\rho|l\rangle\langle l|M_\nu|k\rangle\langle k|M_\tau|j\rangle\langle j|M_\sigma|g\rangle}{(\omega_{jg} - \omega_1)(\omega_{kg} - \omega_1 + \omega_2)(\omega_{lg} - \omega_0)} \\
& + \frac{\langle g|M_\rho|l\rangle\langle l|M_\tau|k\rangle\langle k|M_\sigma|j\rangle\langle j|M_\nu|g\rangle}{(\omega_{jg} - \omega_3)(\omega_{kg} - \omega_1 - \omega_3)(\omega_{lg} - \omega_0)} + \frac{\langle g|M_\rho|l\rangle\langle l|M_\nu|k\rangle\langle k|M_\sigma|j\rangle\langle j|M_\tau|g\rangle}{(\omega_{jg} + \omega_2)(\omega_{kg} - \omega_1 + \omega_2)(\omega_{lg} - \omega_0)} \\
& + \frac{\langle g|M_\rho|l\rangle\langle l|M_\sigma|k\rangle\langle k|M_\tau|j\rangle\langle j|M_\nu|g\rangle}{(\omega_{jg} - \omega_3)(\omega_{kg} - \omega_3 + \omega_2)(\omega_{lg} - \omega_0)} + \frac{\langle g|M_\rho|l\rangle\langle l|M_\sigma|k\rangle\langle k|M_\nu|j\rangle\langle j|M_\tau|g\rangle}{(\omega_{jg} + \omega_2)(\omega_{kg} - \omega_3 + \omega_2)(\omega_{lg} - \omega_0)} \\
& + \frac{\langle g|M_\tau|l\rangle\langle l|M_\rho|k\rangle\langle k|M_\nu|j\rangle\langle j|M_\sigma|g\rangle}{(\omega_{jg} - \omega_1)(\omega_{kg} - \omega_1 - \omega_3)(\omega_{lg} - \omega_2)} + \frac{\langle g|M_\nu|l\rangle\langle l|M_\rho|k\rangle\langle k|M_\tau|j\rangle\langle j|M_\sigma|g\rangle}{(\omega_{jg} - \omega_1)(\omega_{kg} - \omega_1 + \omega_2)(\omega_{lg} + \omega_3)} \\
& + \frac{\langle g|M_\tau|l\rangle\langle l|M_\rho|k\rangle\langle k|M_\sigma|j\rangle\langle j|M_\nu|g\rangle}{(\omega_{jg} - \omega_3)(\omega_{kg} - \omega_1 - \omega_2)(\omega_{lg} - \omega_2)} + \frac{\langle g|M_\nu|l\rangle\langle l|M_\rho|k\rangle\langle k|M_\sigma|j\rangle\langle j|M_\tau|g\rangle}{(\omega_{jg} + \omega_2)(\omega_{kg} - \omega_1 + \omega_2)(\omega_{lg} + \omega_3)} \\
& + \frac{\langle g|M_\sigma|l\rangle\langle l|M_\rho|k\rangle\langle k|M_\tau|j\rangle\langle j|M_\nu|g\rangle}{(\omega_{jg} - \omega_3)(\omega_{kg} - \omega_1 + \omega_2)(\omega_{lg} + \omega_1)} + \frac{\langle g|M_\sigma|l\rangle\langle l|M_\rho|k\rangle\langle k|M_\nu|j\rangle\langle j|M_\tau|g\rangle}{(\omega_{jg} + \omega_2)(\omega_{kg} - \omega_3 + \omega_2)(\omega_{lg} + \omega_1)} \\
& + \frac{\langle g|M_\tau|l\rangle\langle l|M_\nu|k\rangle\langle k|M_\rho|j\rangle\langle j|M_\sigma|g\rangle}{(\omega_{jg} - \omega_1)(\omega_{kg} + \omega_3 - \omega_2)(\omega_{lg} - \omega_2)} + \frac{\langle g|M_\nu|l\rangle\langle l|M_\tau|k\rangle\langle k|M_\rho|j\rangle\langle j|M_\sigma|g\rangle}{(\omega_{jg} - \omega_1)(\omega_{kg} + \omega_3 - \omega_2)(\omega_{lg} + \omega_3)} \\
& + \frac{\langle g|M_\tau|l\rangle\langle l|M_\sigma|k\rangle\langle k|M_\rho|j\rangle\langle j|M_\nu|g\rangle}{(\omega_{jg} - \omega_3)(\omega_{kg} + \omega_1 - \omega_2)(\omega_{lg} - \omega_2)} + \frac{\langle g|M_\nu|l\rangle\langle l|M_\sigma|k\rangle\langle k|M_\rho|j\rangle\langle j|M_\tau|g\rangle}{(\omega_{jg} + \omega_2)(\omega_{kg} + \omega_1 + \omega_3)(\omega_{lg} + \omega_3)} \\
& + \frac{\langle g|M_\sigma|l\rangle\langle l|M_\tau|k\rangle\langle k|M_\rho|j\rangle\langle j|M_\nu|g\rangle}{(\omega_{jg} - \omega_3)(\omega_{kg} + \omega_1 - \omega_2)(\omega_{lg} + \omega_1)} + \frac{\langle g|M_\sigma|l\rangle\langle l|M_\nu|k\rangle\langle k|M_\rho|j\rangle\langle j|M_\tau|g\rangle}{(\omega_{jg} + \omega_2)(\omega_{kg} + \omega_1 + \omega_3)(\omega_{lg} + \omega_1)} \\
& + \frac{\langle g|M_\tau|l\rangle\langle l|M_\nu|k\rangle\langle k|M_\sigma|j\rangle\langle j|M_\rho|g\rangle}{(\omega_{jg} + \omega_0)(\omega_{kg} + \omega_3 - \omega_2)(\omega_{lg} - \omega_2)} + \frac{\langle g|M_\nu|l\rangle\langle l|M_\tau|k\rangle\langle k|M_\sigma|j\rangle\langle j|M_\rho|g\rangle}{(\omega_{jg} + \omega_0)(\omega_{kg} + \omega_3 - \omega_2)(\omega_{lg} + \omega_3)} \\
& + \frac{\langle g|M_\tau|l\rangle\langle l|M_\sigma|k\rangle\langle k|M_\nu|j\rangle\langle j|M_\rho|g\rangle}{(\omega_{jg} + \omega_0)(\omega_{kg} + \omega_1 - \omega_2)(\omega_{lg} - \omega_2)} + \frac{\langle g|M_\nu|l\rangle\langle l|M_\sigma|k\rangle\langle k|M_\tau|j\rangle\langle j|M_\rho|g\rangle}{(\omega_{jg} + \omega_0)(\omega_{kg} + \omega_1 + \omega_3)(\omega_{lg} + \omega_3)} \\
& + \frac{\langle g|M_\sigma|l\rangle\langle l|M_\tau|k\rangle\langle k|M_\nu|j\rangle\langle j|M_\rho|g\rangle}{(\omega_{jg} + \omega_0)(\omega_{kg} + \omega_1 - \omega_2)(\omega_{lg} + \omega_1)} + \frac{\langle g|M_\sigma|l\rangle\langle l|M_\nu|k\rangle\langle k|M_\tau|j\rangle\langle j|M_\rho|g\rangle}{(\omega_{jg} + \omega_0)(\omega_{kg} + \omega_1 + \omega_3)(\omega_{lg} + \omega_1)} \Bigg].
\end{aligned}
\tag{1.37}
$$

The Raman resonant enhancement occurs as a result of frequency factors like $\omega_{kg} - (\omega_1 - \omega_2)$ in the denominator of the second term in this expression for $\gamma_{\rho\sigma\tau\nu}$. When $k = r$ this frequency factor becomes $\omega_{rg} - (\omega_1 - \omega_2)$, where r and g are two molecular states connected by a Raman allowed transition (cf. Fig. 1.3), and as $\omega_1 - \omega_2 \to \omega_{rg}$ the denominator in the second term in the above expression approaches zero. Note that denominators such as $\omega_{jg} - \omega_1$ give rise to one-photon resonances in $\gamma_{\rho\sigma\tau\nu}$. The effect of these one-photon resonances is termed resonance CARS and is directly analogous to the resonance Raman effect. Other frequency factors like $\omega_{kg} - (\omega_1 + \omega_3)$ represent two-photon absorption resonances in $\gamma_{\rho\sigma\tau\nu}$. The resonant and nonresonant contributions to $\gamma_{\rho\sigma\tau\nu}$ are illustrated in Fig. 1.5.

Actually, $\gamma_{\rho\sigma\tau\nu} = \infty$ at one-photon, Raman, and two-photon absorption resonances. This unphysical behavior arises because Eq. (1.37) is strictly valid only in the *absence* of any resonance. Orr and Ward have carried out a perturbation theory treatment of $\boldsymbol{\gamma}$ which properly deals with secular divergences, e.g., $\omega_{jg} = \omega_{gg} = 0$ and $\omega_1 = 0$ in the first term of Eq. (1.37), as well as the resonant divergences in $\boldsymbol{\gamma}$ (Orr and Ward, 1971). This leads to a considerably more complicated formulation for $\boldsymbol{\gamma}$. However, we are concerned only with Raman resonances in $\boldsymbol{\gamma}$, and in this case Eq. (1.37) is adequate if we introduce damping of the molecular states j, k, and l. That is, we make the various Raman resonant frequency denominators complex by replacing ω_{ng}, where $n = j, k, l$, by Ω_{ng}, where

$$\Omega_{ng} = \omega_{ng} - i\Gamma_{ng} \tag{1.38}$$

and Γ_{ng} is the damping constant. Thus, for example, when $n = k = r$ and $\omega_1 - \omega_2 = \omega_{rg}$ the denominator $\Omega_{kg} - (\omega_1 - \omega_2)$ becomes $-i\Gamma_{rg}$.

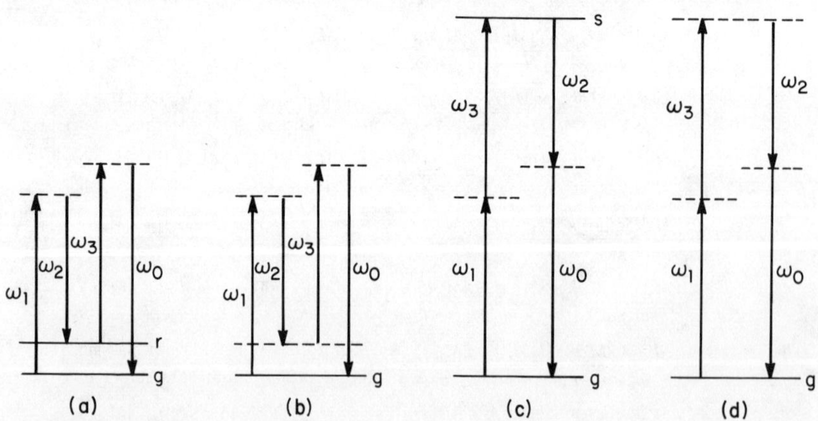

FIG. 1.5. Energy-level schematic for (a) CARS resonant, (b) nonresonant, (c) two-photon absorption resonant, and (d) nonresonant contributions to $\chi^{(3)}$. Dashed lines indicate virtual electronic states.

This approach leads quite naturally to a separation of γ and hence $\chi^{(3)}$ into resonant (i.e., Raman resonant) and nonresonant contributions:

$$\chi^{(3)} \equiv \chi' + i\chi'' + \chi^{\mathrm{NR}}, \tag{1.39}$$

where $\chi' + i\chi''$ is the resonant part of $\chi^{(3)}$ and χ^{NR} the nonresonant part. Note that to avoid excessive superscripts the (3) identification is deleted from χ', χ'', and χ^{NR}, since only $\chi^{(3)}$ is important in CARS. In this separation of resonant and nonresonant contributions to $\chi^{(3)}$ we assume that χ^{NR} is real and independent of ω_0, ω_1, ω_2, and ω_3.

The third-order dielectric susceptibility $\chi^{(3)}$ is related to the molecular hyperpolarizability γ by the molecular density N of the sample and a factor that relates the magnitude of the applied macroscopic electric fields to the fields acting on the individual molecules (Armstrong *et al.*, 1962; Kittel, 1971; Pantell and Puthoff, 1969):

$$\chi^{(3)}(-\omega_0, \omega_1, -\omega_2, \omega_3) = N\zeta(\omega_0, \omega_1, \omega_2, \omega_3)\gamma(-\omega_0, \omega_1, -\omega_2, \omega_3), \tag{1.40}$$

where

$$\zeta(\omega_0, \omega_1, \omega_2, \omega_3) = \prod_{i=0}^{3} \frac{n^2(\omega_i) + 2}{3}, \tag{1.41}$$

and $n(\omega_i)$ is the index of refraction at frequency ω_i. For simplicity we shall assume that all the local field magnitudes are equal to the macroscopic field magnitudes and accept the usual identification of $\chi^{(3)}$ as $N\gamma$ [cf. Eq. (1.12)], which is valid in all but high-refractive-index materials.

Thus the perturbation theory treatment of γ shows how Raman resonances appear in $\chi^{(3)}$ and hence CARS. Now we must inquire how the amplitude of $\chi^{(3)}$ at these resonances is related to $d\sigma/d\Omega$, the spontaneous Raman scattering cross sections for the Raman transitions that cause these $\chi^{(3)}$ resonances. The simplest approach (Tolles *et al.*, 1977) identifies the resonant frequency ω_{rg} as the frequency of a damped harmonic oscillator and, following Placzek's treatment (Placzek, 1934), relates the linear polarizability tensor $\boldsymbol{\alpha}$ of the molecule to the harmonic oscillator coordinate q:

$$\boldsymbol{\alpha} = \boldsymbol{\alpha}_0 + (\partial\boldsymbol{\alpha}/\partial\mathbf{q})_0 q + \cdots. \tag{1.42}$$

The equation of motion for this oscillator in the presence of a driving electric field $\mathbf{E}(\mathbf{r}, t)$ is (Pantell and Puthoff, 1969)

$$\ddot{q} + \Gamma_{rg}\dot{q} + \omega_{rg}^2 q = \frac{1}{2m}\left(\frac{\partial\boldsymbol{\alpha}}{\partial\mathbf{q}}\right)_0 \mathbf{E}^2(\mathbf{r}, t), \tag{1.43}$$

where again [cf. Eq. (1.38)] Γ_{rg} is the damping constant.

Writing the field in terms of its Fourier components as before [Eq. (1.15)] with real fields at frequencies ω_1 and ω_2, we find that q must have a Fourier component at $\omega_1 - \omega_2$

$$\ddot{q} + \Gamma_{rg}\dot{q} + \omega_{rg}^2 q = \frac{1}{2m}\left(\frac{\partial \boldsymbol{\alpha}}{\partial \mathbf{q}}\right)_0 \frac{1}{4}\mathbf{E}(\omega_1, \mathbf{r})\mathbf{E}^*(\omega_2, \mathbf{r}) \times \exp\{i[(\mathbf{k}_1 - \mathbf{k}_2)\cdot\mathbf{r} - (\omega_1 - \omega_2)t]\}, \quad (1.44)$$

for which the solution is

$$q(\omega_1 - \omega_2) = \frac{1}{8m}\left(\frac{\partial \boldsymbol{\alpha}}{\partial \mathbf{q}}\right)_0 \frac{\mathbf{E}(\omega_1, \mathbf{r})\mathbf{E}^*(\omega_2, \mathbf{r})\exp\{i[(\mathbf{k}_1 - \mathbf{k}_2)\cdot\mathbf{r} - (\omega_1 - \omega_2)t]\}}{[\omega_{rg}^2 - (\omega_1 - \omega_2)^2 - i\Gamma_{rg}(\omega_1 - \omega_2)]}. \quad (1.45)$$

This field-driven oscillation in q at $\omega_1 - \omega_2$ produces a field-driven oscillation in the molecular polarizability, given by

$$\left(\frac{\partial \boldsymbol{\alpha}}{\partial \mathbf{q}}\right)_0 q(\omega_1 - \omega_2). \quad (1.46)$$

By Eq. (1.8) this gives rise to a Fourier component of the dipole moment $\boldsymbol{\mu}$ at the anti-Stokes frequency $\omega_0 = 2\omega_1 - \omega_2 = \omega_1 + (\omega_1 - \omega_2)$, via the interaction of the field at ω_1 with this oscillating polarizability:

$$\begin{aligned}\boldsymbol{\mu}(\mathbf{r}, t) &= \left(\frac{\partial \boldsymbol{\alpha}}{\partial \mathbf{q}}\right)_0 q(\omega_1 - \omega_2)\frac{1}{2}\mathbf{E}(\omega_1, \mathbf{r})\exp[i(\mathbf{k}_1\cdot\mathbf{r} - \omega_1 t)] + \text{c.c.} \\ &= \frac{1}{16m}\left(\frac{\partial \boldsymbol{\alpha}}{\partial \mathbf{q}}\right)_0\left(\frac{\partial \boldsymbol{\alpha}}{\partial \mathbf{q}}\right)_0 \frac{\mathbf{E}(\omega_1, \mathbf{r})\mathbf{E}^*(\omega_2, \mathbf{r})\mathbf{E}(\omega_1, \mathbf{r})}{[\omega_{rg}^2 - (\omega_1 - \omega_2)^2 - i\Gamma_{rg}(\omega_1 - \omega_2)]} \\ &\quad \times \exp\{i[(2\mathbf{k}_1 - \mathbf{k}_2)\cdot\mathbf{r} - \omega_0 t]\} + \text{c.c.} \qquad (1.47)\end{aligned}$$

We can equate this Fourier component of the induced dipole with a component of the bulk polarization through Eq. (1.11):

$$\mathbf{P}(\mathbf{r}, t) = \frac{N}{16m}\left(\frac{\partial \boldsymbol{\alpha}}{\partial \mathbf{q}}\right)_0\left(\frac{\partial \boldsymbol{\alpha}}{\partial \mathbf{q}}\right)_0 \frac{\mathbf{E}(\omega_1, \mathbf{r})\mathbf{E}^*(\omega_2, \mathbf{r})\mathbf{E}(\omega_1, \mathbf{r})}{[\omega_{rg}^2 - (\omega_1 - \omega_2)^2 - i\Gamma_{rg}(\omega_1 - \omega_2)]} \times \exp\{i[(2\mathbf{k}_1 - \mathbf{k}_2)\cdot\mathbf{r} - \omega_0 t]\} + \text{c.c.} \quad (1.48)$$

We will again assume that the driving electric fields have parallel field vectors and parallel propagation vectors aligned along the space-fixed z axis. This allows us to neglect the vector nature of the electric fields and the tensor nature of the molecular polarizability. In this case Eq. (1.48) becomes

$$P(z, t) = \frac{3N}{16m}\left(\frac{\partial \alpha}{\partial q}\right)_0^2 \frac{E^2(\omega_1)E^*(\omega_2)\exp\{i[(2k_1 - k_2)z - \omega_0 t]\}}{[\omega_{rg}^2 - (\omega_1 - \omega_2)^2 - i\Gamma_{rg}(\omega_1 - \omega_2)]} + \text{c.c.}, \quad (1.49)$$

where the factor of 3 arises because each distinct permutation of the order of the electric fields contributes to $P(z, t)$ [cf. Eq. (1.20)].

Comparing Eqs. (1.49) and (1.26), we find that

$$\chi^{(3)}(-\omega_0, \omega_1, -\omega_2, \omega_1) = \frac{N}{2m}\left(\frac{\partial\alpha}{\partial q}\right)_0^2 \frac{1}{[\omega_{rg}^2 - (\omega_1 - \omega_2)^2 - i\Gamma_{rg}(\omega_1 - \omega_2)]}. \tag{1.50}$$

The Raman differential scattering cross section $d\sigma/d\Omega$ is related to $(\partial\alpha/\partial q)_0^2$ by (Tolles *et al.*, 1977)

$$(\partial\alpha/\partial q)_0^2 = (2m\omega_{rg}c^4/\hbar\omega_2^4)(d\sigma/d\Omega). \tag{1.51}$$

Therefore

$$\chi^{(3)}(-\omega_0, \omega_1, -\omega_2, \omega_1) = \frac{Nc^4}{\hbar\omega_2^4}\frac{d\sigma}{d\Omega}\frac{\omega_{rg}}{[\omega_{rg}^2 - (\omega_1 - \omega_2)^2 - i\Gamma_{rg}(\omega_1 - \omega_2)]}. \tag{1.52}$$

This purely classical derivation does not take account of the quantum-mechanical effect that the magnitude of the oscillation $q(\omega_1 - \omega_2)$, given by Eq. (1.45), is linearly dependent on the *difference* in population between the harmonic oscillator levels r and g, Δ_{rg} (Tolles *et al.*, 1977). We must thus add the factor Δ_{rg} to Eq. (1.52), giving

$$\chi^{(3)}(-\omega_0, \omega_1, -\omega_2, \omega_1) = \frac{N\,\Delta_{rg}\,c^4}{\hbar\omega_2^4}\frac{d\sigma}{d\Omega}\frac{\omega_{rg}}{[\omega_{rg}^2 - (\omega_1 - \omega_2)^2 - i\Gamma_{rg}(\omega_1 - \omega_2)]}. \tag{1.53}$$

At resonance $\omega_1 - \omega_2 = \omega_{rg}$, and

$$|\chi^{(3)}|^2 = (N\,\Delta_{rg}\,c^4/\hbar\omega_2^4)^2(d\sigma/d\Omega)^2(1/\Gamma_{rg})^2. \tag{1.54}$$

Thus the magnitude of a CARS signal at resonance depends on the square of the magnitude of the Raman cross section for that Raman transition, as well as the square of the difference in population between the states r and g, Δ_{rg}, and the square of the Raman transition linewidth Γ_{rg}.

D. Symmetry Properties of $\chi^{(3)}$

As a fourth-rank tensor $\boldsymbol{\chi}^{(3)}$ has $3^4 = 81$ elements of the form $\chi^{(3)}_{\rho\sigma\tau\nu}(-\omega_0, \omega_1, -\omega_2, \omega_3)$, where $\rho, \sigma, \tau, \nu = x, y$, or z and $\omega_0 = \omega_1 - \omega_2 + \omega_3$. Symmetry restrictions, however, will limit the number of the elements that are independent and nonvanishing. We have noted already (cf. Subsection 1.2.A) the intrinsic symmetry of $\chi^{(3)}_{\rho\sigma\tau\nu}(-\omega_0, \omega_1, -\omega_2, \omega_3)$ with respect to permutation of the pairs $(1, \sigma)$, $(2, \tau)$, $(3, \nu)$. $\boldsymbol{\chi}^{(3)}$ must also transform in the indices

ρ, σ, τ, and ν according to the macroscopic spatial symmetry properties of the nonlinear medium. Butcher has tabulated the relationships among the the nonzero elements of $\boldsymbol{\chi}^{(3)}$ for all the crystallographic point groups as well as for isotropic media such as liquids and gases (Butcher, 1965; Levenson and Song, 1980).

Since the vast majority of CARS experimental work has been done in isotropic media we will explicitly consider the symmetry properties of $\boldsymbol{\chi}^{(3)}$ only in isotropic materials. For such $\boldsymbol{\chi}^{(3)}$ has 21 nonzero elements:

$$
\begin{aligned}
\chi^{(3)}_{1111} &= \chi^{(3)}_{xxxx} = \chi^{(3)}_{yyyy} = \chi^{(3)}_{zzzz}, \\
\chi^{(3)}_{1122} &= \chi^{(3)}_{xxyy} = \chi^{(3)}_{xxzz} = \chi^{(3)}_{yyxx} = \chi^{(3)}_{yyzz} = \chi^{(3)}_{zzxx} = \chi^{(3)}_{zzyy}, \\
\chi^{(3)}_{1212} &= \chi^{(3)}_{xyxy} = \chi^{(3)}_{xzxz} = \chi^{(3)}_{yxyx} = \chi^{(3)}_{yzyz} = \chi^{(3)}_{zxzx} = \chi^{(3)}_{zyzy}, \\
\chi^{(3)}_{1221} &= \chi^{(3)}_{xyyx} = \chi^{(3)}_{xzzx} = \chi^{(3)}_{yxxy} = \omega^{(3)}_{yzzy} = \chi^{(3)}_{zxxz} = \omega^{(3)}_{zyyz}.
\end{aligned}
\tag{1.55}
$$

Of these 21 nonvanishing elements only 3 are independent, since

$$\chi^{(3)}_{1111} = \chi^{(3)}_{1122} + \chi^{(3)}_{1212} + \chi^{(3)}_{1221}. \tag{1.56}$$

In almost all CARS experiments $\omega_1 = \omega_3$, so

$$\chi^{(3)}_{1122} = \chi^{(3)}_{1221}, \tag{1.57}$$

and

$$\chi^{(3)}_{1111} = 2\chi^{(3)}_{1122} + \chi^{(3)}_{1212}. \tag{1.58}$$

In Subsection 1.2.B, in which we derived the plane wave solution to Maxwell's equations for the anti-Stokes signal, we suppressed the tensor nature of $\boldsymbol{\chi}^{(3)}$ by having the electric fields at ω_1 and ω_2 have parallel field vectors. This is equivalent to identifying $\chi^{(3)}$ in Eqs. (1.32) and (1.34) as $\chi^{(3)}_{1111}$, and we find that the anti-Stokes signal electric field vector must also be parallel to the fields at ω_1 and ω_2. If we choose the field vectors at ω_1 and ω_2 to be perpendicular, we find that $\chi^{(3)}$ in Eqs. (1.32) and (1.34) must be $\chi^{(3)}_{1212}$, and the electric field vector of the anti-Stokes beam will be parallel to the field vector at ω_2, the Stokes beam. Thus, when $\omega_1 = \omega_3$, as is usually the case, two measurements, one with the fields at ω_1 and ω_2 parallel and one with the fields perpendicular, determine all elements of the macroscopic susceptibility tensor.

E. Selection Rules

Although the CARS signal is directly related to the ordinary Raman cross section [cf. Eq. (1.54)], the fact that it is a nonlinear three-wave mixing technique might lead one to expect different selection rules in CARS and spontaneous Raman scattering. Slightly relaxed Raman selection rules in CARS were suggested by Hudson (1974), but an exact analysis (Yuratich and Hanna, 1977) shows that the selection rules for CARS and ordinary Raman scattering are the same.

F. Signal Intensity

Although coherent anti-Stokes Raman scattering has been used to investigate the nature of optical nonlinearities in matter (Levenson and Bloembergen, 1974; Rado, 1967), interest in it today derives mainly from its use as a method for fundamental and applied Raman spectroscopy. The importance of CARS for Raman spectroscopy is principally a consequence of the fact that the CARS signal intensity can be several orders of magnitude greater than that produced in ordinary Raman scattering. This large signal enhancement arises because CARS is a coherent process. The laser fields at ω_1 and ω_2 drive a Raman mode at $\omega_{rg} = \omega_1 - \omega_2$, which then interacts with the field at ω_1 to produce a coherently oscillating polarization at a frequency corresponding to a three-fold sum of the incident frequencies. This leads to the generation of a coherent output beam at $\omega_0 = 2\omega_1 - \omega_2$. Ordinary Raman scattering is the result of the oscillating dipole term proportional to $(\partial\alpha/\partial\alpha)_0 q(\omega_{rg})\mathbf{E}(\omega_1)$, and results in an incoherent output at $\omega_1 \pm \omega_{rg}$.

In spontaneous Raman scattering the signal power at the Stokes or anti-Stokes shifted frequency ω_0 is given by

$$P_0 = N(d\sigma/d\Omega)LP_1\,\delta\Omega. \tag{1.59}$$

Here P_1 is the incident power, $\delta\Omega$ the solid angle over which the scattered light is collected, L the sample length, $d\sigma/d\Omega$ the Raman cross section, and N the particle density. The CARS signal, given by Eq. (1.32), depends on the incident laser intensity, i.e., the power per unit area. We can rewrite Eq. (1.32) in terms of powers instead of intensities as:

$$P_0 = (12\pi^2\omega_0/c^2)^2 P_1^2 P_2 (A_0/A_1^2 A_2)|\chi^{(3)}|^2 L^2, \tag{1.60}$$

where A_i is the cross-sectional area of the beam at frequency ω_i. Taking $A_0 = A_1 = A_2 = A$ we have

$$P_0 = (12\pi^2\omega_0/c^2)^2 P_1^2 P_2 (1/A^2)|\chi^{(3)}|^2 L^2, \tag{1.61}$$

and the CARS signal power will increase as the square of the decrease in area of the beams. Because of this, it is common in CARS experiments to focus the incident beams to cross-sectional areas of 10^{-4} cm^2 and even smaller. Equation (1.61), derived from a plane wave analysis will be valid only when the sample length L is much smaller than the confocal parameter

b of the focus, given by (Kogelnik and Li, 1966)

$$b = 2\pi d_0^2/\lambda, \tag{1.62}$$

where λ is the wavelength and d_0 the beam diameter at the focus:

$$d_0 = 4\lambda f/\pi d. \tag{1.63}$$

Here f is the focal length and d the beam diameter at the focusing lens.

Bjorklund (1975) has carried out a rigorous theoretical analysis of the effects of focusing on nonlinear processes such as third-harmonic generation and CARS, using Gaussian input beams. Applying this analysis, Shaub *et al.* (1977a) showed that for coherent anti-Stokes Raman scattering with focused lasers the anti-Stokes signal power is given by

$$\begin{aligned} P_0 &= (12\pi^2\omega_0/c^2)^2 P_1^2 P_2 |\chi^{(3)}|^2 (64\omega_0^2/c^2) F_2 \\ &= (96\pi^2\omega_0^2/c^3)^2 P_1^2 P_2 |\chi^{(3)}|^2 F_2 \\ &= (96\pi^2\omega_0^2 c/\hbar\omega_2^4)^2 P_1^2 P_2 (N\,\Delta_{rg})^2 (1/\Gamma_{rg})^2 (d\sigma/d\Omega)^2 F_2. \end{aligned} \tag{1.64}$$

Here F_2 is a dimensionless function of the sample length L, the focal length of the lens f, the wave vectors k_0, k_1, and k_2, and the confocal parameter b, which is assumed the same for both input beams. Computation of F_2 indicates that the CARS signal power is always optimized by focusing as tightly as possible and by having perfect phase matching, $\Delta k = 0$. There is little gain, however, in focusing any tighter than $b/L \sim 0.3$. Recently, Guha and Falk (1981) considered the case of a CARS signal generated by two Gaussian input beams with *unequal* confocal parameters. In this case the maximum signal does not occur when the beams are phase matched, but this effect is important only in the weak focusing limit, $L < b$.

In computing the CARS signals we assume unit signal collection efficiency. This assumption is warranted by the fact that the CARS signal, being a coherent beam, has a spatial distribution like that of the driving laser beams at ω_1 and ω_2, and hence is well collimated and typically has a divergence of 10^{-6} sr or less. In contrast, the incoherent spontaneous Raman signal is distributed over 4π sr. This limited beam divergence makes CARS particularly useful in remote sensing, where light collection optics must be placed a considerable distance from the sample.

In the above CARS signal relationships we also assume that the beams at ω_1 and ω_2 have ideal Gaussian profiles and are diffraction limited, and that they are exactly concentric and perfectly overlapped, with identical beam waist locations. Since ideal, perfectly overlapped beams like these are not encountered in the laboratory, the observed signal intensities will be somewhat smaller than the computed intensities. In practice we observe signals that are within a factor of 10 of those calculated, and others (Nibler and Knighten, 1977) report similar results. With typical pulsed laser experiments the CARS signals from nitrogen and oxygen in room air are readily visible when projected on a white card.

From Eq. (1.64) one might expect that the magnitude of CARS signals would be restricted only by the power of available laser sources. As with any other type of spectroscopy, however, there are effects that limit the maximum signals that can be obtained. Probably most important among these is saturation, that is, saturation of the molecular transition from state g to state r via the two-photon $\omega_1 - \omega_2$ transition (cf. Fig. 1.3). With high-power Nd:YAG and ruby pulsed lasers saturation can be achieved fairly easily, so experiments utilizing such sources must be done with care. While estimates of saturation power levels can be made (Eckbreth and Schreiber, 1981; Tolles *et al.*, 1977), the best procedure to follow to ensure that spectra are not affected by saturation is to determine the response of the spectra to changes in laser power. Since the saturation will have a P_1P_2 power dependence ($\omega_1 - \omega_2$ two-proton process), while the CARS signal scales as $P_1^2P_2$, keeping the ratio P_1/P_2 large will optimize the signal level while minimizing saturation. Weil and Schreiber (1982) and Wilson-Gordon *et al.* (1982) present detailed theoretical treatments of saturation in CARS, while recent high-resolution experiments by Duncan *et al.* (1981) on acetylene in a molecular beam show the effects of saturation on CARS spectra.

Other limiting mechanisms in CARS experiments include optical breakdown and the dynamic Stark effect. Tight focusing and high laser powers can lead to optical breakdown, i.e., large-scale ionization, in the sample due to the strong electric field at the laser focus. The importance of breakdown, which is extensively discussed by Smith and Meyerand (1974), is a strong function of the chemical identity and density of the sample, as well as the level of particulates. The dynamic Stark effect is probably significant only in high-resolution spectroscopy. It has been invoked (Rahn *et al.*, 1980) to account for shifts and broadening in vibrational and rotational transitions in CARS spectra taken with large laser field strengths.

G. Spectral Line Shape

In Subsection 1.2.C we expressed $\chi^{(3)}$ as a sum of resonant and nonresonant components, with the resonant contribution having real and imaginary parts

$$\chi^{(3)} \equiv \chi' + i\chi'' + \chi^{\mathrm{NR}}. \tag{1.65}$$

The 1111 Cartesian component of the resonant contribution $\chi' + i\chi''$ can be identified with $\chi^{(3)}$ given in Eq. (1.53). Separating Eq. (1.53) into real and

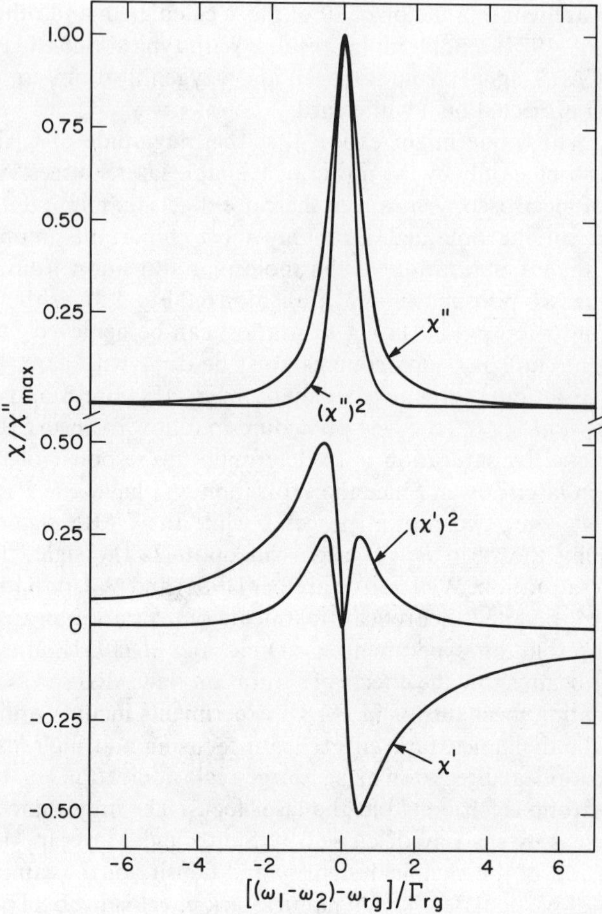

FIG. 1.6. Real and imaginary components of the resonant third-order dielectric susceptibility $\chi^{(3)}$ in the region of the resonance. See Eqs. (1.66) and (1.67).

imaginary parts, we find

$$\chi' = \frac{N\,\Delta_{rg}\,c^4}{\hbar\omega_2^4}\frac{d\sigma}{d\Omega}\frac{\omega_{rg}[\omega_{rg}^2 - (\omega_1 - \omega_2)^2]}{[\omega_{rg}^2 - (\omega_1 - \omega_2)^2]^2 + \Gamma_{rg}^2(\omega_1 - \omega_2)^2} \tag{1.66}$$

and

$$\chi'' = \frac{N\,\Delta_{rg}\,c^4}{\hbar\omega_2^4}\frac{d\sigma}{d\Omega}\frac{\omega_{rg}\Gamma_{rg}(\omega_1 - \omega_2)}{[\omega_{rg}^2 - (\omega_1 - \omega_2)^2]^2 + \Gamma_{rg}^2(\omega_1 - \omega_2)^2}. \tag{1.67}$$

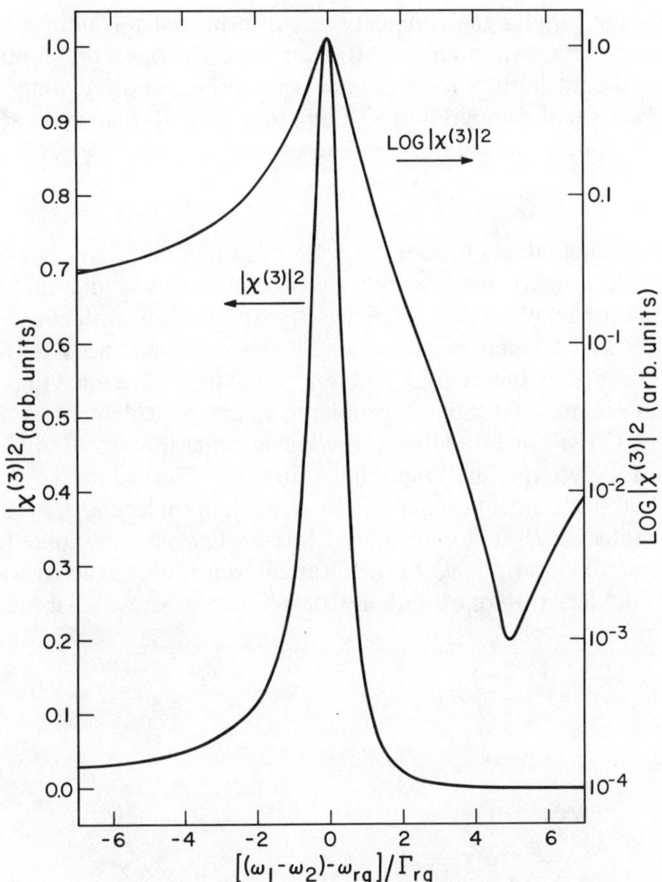

FIG. 1.7. Square of the third-order dielectric susceptibility $\chi^{(3)}$ in the region of a Raman resonance. $\chi^{NR} = 0.1$ arbitrary unit. See Eq. (1.69).

As before we assume χ^{NR} to be real and independent of ω_0, ω_1, and ω_2, so

$$\chi^{NR} = \text{const.} \tag{1.68}$$

These contributions to $\chi^{(3)}$ are plotted in Fig. 1.6, while

$$|\chi^{(3)}|^2 = (\chi')^2 + (\chi'')^2 + (\chi^{NR})^2 + 2\chi'\chi^{NR} \tag{1.69}$$

is shown in Fig. 1.7. Since the frequency dependence of the CARS signal is determined by $|\chi^{(3)}|^2$, Fig. 1.7 gives the expected CARS line shape, which is asymmetric for $\chi^{NR} \neq 0$.

Just as the large signal intensity is the principal advantage of CARS spectroscopy over spontaneous Raman spectroscopy, the nonresonant background contribution to the signal is the principal disadvantage. When χ' and χ'' are small compared to χ^{NR}, due to a small Raman cross section or low species concentration, Eq. (1.69) becomes

$$|\chi^{(3)}|^2 \cong (\chi^{NR})^2 + 2\chi'\chi^{NR}. \tag{1.70}$$

In this case fluctuations (noise) in $(\chi^{NR})^2$ can often be as large as or larger than $2\chi'\chi^{NR}$, severely limiting the signal-to-noise ratio in the spectrum. Nonresonant background interference is particularly a problem in mixture diagnostics and condensed-phase samples. Several advanced CARS techniques described in Subsections 1.3.C and 1.3.D were developed to overcome this nonresonant background problem, either by enhancing the signal (resonance CARS) or by reducing the background (polarization CARS).

Figure 1.7 gives the line shape that would be observed for a Raman line far removed from other resonances. In general, in molecular CARS spectra one encounters several closely spaced Raman lines, for example, the rotational lines in a vibrational Q-branch Raman transition. In this case adjacent lines can interfere with one another. Considering only two adjacent lines we can write

$$\chi^{(3)} = \sum_{j=1}^{2} (\chi'_j + i\chi''_j) + \chi^{NR}, \tag{1.71}$$

and

$$|\chi^{(3)}|^2 = (\chi'_1)^2 + (\chi'_2)^2 + (\chi''_1)^2 + (\chi''_2)^2 + (\chi^{NR})^2 + 2\chi'_1\chi'_2 + 2\chi''_1\chi''_2 + 2\chi'_1\chi^{NR} + 2\chi'_2\chi^{NR}. \tag{1.72}$$

Clearly, when there are several closely spaced lines the CARS line shape function can become quite complicated. Figure 1.8 illustrates some of these adjacent line and nonresonant background interference effects in the vibrational Q-branch spectrum of H_2. When the spacing between lines is not much greater than the linewidth Γ_{rg}, numerical analysis of the CARS spectrum is often necessary if one wishes to obtain a quantum state population distribution or temperature from the observed spectrum. This computational analysis is straightforward except in the case that the spectral lines are unresolved or barely resolved and the linewidth is not known. This situation arises often in determination of temperatures from CARS Q-branch rotational profiles at total pressures of an atmosphere or more, where the linewidth is determined not by Doppler effects but by collisional broadening. Since collisional broadening pressure coefficients and linewidths

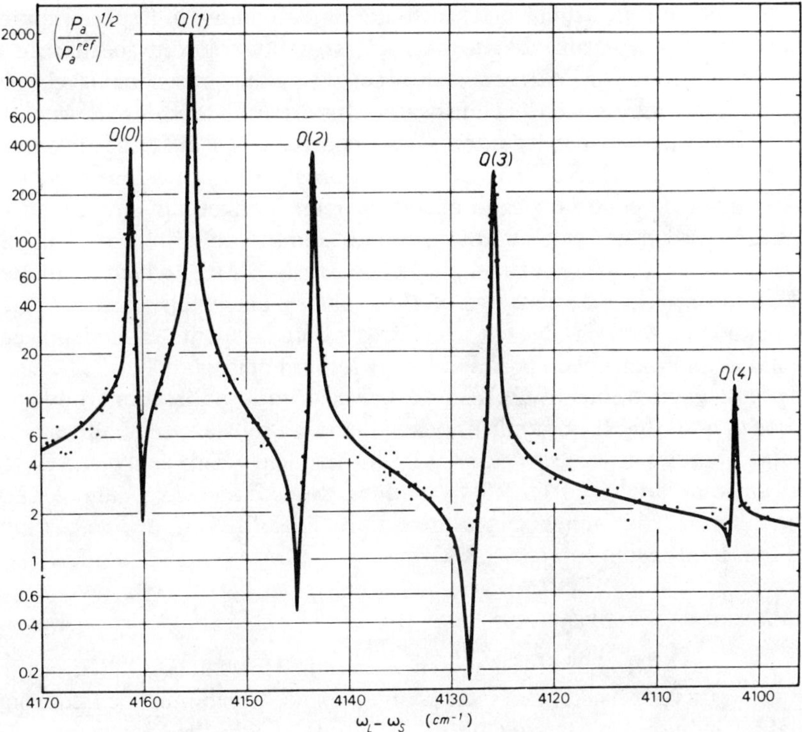

FIG. 1.8. CARS spectrum of pure hydrogen at STP. The quantity $(P_a/P_a^{ref})^{1/2}$ is the square root of the anti-Stokes signal intensity divided by a reference intensity. $\mathrm{Log}(P_a/P_a^{ref})^{1/2}$ is plotted versus the Raman frequency $\omega_L - \omega_S\,[\equiv(\omega_1 - \omega_2)/(2\pi c)]$. The points are experimental; the solid line is calculated. [From Moya *et al.* (1975). © North-Holland Publishing Company, Amsterdam, 1975.]

have been measured for only a few molecules, this can lead to ambiguity in the spectral interpretation.

1.3. The Practice and Application of CARS

A. General Applicability

In general CARS can be applied in all areas of research where spontaneous Raman spectroscopy can be used, as well as environments where spontaneous Raman is difficult or impractical to implement. CARS has been shown to be of particular usefulness in high-resolution spectroscopy, combustion diagnostics, time-resolved spectroscopy (particularly in photochemistry), spectroscopy of absorbing and/or fluorescing compounds (especially biological samples), plasma diagnostics, and spatially resolved spectroscopy. These applications of CARS are made possible by the large signal levels and high discrimination ($\sim 10^9$) against sample fluorescence and luminescence.

The high signal intensity often allows spectra to be obtained in only a few laser pulses and, even when this is not possible, at much lower average powers than necessary for spontaneous Raman spectroscopy. This reduces problems associated with photolysis and degradation of absorbing samples in the condensed phase. The high sensitivity of CARS, which facilitates detection of species at densities of 10^{11} to 10^{12} cm^{-3} (Druet and Taran, 1981), makes CARS suitable for detection of photofragments, excited molecular states, and molecular species in highly ionized plasmas.

Specific applications of CARS will be discussed in Subsections 1.3.E–H. Before considering these applications in detail we must examine the experimental apparatus necessary for CARS experiments (Subsection 1.3.B), as well as some advanced CARS techniques. (Subsections 1.3.C and 1.3.D), which enhance the minor species detection capabilities, spatial resolution, and temporal resolution of CARS.

B. Experimental Apparatus

A typical CARS apparatus is shown in simplified form in Fig. 1.9. Basically, the apparatus consists of two laser sources, one of which must be frequency tunable; laser beam steering optics for adjusting the beam overlap and crossing angle θ in the sample; focusing and recollimating lenses at the en-

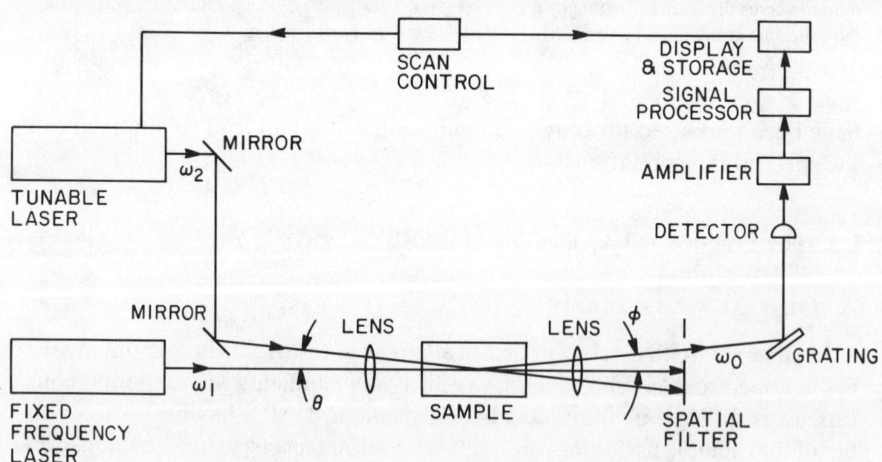

FIG. 1.9. Block diagram of a typical CARS experiment.

trance and exit of the cell; spatial and spectral filters for discriminating against scattered laser light and sample luminescence and fluorescence; a photodiode or photomultiplier to detect the signal; and signal processing and recording electronics.

The crossing angle θ is chosen to satisfy the phase-matching condition

$$\mathbf{k}_0 = 2\mathbf{k}_1 - \mathbf{k}_2, \tag{1.73}$$

as discussed in Subsection 1.2.B and illustrated in Fig. 1.4. The magnitude of the wave vector $|\mathbf{k}_i|$ is given by $\omega_i n_i/c$, where n_i is the index of refraction of the medium at frequency ω_i and c is the velocity of light. In liquids $\theta \approx 1°–3°$, while for low-density gases, for which the wavelength dispersion in the index of refraction is negligible, $\theta = 0$ and therefore $\phi = 0$, and the pump and Stokes incident beams and the anti-Stokes signal beam are collinear. In this collinear case spatial filtering of the signal beam from the input beams can be accomplished only after some dispersive spectral filtering via prisms or gratings.

Because of the nonlinear nature of the CARS process most of the signal is generated in a small region about the focus of the pump and Stokes beams. Consequently, it is crucial for efficient signal generation that the pump and Stokes beams are spatially overlapped at a common focus. This overlap can be ensured by performing simple experimental tests with equipment not shown in Fig. 1.9. In our laboratory we use a pinhole test of beam overlap. We reflect a small fraction of the pump and Stokes beams that have passed through the focusing lens to a pinhole located at the focal point of the lens. This pinhole has a diameter approximately equal to the beam waist diameter of the beams at the focus [cf. Eq. (1.63)]. If the beams are spatially overlapped and have a common focus they will simultaneously pass through the pinhole and be projected on a white card placed after the pinhole. If the beams have a common focus at the pinhole the beam images projected on the card will be uniformly and simultaneously extinguished as the pinhole is translated across the beams. We use the beam steering mirrors to achieve spatial overlap and telescopes (not shown in Fig. 1.9) in the Stokes and pump beam paths to adjust the focal points of the beams. Chabay *et al.* (1976) describe a similar beam overlap test in which the pinhole is replaced by two razor blades lying in a common plane normal to the laser beams, their edges perpendicular to each other.

Several different kinds of laser systems have been used in CARS spectroscopy. In a few cases cw laser systems have been employed (see, for example, Barrett and Begley, 1975; Bulatov *et al.*, 1980; Henesian *et al.*, 1977), generally with an ion laser as the fixed-frequency source and an ion-pumped dye laser as the tunable source. Continuous-wave laser systems allow very high-resolution spectroscopy, because of the very narrow ($\sim$0.001 cm^{-1})

linewidths achievable with single-frequency cw sources. However, cw sources have very low power outputs, typically a few watts for the ion lasers and less than 1 W for the single-frequency ion-pumped dye lasers. As a result the CARS signals obtained with cw lasers are of quite low intensity relative to the signal levels possible with high-power pulsed lasers, because of the $P_1^2P_2$ dependence of the anti-Stokes signal intensity.

A typical pulsed laser system with $P_1 = 1$ MW and $P_2 = 100$ kW in 10 ns with a 0.1-cm^{-1} laser linewidth and 10 pulses per second would give an instantaneous CARS signal at least 10^{10} times larger than a cw system of $P_1 = 5$ W and $P_2 = 0.5$ W and 10^{-3}-cm^{-1} linewidth, and a time-averaged signal at least 10^3 times larger. The cw power level can be increased by a factor of ~ 100 by placing the sample inside the ion laser and dye laser cavities (Hirth and Vollrath, 1976), but such an experiment is considerably more difficult to set up. "Quasi-cw" CARS laser systems (Duncan *et al.*, 1981), which generate high-power (~ 0.5-MW) but narrow-linewidth (~ 0.003-cm^{-1}) laser beams through pulsed laser amplification of single-frequency cw laser outputs, seem promising for overcoming the low signal levels of cw experiments.

Pulsed laser systems used to obtain CARS spectra have included ruby lasers with ruby-laser-pumped dye lasers (see, for example, Moya *et al.*, 1975), Nd:YAG lasers with Nd:YAG-pumped dye lasers (see, for example, Begley *et al.*, 1974), and nitrogen-pumped dye lasers (see, for example, Itzkan and Leonard, 1975). Whereas high peak powers (>1 MW) are available with ruby laser systems, the low repetition rate, typically 1 pulse per second or less, presents some problems. In addition, the long wavelength of the ruby system, 694.3 nm, requires that the Stokes beam be generated by a dye laser operating in the red or infrared, where dye efficiency and lifetime are limited and the beam is often invisible to the unaided eye.

Nitrogen-pumped dye lasers do not have the high peak powers of Nd:YAG or ruby systems but are adequate for many gas-phase spectroscopy applications and condensed-phase experiments. The poor beam quality of the nitrogen laser precludes its use as one of the incident CARS beams, so nitrogen laser systems must employ two dye lasers, pumped by one or two nitrogen lasers. Recently developed excimer-pumped dye laser systems, which are similar to nitrogen-pumped systems, will likely be used in some CARS applications due to the higher power achievable with these lasers relative to the nitrogen-pumped dye lasers.

The most versatile and widely used CARS laser system is the Nd:YAG laser plus Nd:YAG-pumped dye laser. The most common configuration uses the second harmonic of the Nd:YAG at 532 nm as the CARS pump beam ω_1, as well as the pump for the dye laser, which produces the tunable

Stokes beam ω_2. The high repetition rate, typically 10 pulses per second, and high peak power, typically $\gtrsim 1$ MW for both the pump and Stokes beams, make the Nd:YAG the system of choice for all gas-phase CARS applications.

Because of the high signal levels achievable in pulsed laser CARS experiments it is possible in many circumstances to get adequate signal-to-noise ratio in only a few laser pulses and in some cases in a single laser pulse. This makes CARS a very powerful technique for observing fast transient phenomena. However, the time required to scan the tunable laser source ω_2 through the Raman spectrum of interest is typically at least several minutes, so with a conventional scanning CARS apparatus like that shown in Fig. 1.9 the potential of CARS for studying transient phenomena cannot be fully realized.

An approach commonly referred to as multiplex CARS overcomes this difficulty. In multiplex CARS one operates the "tunable" laser in a broadband mode to produce output over a relatively wide spectral range. Carried out with a broadband Stokes laser source, coherent anti-Stokes Raman scattering generates a signal at all frequencies within the range $\omega_0 = 2\omega_1 - (\omega_2' \pm \Delta\omega_2/2)$, where $\Delta\omega_2$ is the spectral width of the Stokes radiation centered at ω_2', accessing all Raman resonances such that $\omega_{rg} = \omega_1 - (\omega_2' \pm \Delta\omega_2/2)$. A broadband dye laser, formed by replacing the laser grating or other spectrally dispersive elements by a mirror, can be made to oscillate over a bandwidth $\Delta\omega_2$ of 100 cm^{-1} or more, a spectral range adequate to span an entire Raman band for most molecular species. With such a broadband source for the Stokes beam the CARS spectrum from an entire Raman band, e.g., the vibrational Q branch of a diatomic molecule, can be generated in each laser pulse, eliminating the need for spectral scanning. To record the spectrum one can use a spectrograph to disperse the anti-Stokes signal and an optical multichannel analyzer to collect the light.

Roh *et al.* (1976) were the first to demonstrate the power of multiplex CARS by recording the entire vibrational Q-branch spectrum of H_2 generated in a single 20-ns laser pulse. Multiplex CARS is now frequently used in combustion studies (Eckbreth and Hall, 1979; Eckbreth, 1980; Klick *et al.*, 1981). Multiplex CARS is important here because it allows accurate, instantaneous temperature measurements based on Raman band contour analysis. Figure 1.10 shows single-pulse and multiple-pulse multiplex CARS spectra of nitrogen within the cylinder of a firing internal combustion engine (Klick *et al.*, 1981). Even in the single-pulse spectra, indicated by dotted lines in a and b of Fig. 1.10, the signal-to-noise ratio is quite good. Lau *et al.* (1977) have reported single-pulse CARS spectra of dye solutions, while Tretzel and Schneider (1979) have obtained single-pulse multiplex spectra of bacteriorhodopsin. Two of the spectra reported by Tretzel and Schneider are shown in Fig. 1.11. Even in a single 1-ns-duration laser pulse the spectral differences between the dark-adapted and light-adapted forms of bacteriorhodopsin are clearly evident.

Special CARS techniques are also necessary to take full advantage of another attractive feature of coherent anti-Stokes Raman scattering, namely the potential for highly spatially resolved spectroscopy. Whereas the beam crossing required for phase matching [Eq. (1.73) and Fig. 1.4] in liquids and solids will generally permit high spatial resolution, the normal collinear phase-matched geometry in gas-phase experiments usually leads to very

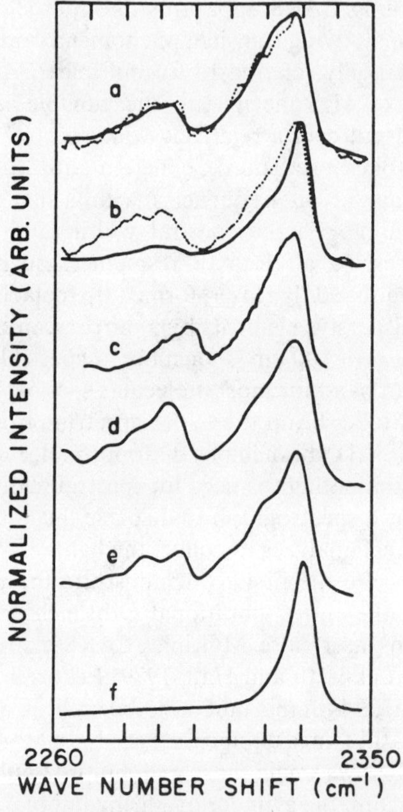

FIG. 1.10. Multiplex CARS spectra of nitrogen within the cylinder of a firing internal combustion engine: (a) single-pulse (dotted line) and three-pulse average (solid line) taken 20 ms after firing a propane-fueled engine; (b) single-pulse (dotted line) and 15-pulse average (solid line) taken 10 ms after firing a propane-fueled engine (one or more misfires must have occurred during averaging); (c) calculated spectrum with $T = 2200$ K; (d, e, f) three-pulse average spectra taken 10, 20, and 30 ms, respectively, after firing a methanol-fueled engine. [From Klick *et al.* (1981).]

poor spatial resolution. For this reason two-frequency, three-beam CARS techniques have been developed to permit crossed-beam geometries in dispersionless media.

In liquids and solids the requirement for phase matching, Eq. (1.73), necessitates the crossing of the pump and Stokes beams at an angle θ of approximately 1°–3°. Since the lasers are focused this beam crossing will limit CARS signal generation to a quite small volume element. For a crossing angle of 2° with ω_1 and ω_2 beams of 1-cm diameter focused by a 50-cm lens, the beams overlap only at the focus. The overlap region has a diameter at the focus given by Eq. (1.63), which for $\lambda = 532$ nm is only 3×10^{-3} cm. The length of the overlap region, determined by the 2° crossing angle, would be less than 0.2 cm. The sampled volume in this case is only $\sim 2 \times 10^{-6}$ cm^3. Since Eq. (1.63) gives the focal beam waist for diffraction-limited incident

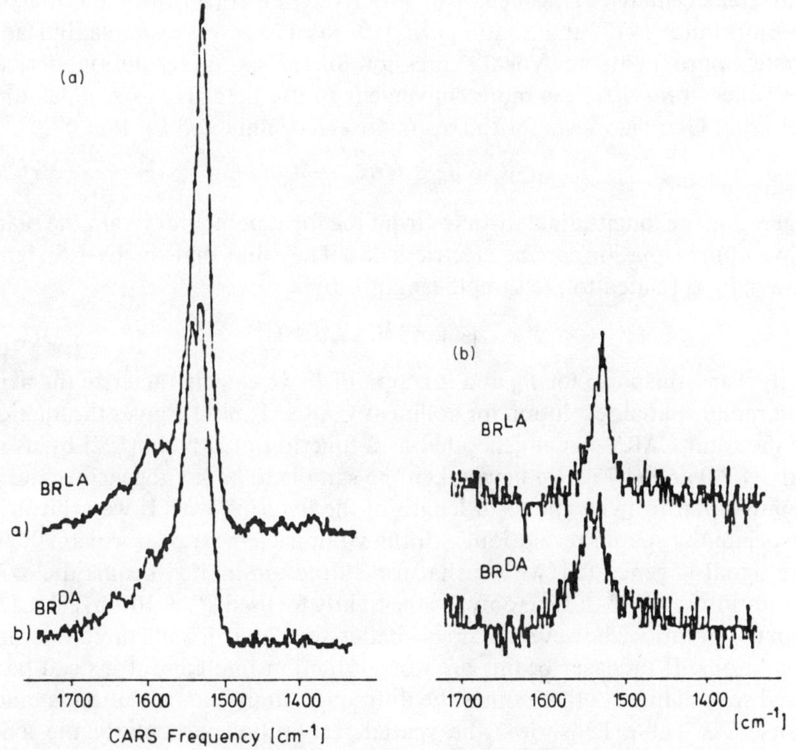

FIG. 1.11. Multiplex CARS spectra of light-adapted (LA) and dark-adapted (DA) bacteriorhodopsin: (a) accumulation of one thousand 1-ns laser pulses; (b) after a single 1-ns laser pulse. [From Tretzel and Schneider (1979). © North-Holland Publishing Company, Amsterdam, 1979.]

beams whereas actual laser beams have divergences somewhat larger than the diffraction limit, this computation will underestimate the extent of the sampled volume somewhat. However, if the beam diameter at the focus were three times the diffraction limit the probed volume would still be less than 5×10^{-5} cm^3, with diameter 1×10^{-2} cm and length 0.6 cm.

In CARS spectroscopy in low-density gases high spatial resolution is not so easily achieved, since the negligible wavelength dispersion of the index of refraction in gases requires collinear ω_1 and ω_2 beams to satisfy the phase-matching condition. Despite the fact that the CARS signal, due to the $P_1^2 P_2$ laser power dependence, is generated predominantly near the focus, the large confocal parameters [Eq. (1.62)] typical of focused beams in CARS experiments results in relatively long focal volumes.

The collinear CARS axial and radial spatial resolution, which is related to the fraction of the signal generated in a volume element of length L and diameter d centered at the focus, can be derived numerically from the analysis of Bjorklund (1975) and Shaub *et al.* (1977a). However, a simple, but adequate, approximate analytical expression for the spatial resolution, derived by Tolles *et al.* (1977), is more convenient to use here. Tolles *et al.* assume the usual Gaussian form for the beam area (Kogelnik and Li, 1966):

$$d(z)^2 = d_0^2[1 + (4\lambda z/\pi d_0^2)]^2, \tag{1.74}$$

where z is the longitudinal distance from the focal point, but retain the plane wave approximation for the electric fields. They find that the CARS signal power P_0 is related to the sample length L by

$$P_0 \propto [2 \tan^{-1}(2L\lambda/\pi d_0^2)]^2. \tag{1.75}$$

By using this form for P_0 as a function of L, we can characterize the axial and radial spatial resolution for collinear CARS. Table 1.1 gives the fraction of the total CARS signal generated as a function of L and $d(L/2)$ by using Eqs. (1.74) and (1.75). We have taken the sample to be homogeneous and of length equal to twice the focal length of the focusing lens. If we arbitrarily associate the spatial resolution with the volume element over which 90% of the signal is generated, we see that for diffraction-limited beams the axial resolution is less than 1 cm only for the tightly focused ($f = 10$ cm) case. The radial resolution, however, is much better than that for all three focusing conditions. If the laser beams are not diffraction limited, but instead have focal spot diameters three times the diffraction limit, the resolution is much worse. As Table 1.1 shows, the spatial resolution, particularly the axial resolution, can be significantly improved by tight focusing. But, as discussed in Subsection 1.2.F, optical breakdown can limit the laser beam intensities that can be used with tight focusing, diminishing the CARS signal intensities.

TABLE 1.1

AXIAL AND RADIAL SPATIAL RESOLUTION OF CARS USING COLINEAR, FOCUSED BEAMS[a]

Fraction of total signal	$f = 100$ cm		$f = 50$ cm		$f = 10$ cm	
	L^b (cm)	$d(L/2)^c$ (cm)	L (cm)	$d(L/2)$ (cm)	L (cm)	$d(L/2)$ (cm)
0.50	2.71	0.015	0.680	0.008	0.027	0.002
0.70	5.07	0.026	1.28	0.013	0.052	0.003
0.90	15.6	0.078	4.04	0.040	0.167	0.008
0.95	29.3	0.147	7.88	0.079	0.335	0.017

[a] Pump and Stokes laser beams assumed to be diffraction limited and of 1-cm diamter at the focusing lens and to have identical confocal parameters.

[b] From Eq. (1.75) with $\lambda = 532$ nm and d_0 from Eq. (1.63).

[c] From Eq. (1.74) with $z = L/2$, L from Eq. (1.75), d_0 from Eq. (1.63), and $\lambda = 532$ nm.

Gas-phase spatial resolution can be increased simply by crossing the pump and Stokes input beams. Some compromise between resolution and signal intensity must be reached, since the crossed beams will be phase-mismatched. With a 1-cm-diameter diffraction-limited laser beam and a 50-cm focal length lens an axial spatial resolution of 0.1 cm would be possible at a 4° crossing angle. The phase mismatch for this crossing angle would be ~92 cm^{-1} for $\omega_1 = 3.54 \times 10^{15}\ \text{s}^{-1}$ (18,797 cm^{-1}) and $\omega_2 = 3.10 \times 10^{15}\ \text{s}^{-1}$ (16,466 cm^{-1}), probing the nitrogen $v = 0 \rightarrow v = 1$ transition. From the plane wave solution for the CARS signal power [Eq. (1.34)] we expect that this phase mismatch will decrease the signal by a factor of ~20 relative to

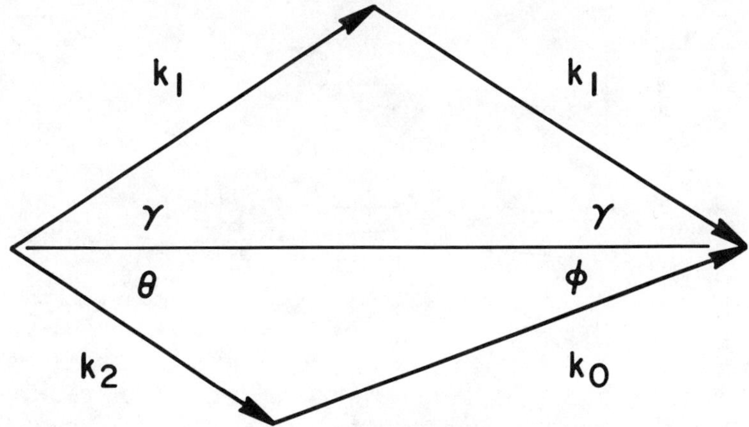

FIG. 1.12. BOXCARS phase-matching diagram.

that which would be obtained over the same 0.1-cm sample length in the phase-matched case.

Eckbreth (1978) has developed a method for achieving any desired spatial resolution without sacrificing signal due to phase mismatching. His technique is a crossed two-frequency, three-beam approach with a phase-matching diagram as shown in Fig. 1.12. This technique is termed BOXCARS because of the shape of the phase-matching diagram. In BOXCARS, the pump beam ω_1 is split into two parts, which are separately imaged into the sample at a crossing angle 2γ, as shown in the simplified experimental schematic of Fig. 1.13. The angles θ and ϕ are then chosen to satisfy phase matching, and are related by

$$2n_1\omega_1 \cos \gamma = n_2\omega_2 \cos \theta + n_0\omega_0 \cos \phi \tag{1.76}$$

and

$$n_2\omega_2 \sin \theta = n_0\omega_0 \sin \phi. \tag{1.77}$$

Since phase matching can be satisfied for any desired spatial resolution down to a limit set by the beam waist at the focus, increasing resolution is accompanied only by the unavoidable loss in signal intensity due to decreasing sample volume. The interaction volume and spatial resolution are determined simply by beam overlap at the focus as in the case of only two crossed beams.

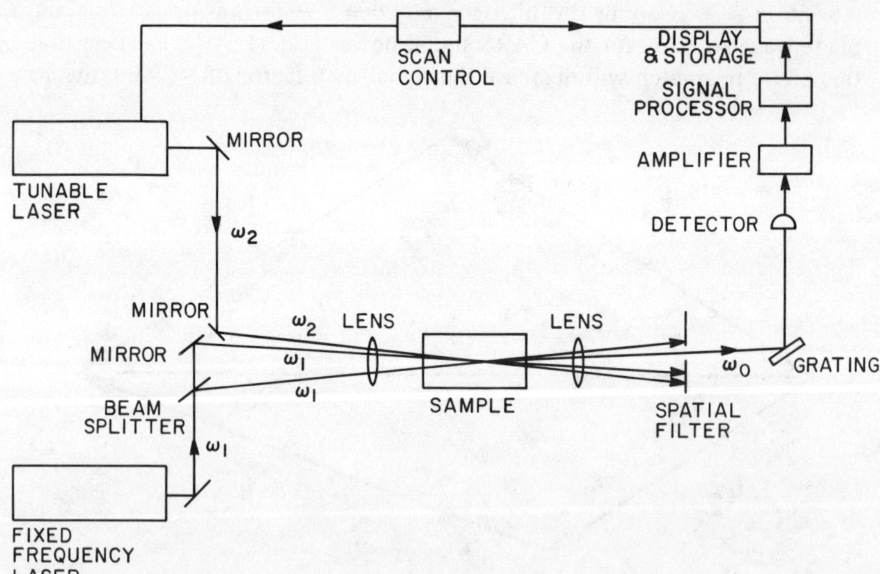

FIG. 1.13. Block diagram of a typical BOXCARS experiment.

Marko and Rimai (1979) have demonstrated a simplified variation of the BOXCARS technique that uses only two laser beams. Here a Gaussian beam at ω_2 crosses an annular beam, such as the diffraction-coupled output of a Nd:YAG laser at ω_1, and phase matching is achieved through a combination of appropriately crossed k_1 wave vectors present in different parts of the focused annular beam.

Clearly, one can imagine many crossed-beam geometries that will satisfy the phase-matching criterion. Some of these arrangements can be exploited to enhance the application of CARS. Laufer *et al.* (1979) developed a two-frequency, three-beam crossed CARS geometry that leads to angular separation of anti-Stokes signals with different frequencies ω_0. By using a broadband dye laser they were able to simultaneously observe angularly resolved signals from carbon monoxide and nitrogen in a CO/N_2 mixture. Murphy *et al.* (1979) describe a large-angle ($\gamma \cong \theta \cong \phi \cong 90°$) BOXCARS arrangement. By focusing the ω_1 beams into "sheets" with cyclindrical lenses, and focusing ω_2 with a spherical lens into the intersection region of the ω_1 beams, they were able to make spatially resolved measurements along a line across a methane jet. CARS signals generated in a region 0.5 cm long and 0.04 cm in diameter were spatially distinguished by an optical multichannel analyzer. Compaan and Chandra (1979) have reported a three-beam, three-frequency crossed-beam CARS geometry utilizing counterpropagating beams. Their method can provide good spatial resolution independent of the refractive index and the Raman frequency.

C. Background-Free Techniques

Because of the high intensity of CARS signals, one seldom encounters in the application of CARS a situation for which the signal *per se* is too small to detect. However, one frequently finds that although the resonant signal of interest is large the nonresonant background signal is equally large or larger, and the signal-to-noise ratio is limited not by the magnitude of the resonant signal but by the ratio of the resonant signal magnitude to the nonresonant signal magnitude. An example of such a situation is depicted in Fig. 1.14. This figure, taken from the work of Hall (1979), shows the computed CARS spectrum of a methane/air flame in the vicinity of the carbon monoxide vibrational Q-branch resonance at 2143 cm^{-1}. Here, $\omega_1 = 3.54 \times 10^{15}$ s^{-1} ($\lambda_1 = 532$ nm), so $\omega_0 = 3.94 \times 10^{15}$ s^{-1} ($\lambda_0 = 478$ nm), and $|\chi^{NR}|$ is assumed to be 9.2×10^{-19} cm^3 erg^{-1}. Although the CO $v = 0 \rightarrow v = 1$ bandhead at 20,940 cm^{-1} and the $v = 1 \rightarrow v = 2$ hot-band bandhead at 20,913 cm^{-1} are clearly evident at 4% CO concentration, the nonresonant background is about as large as the resonant signal. At 0.1% CO the resonant signal is nearly completely lost in the nonresonant background.

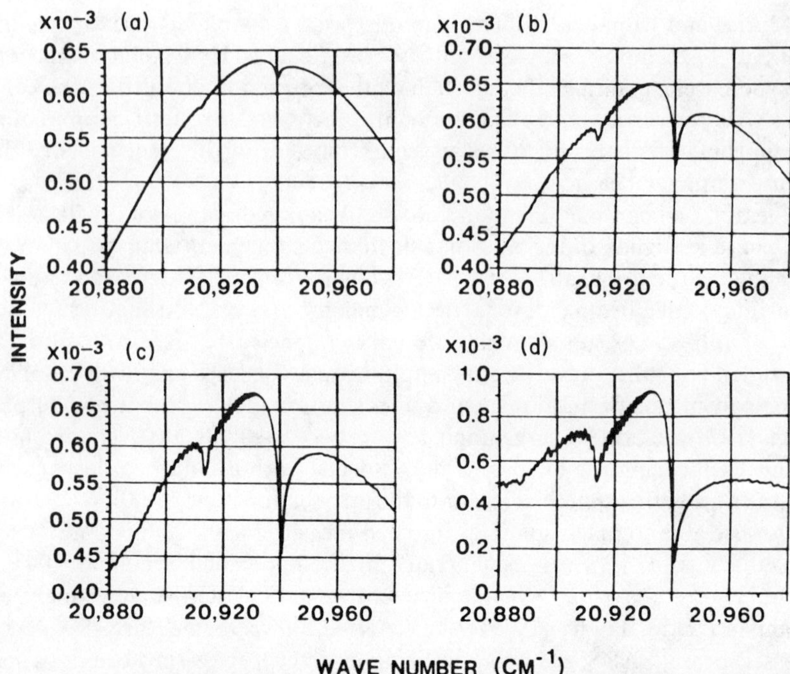

FIG. 1.14. Predicted CARS spectra of CO at various concentrations in a methane/air atmospheric-pressure flame at 1700 K: (a) 0.1%, (b) 0.5%, (c) 1%, and (d) 4%. χ^{NR} is taken to be 9.2×10^{-19} cm^3/erg. [From Hall (1979). Reprinted by permission of the publisher, Copyright 1979 by the Combustion Institute.]

Several special CARS techniques have been developed to reduce such problems with nonresonant background interference by separating the resonant signal from the nonresonant background on the basis of the different polarization† behavior of the resonant and nonresonant third-order susceptibilities. As discussed in Subsection 1.2.D, $\chi^{(3)}$ is a fourth-rank tensor with up to $3^4 = 81$ elements. For isotropic media such as gases and liquids there are only four nonzero elements that are related:

$$\chi^{(3)}_{1111} = \chi^{(3)}_{1122} + \chi^{(3)}_{1212} + \omega^{(3)}_{1221}. \tag{1.56}$$

In almost all CARS experiments $\omega_1 = \omega_3$, so that

$$\chi^{(3)}_{1111} = 2\chi^{(3)}_{1122} + \chi^{(3)}_{1212}. \tag{1.58}$$

Generally the lasers at ω_1 and ω_2 are plane polarized in the same direction,

† Polarization here refers to the direction of the electric vector of the fields at ω_0, ω_1, ω_2, and ω_3. It should not be confused with the polarization **P** induced in the sample by the incident electric fields.

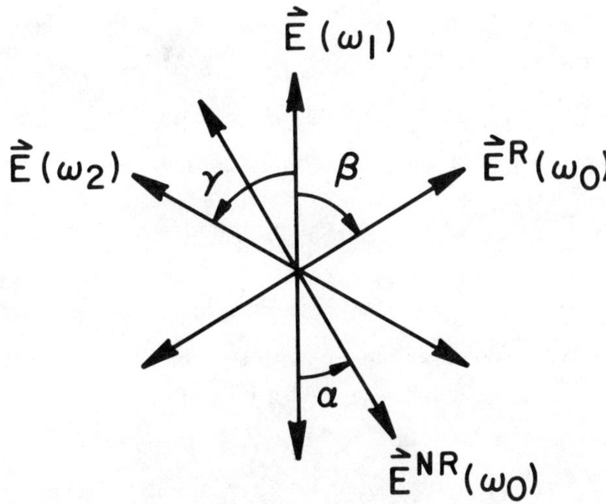

FIG. 1.15. Electric field polarization diagram for coherent anti-Stokes Raman ellipsometry (CARE). $\mathbf{E}^{\mathrm{R}}(\omega_0)$ and $\mathbf{E}^{\mathrm{NR}}(\omega_0)$ are the electric field vectors of the resonant and nonresonant contributions to the anti-Stokes signal.

so the tensor component sampled is $\chi_{1111}^{(3)}$, and the signal ω_0 is plane polarized in the same direction as ω_1 and ω_2. However, if we do not have ω_1 and ω_2 polarized in the same direction the effective $\boldsymbol{\chi}^{(3)}$ will be some combination of $\chi_{1111}^{(3)}$, $\chi_{1122}^{(3)}$, and $\chi_{1212}^{(3)}$, and ω_0 can be plane polarized in a direction different from both ω_1 and ω_2. Since $\boldsymbol{\chi}^{\mathrm{NR}}$ and $\boldsymbol{\chi}^{\mathrm{R}}$ in general have different polarization behavior, it is possible, by appropriate choice of the direction of polarization of ω_1 and ω_2, to generate a resonant signal with an electric field component in a direction along which the nonresonant signal has no electric field component. By coupling this polarization orientation with polarization-sensitive detection it is possible to eliminate the nonresonant contribution to the signal.

A laser polarization diagram for a CARS experimental arrangement that takes advantage of the different polarization behavior of $\boldsymbol{\chi}^{\mathrm{NR}}$ and $\boldsymbol{\chi}^{\mathrm{R}}$ to eliminate the nonresonant background signal is shown in Fig. 1.15. The induced polarization at the anti-Stokes frequency ω_0 will have components perpendicular to and parallel to $\mathbf{E}(\omega_1)$. If we define x and y axes to be perpendicular to and parallel to $\mathbf{E}(\omega_1)$ we can write these components of the induced polarization as [see Eq. (1.21)]

$$P_x^{(3)}(\omega_0, z) = \tfrac{3}{4}\chi_{1212}^{(3)}(-\omega_0, \omega_1, -\omega_2, \omega_1)E^2(\omega_1, z)E^*(\omega_2, z) \times \sin\gamma \exp[i(2k_1 - k_2)z], \tag{1.78}$$

and

$$P_y^{(3)}(\omega_0, z) = \tfrac{3}{4}\chi_{1111}^{(3)}(-\omega_0, \omega_1, -\omega_2, \omega_1)E^2(\omega_1, z)E^*(\omega_2, z) \times \cos\gamma \exp[i(2k_1 - k_2)z]. \quad (1.79)$$

There are both resonant and nonresonant contributions to $P_x^{(3)}(\omega_0, z)$ and $P_y^{(3)}(\omega_0, z)$. Defining α as the angle, with respect to $\mathbf{E}(\omega_1)$, of the nonresonant contribution $\mathbf{P}^{\mathrm{NR}}(\omega_0, z)$ characterized by the electric field vector $\mathbf{E}^{\mathrm{NR}}(\omega_0)$, we have

$$\alpha = \tan^{-1}(\chi_{1212}^{\mathrm{NR}}/\chi_{1111}^{\mathrm{NR}} \tan\gamma). \quad (1.80)$$

A similar expression gives the angle, with respect to $\mathbf{E}(\omega_1)$, of the resonant contribution $\mathbf{P}^{\mathrm{R}}(\omega_0, z)$ having field vector $\mathbf{E}^{\mathrm{R}}(\omega_0)$:

$$\delta = \tan^{-1}(\chi_{1212}^{\mathrm{R}}/\chi_{1111}^{\mathrm{R}} \tan\gamma). \quad (1.81)$$

However, $\chi_{1212}^{\mathrm{R}}/\chi_{1111}^{\mathrm{R}} \neq \chi_{1212}^{\mathrm{NR}}/\chi_{1111}^{\mathrm{NR}}$, so $\alpha \neq \delta$, and the resonant signal at ω_0 will have a polarization component perpendicular to the direction of polarization of the nonresonant signal.

This component of the resonant signal I_0 will be at an angle $\beta = 90° - \alpha$ with respect to $\mathbf{E}(\omega_1)$, and in the case of plane wave fields can be shown from Eqs. (1.34), (1.78), and (1.79) to be

$$I_0(L) = \left(\frac{12\pi^2\omega_0}{c^2}\right)^2 I_1^2 I_2 |\chi_{1111}^{\mathrm{R}}|^2 L^2 \left[\frac{\sin(\Delta k\, L/2)}{\Delta k\, L/2}\right]^2 \times \left[\left(1 - \frac{\chi_{1111}^{\mathrm{NR}}\,\chi_{1212}^{\mathrm{R}}}{\chi_{1212}^{\mathrm{NR}}\,\chi_{1111}^{\mathrm{R}}}\right)\sin\alpha\cos\gamma\right]^2. \quad (1.82)$$

Now since $\boldsymbol{\chi}^{\mathrm{NR}}$ is independent of frequency, $\chi_{1111}^{\mathrm{NR}}/\chi_{1212}^{\mathrm{NR}} = \text{const}$, while $\chi_{1212}^{\mathrm{R}}/\chi_{1111}^{\mathrm{R}} = \rho$, the depolarization ratio of the Raman mode; therefore the signal is proportional only to $|\chi_{1111}^{\mathrm{R}}|^2$ and has no contribution from the nonresonant signal. The optimum angles α, β, γ are found by maximizing the quantity $\sin\alpha\cos\gamma = \sin[\tan^{-1}(\chi_{1212}^{\mathrm{NR}}/\chi_{1111}^{\mathrm{NR}} \tan\gamma)]\cos\gamma$. If we assume that the nonresonant susceptibilities obey Kleinmann symmetry (Kleinmann, 1962),

$$\tfrac{1}{3}\chi_{1111}^{\mathrm{NR}} = \chi_{1122}^{\mathrm{NR}} = \chi_{1212}^{\mathrm{NR}} = \chi_{1221}^{\mathrm{NR}}, \quad (1.83)$$

we find that the signal is maximized when $\gamma = 60°$, so $\alpha = 30°$ and $\beta = 60°$.

Although this polarization CARS technique, which is sometimes referred to as coherent anti-Stokes Raman ellipsometry (CARE), has not been used extensively in practical applications, several groups have demonstrated the large nonresonant background suppression and concomitant increased sensitivity that can be achieved with it. Oudar *et al.* (1979) carried out CARE experiments in dilute liquid mixtures of benzene in carbon tetrachloride. They were able to reduce the background by more than 10^4 so that very weak resonant signals could be detected. They could detect 200-ppm benzene in carbon tetrachloride and predicted 10-ppm sensitivity with more powerful lasers. Akhmanov *et al.* (1978) were able to increase the detectability of carbon dioxide in carbon dioxide/nitrogen gas mixtures by a factor of 10, bringing

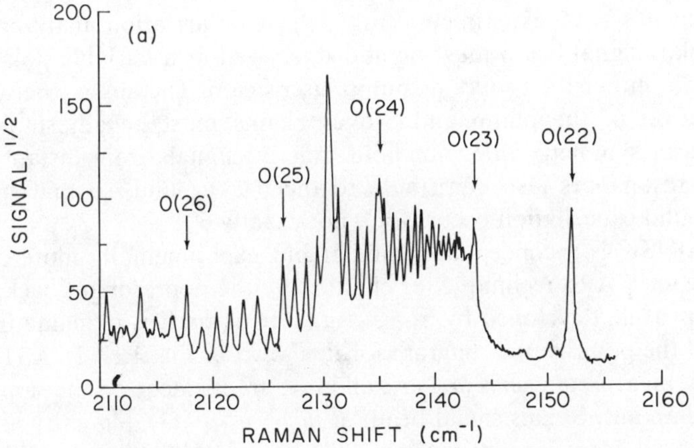

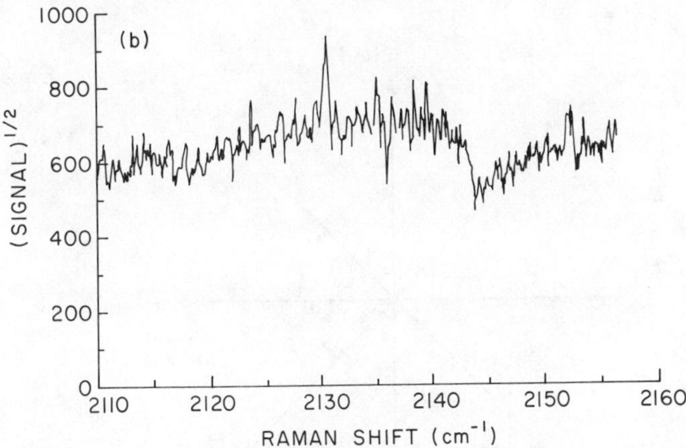

FIG. 1.16. Square root of the CARS signal from a methane/air flame in the region of the CO resonance: (a) background-free (CARE) spectrum with $\gamma = 60°$, $\beta = 57°$ (cf. Fig. 1.15) with the O-branch lines of N_2 labeled; (b) conventional CARS spectrum with all electric field polarizations parallel. [From Rahn *et al.* (1979). © North-Holland Publishing Company, Amsterdam, 1979.]

the sensitivity up to 100-ppm CO_2, and they expect improvements in the experiment to increase the sensitivity to 0.1 to 10 ppm. Rahn *et al.* (1979) have demonstrated the advantages of CARE in real-world environments by showing enhanced sensitivity for detection of CO in a methane/air flame. Their results, which are shown in Fig. 1.16, indicate an increase in signal-to-noise ratio of more than 200 in going from CARS to CARE, with an increase of more than 25 in the detectability of CO in the flame.

The apparatus needed for CARE experiments is essentially identical to that used in CARS experiments (Fig. 1.9). A polarization analyzer for the anti-Stokes signal beam must be added, as well as a variable polarization rotator for either the Stokes or pump laser beam. The angle γ between the polarization of the pump and Stokes beams must be adjustable, since Kleinmann symmetry does not hold exactly; signals from distant, strong Raman resonances also contribute to the background, so that optimum background cancellation occurs for γ not exactly 60°.

ASTERISK is a conceptually similar but experimentally more complex polarization CARS technique for eliminating the nonresonant background. This approach, developed by Song *et al.* (1976), derives its name from the shape of the polarization diagram for it, shown in Fig. 1.17. In ASTERISK three lasers, at frequencies ω_1, ω_2, and ω_3, are incident on the sample and generate an anti-Stokes signal beam at $\omega_0 = \omega_1 - \omega_2 + \omega_3$. By assuming that all input beams as well as the signal beam are plane waves and by using the polarization arrangement of Fig. 1.17, we find that the signal intensity is

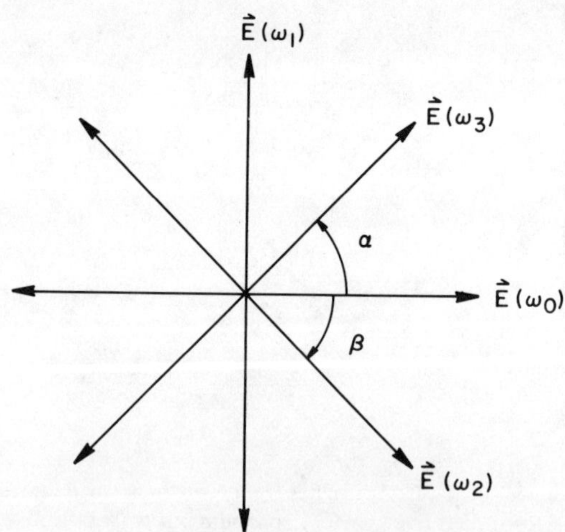

FIG. 1.17. Electric field polarization diagram for ASTERISK.

given by

$$I_0(L) = (24\pi^2\omega_0/c^2)^2 I_1 I_2 I_3 L^2[\sin(\Delta k\, L/2)/\Delta k\, L/2]^2$$
$$\times\, |\chi^{(3)}_{1212}(-\omega_0, \omega_1, -\omega_2, \omega_3) \sin\alpha \cos\beta$$
$$-\, \chi^{(3)}_{1221}(-\omega_0, \omega_1, -\omega_2, \omega_3) \cos\alpha \sin\beta|^2. \qquad (1.84)$$

The nonresonant contribution to $I_0(L)$ vanishes when

$$\chi^{\mathrm{NR}}_{1212} \sin\alpha \cos\beta = -\chi^{\mathrm{NR}}_{1221} \cos\alpha \sin\beta. \qquad (1.85)$$

If Kleinmann symmetry holds for $\boldsymbol{\chi}^{\mathrm{NR}}$ $\alpha = \beta = 45°$, and Eq. (1.84) becomes

$$I_0(L) = (24\pi^2\omega_0/c^2)^2 I_1 I_2 I_3 L^2[\sin(\Delta k\, L/2)/\Delta k\, L/2]^2$$
$$\times\, |\chi^{\mathrm{R}}_{1212}(-\omega_0, \omega_1, -\omega_2, \omega_3) - \chi^{\mathrm{R}}_{1221}(-\omega_0, \omega_1, -\omega_2, \omega_3)|^2. \qquad (1.86)$$

Using ASTERISK, Song *et al.* (1976) found that for a liquid solution of 0.3-M benzene in carbon disulfide the nonresonant background was reduced by a factor of more than 1000 as compared to CARS. The resonant signal from benzene decreased by a factor of only 4. This gives about a 20-fold increase in sensitivity relative to CARS.

With three distinct incident laser frequencies it is also possible to cancel the nonresonant background by using what might be called double-resonance CARS. Considering two Raman resonances A and B, not necessarily from the same molecular species, we have already shown in Subsection 1.2.G that

$$|\chi^{(3)}|^2 = (\chi'_{\mathrm{A}})^2 + (\chi'_{\mathrm{B}})^2 + (\chi''_{\mathrm{A}})^2 + (\chi''_{\mathrm{B}})^2 + (\chi^{\mathrm{NR}})^2$$
$$+\, 2\chi'_{\mathrm{A}}\chi'_{\mathrm{B}} + 2\chi''_{\mathrm{A}}\chi''_{\mathrm{B}} + 2\chi'_{\mathrm{A}}\chi^{\mathrm{NR}} + 2\chi'_{\mathrm{B}}\chi^{\mathrm{NR}}. \qquad (1.87)$$

If, of the incident laser beams at ω_1, ω_2, and ω_3, two, e.g., ω_1 and ω_3, are tunable, we can probe both Raman resonances A and B simultaneously. We can tune ω_1 to scan through the A resonance $\omega_{\mathrm{A}} = \omega_1 - \omega_2$, as we would in normal CARS. We can use the second tunable laser at ω_3 to tune $\omega_3 - \omega_2$ near the B resonance, to make $\chi'_{\mathrm{B}} < 0$ (cf. Fig. 1.6). By appropriate choice of $\omega_3 - \omega_2$ we can adjust the magnitude of χ'_{B} such that the sum of all the background contributions to $|\chi^{(3)}|^2$, that is, the sum of all terms other than $(\chi'_{\mathrm{A}})^2 + (\chi''_{\mathrm{A}})^2$ in Eq. (1.87), is zero. Then the CARS resonant signal at $\omega_0 = \omega_1 - \omega_2 + \omega_3$, with $\omega_1 - \omega_2 = \omega_{\mathrm{A}}$, will be free of nonresonant background.

Such a method for background cancellation was first demonstrated in liquids and solids by Lynch *et al.* (1976) and further explored by Lotem *et al.* (1976), who were able to cancel the nonresonant background present when observing the CARS signal from a liquid solution of cyclohexane in benzene. As shown in Fig. 1.18, Lotem *et al.* (1976) could eliminate the non-resonant background contribution from the benzene solvent at the cyclo-hexane resonance by adjusting $(\omega_3 - \omega_2)/(2\pi c)$ to be approximately 998 cm^{-1}, while scanning $(\omega_1 - \omega_2)/(2\pi c)$ through the cyclohexane resonance at 802 cm^{-1}. In this experiment the benzene solvent CARS resonance at 992 cm^{-1} serves as the B resonance.

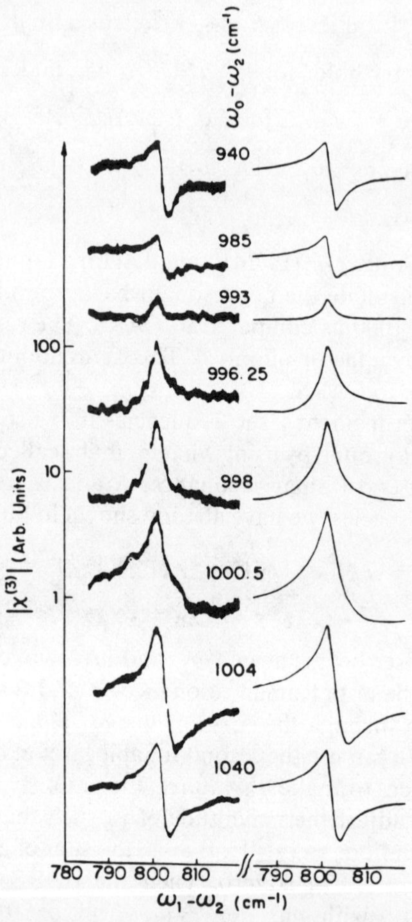

FIG. 1.18. Experimental results (left) and theoretical fits (right) for double-resonance CARS spectra of cyclohexane in benzene. $\chi^{(3)}$ is shown as a function of $(\omega_1 - \omega_2)/(2\pi c)$ in the vicinity of the 802-cm^{-1} cyclohexane Raman resonance for various choices of $(\omega_3 - \omega_2)/(2\pi c)$ near the 992-cm^{-1} benzene resonance. Note that in the notation used in this figure what we have called ω_3 is labeled ω_0. [From Lotem *et al.* (1976).]

The polarization CARS techniques, CARE and ASTERISK, discriminate against nonresonant contributions to $\chi^{(3)}$ and hence against the nonresonant signal, by exploiting the differences in the tensor components of χ^{NR} and χ^{R}. It is also possible to separate the resonant and nonresonant CARS signals on the basis of the different temporal behavior of χ^{NR} and χ^{R}. Zinth *et al.* (1978) recognized that the nonresonant contribution to $\chi^{(3)}$, since in general it is due to virtual electronic transitions, will have a "time constant" of the order of 10^{-14} s. In contrast, the resonant contribution, which is usually due to a real transition from one vibrational state to another, will have a lifetime determined by the vibrational dephasing time. The vibrational dephasing time can be as large as tens of picoseconds in the condensed phase and hundreds of picoseconds in the gas phase.

Zinth *et al.* (1978) measured the temporal behavior of χ^{NR} and χ^{R} by using a two-frequency, three-pulse picosecond laser technique. A laser pulse of 5.2-ps duration containing ω_1 and ω_2 was imaged into a sample cell containing 9% carbon tetrachloride and 91% cyclohexane. The frequency difference $(\omega_1 - \omega_2)/(2\pi c) \cong 459\ \text{cm}^{-1}$ was resonant with the totally symmetric vibration in CCl_4 and nonresonant for C_6H_{12}. A third pulse, at ω_1, with a delay of up to 40 ps with respect to the first ω_1 and ω_2 pulses, was used to probe the temporal behavior of the anti-Stokes scattering at $2\omega_1 - \omega_2$. They found that the nonresonant CARS signal from cyclohexane had a Gaussian temporal profile that followed the first ω_1 and ω_2 pulses, whereas the resonant carbon tetrachloride signal had a delayed maximum with an exponential decay time constant of 3.2 ps. At 15-ps delay of the second ω_1 pulse the nonresonant signal was only 3×10^{-4} of its maximum, whereas the resonant signal was $\sim 1 \times 10^{-2}$ of its maximum value.

Kamga and Sceats (1980) carried out similar experiments on 10% carbon disulfide in toluene, probing the 656-cm^{-1} Raman vibrational resonance of CS_2, which has a dephasing time of 20 ps. By delaying the second ω_1 pulse by 20 ps with respect to the initial ω_1 and ω_2 pulses, they were able to reduce the nonresonant background by a factor of 100 relative to that observed at zero delay time. They claim that in gas-phase samples, where dephasing times are large, complete rejection of the nonresonant background should be possible with the use of long ω_1 probe pulse delays.

These new pulse-sequenced, or PUSCARS (Kamga and Sceats, 1980), techniques, which require lasers having pulse lengths of only a few picoseconds, are quite difficult to implement relative to the usual nanosecond pulsed laser CARS experiments. However, developments in picosecond lasers may eventually make this highly time-resolved background suppression method more accessible.

D. Resonance CARS

In the discussion of Subsection 1.2.C we noted that the two-photon Raman enhancement of the three-wave mixing process that leads to coherent anti-Stokes Raman scattering is the result of terms of the form $\omega_{kg} - (\omega_1 - \omega_2)$ in the denominator of Eq. (1.37). Here $\hbar\omega_{kg}$ is the energy difference between molecular states g and k, where g is the initial state of the system and k spans all other molecular energy levels. We also noted that Eq. (1.37) has terms of the form $\omega_{kg} - \omega_0$, $\omega_{kg} - \omega_1$, $\omega_{kg} - \omega_2$, and $\omega_{kg} - \omega_3$ in its denominator. As a result of these frequency difference terms, whenever any of the laser fields or the anti-Stokes signal field has a frequency equal to that of some one-photon allowed electronic transition, ω_{kg}, the coherent anti-Stokes Raman scattering will be enhanced. This effect is termed resonance CARS, and is analogous to the resonance Raman effect.

As they do in spontaneous Raman spectroscopy, such one-photon resonances can lead to very large signal enhancements in CARS spectroscopy. Increasing the signal in this way increases the ratio of the resonant CARS (i.e., Raman resonant) signal to the nonresonant background and hence increases the signal-to-noise ratio and improves the detectability for species in low relative concentration. Resonance CARS therefore achieves through judicious selection of the magnitude of ω_1, ω_2, and ω_3 what the polarization CARS techniques achieve through appropriate choice of the direction of polarization of the fields at ω_1, ω_2, and ω_3. Like resonance spontaneous Raman, resonance CARS also can be used to investigate structural changes in molecules, particularly large molecules, upon electronic excitation. One-photon resonance enhancement therefore can improve the sensitivity of CARS and also can expand the scope of spectroscopic information that is obtained through CARS.

The potential of electronic resonance enhancement in CARS was recognized and exploited as soon as reliable tunable lasers made such resonance enhancement experimentally accessible. Chabay *et al.* (1976) were the first to demonstrate resonance CARS in recording the spectrum of diphenyloctatetraene in benzene solution. Compared to the resonance spontaneous Raman spectrum, which they also obtained, the CARS signal level, signal-to-noise, and resolution were far better, demonstrating the same advantages of CARS versus spontaneous Raman that are observed without electronic resonance enhancement.

From their spectra Chabay *et al.* estimated a lower limit of detection for diphenyloctatetraene in benzene of 5 ppm. This is comparable to the detectability possible using the background-free CARS techniques described in the previous section. Since one-photon resonance-enhanced CARS is much easier to implement experimentally than the polarization or double-resonance CARS techniques, it is the method of choice for signal-to-noise improvement whenever excited molecular electronic states are accessible. Current tunable pulsed lasers operate in the spectral range from about 220 to 900 nm, so molecules having excited electronic states that are within about 5.5 eV of the ground state are candidates for resonance enhancement in CARS spectroscopy.

This limitation on the wavelength range of availble tunable laser sources at present precludes electronic resonance enhancement in CARS of most small molecules. However, there are many large molecules, such as organic dyes and biological chromophores, in which resonance CARS can be used to significant advantage, and Nestor *et al.* (1976) and Hudson *et al.* (1976) have explored the characteristic features of one-photon resonance enhancement in such molecular systems. Among the many reports of the application of resonance CARS for biological molecules are the work of Dutta *et al.* (1977) on the structure and dynamics of flavin adenine dinucleotide and glucose oxidase and that of Igarashi *et al.* (1980) on porphyrins. One must also note the work of Carreira *et al.* (1977), who have demonstrated detection of β-carotene in benzene solution at 0.05 ppm, considerably better then the early estimates of detectability by Chabay *et al.* (1976) and much better than what has been achieved with the background-free CARS methods.

There are only a few reports of electronic resonance enhancement in the gas phase, due to the absence of low-lying excited electronic states for most small molecules that are permanent gases or at least have appreciable vapor pressure at ambient temperature. Not surprisingly, iodine, which has been the subject of so many spectroscopic studies, was the first molecule for which resonance enhancement was observed in the gas phase (Attal *et al.*, 1978). Since then, reports of resonance enhancement in NO_2 (Guthals *et al.*, 1979; McIlwain and Hindman, 1980) and C_2 (Gross *et al.*, 1979; Hetherington *et al.*, 1981) have been published, as well as further work on iodine (Beckmann *et al.*, 1982). Attal *et al.* (1982) have demonstrated the utility of resonance CARS in practical environments by detecting C_2 in an acetylene welding torch flame at a density of 10^{13} molecules cm^{-3} (0.5 ppm).

In general, one gets improvements in sensitivity of 10^2 to 10^4 through one-photon resonance enhancement in the gas phase. The principal experimental difficulty encountered in these experiments arises from the need to apply high pump and Stokes laser powers to drive the CARS process, and simultaneously small laser powers to avoid saturation of the one-photon resonance. Druet and Taran (1981) suggest the use of long-pulse-length ($\sim$500 ns), large-pulse-energy, but low-peak-power (1–10-kW) flash-lamp-pumped dye lasers to generate the incident laser beams.

Resonantly enhanced gas-phase, small-molecule spectra are considerably more complex than condensed-phase spectra, since a very rich rovibronic one-photon absorption and rovibrational two-photon Raman structure is present in the former, whereas the latter involve only broadband one-photon excitation and Raman spectral features. As a result, the interpretation of gas-phase, high-resolution resonance CARS spectra can be quite complicated (Druet and Taran, 1981). Theoretical treatments deal with the interpretation of these spectra in considerable detail (Druet *et al.*, 1978; Herrmann and Landmann, 1979).

E. High-Resolution Spectroscopy

In view of other recent advances in high-resolution spectroscopy brought on by the development of narrow-linewidth tunable laser sources, it should not be surprising that one of the major applications of coherent anti-Stokes Raman scattering is high-resolution molecular spectroscopy. The large signal intensity produced in CARS greatly facilitates higher spectral resolution than would be possible with spontaneous Raman scattering. However, the coherent nature of the CARS signal yields additional gains for high-resolution applications.

In spontaneous Raman spectroscopy higher resolution is always accompanied by a decrease in signal intensity, since the resolution is increased by decreasing the slit width on the monochromator, which disperses the inelastically scattered light. In CARS, by contrast, the resolution is increased by narrowing the linewidth of the pump and Stokes laser sources. Laser line narrowing can be effected with only small power loss and hence only small decrease in CARS signal intensity. Moreover, as with other stimulated, coherent optical processes, decreasing the laser linewidths at constant laser power actually increases the signal, at least until the linewidth is smaller than the molecular (Doppler) linewidth. Hence, high-resolution CARS spectra can actually be more intense than lower resolution spectra.

The narrowest linewidth tunable laser sources currently available are single-frequency cw dye lasers with linewidths less than 0.001 cm^{-1}, and consequently such sources are used for the highest resolution CARS spectroscopy. The CARS spectra obtained with such cw laser sources have resolution 10^2 to 10^3 times better than high-resolution spontaneous Raman spectra. However, many high-resolution CARS experiments at somewhat lower resolution (10^{-1} to 10^{-2} cm^{-1}) have been carried out with multimode cw lasers and pulsed lasers.

Barrett and Begley (1975) were the first to report cw high-resolution CARS. They observed coherent anti-Stokes Raman scattering from methane with a resolution of 0.1 cm^{-1}. Very shortly after this Hirth and Vollrath (1976) reported high-resolution cw, intracavity CARS of nitrogen in air. Since then there have been several more reports of cw high-resolution spectroscopy on methane (Henesian *et al.*, 1976; Aliev *et al.*, 1977), deuterium (Krynetsky *et al.*, 1977; Henesian *et al.*, 1977), and ethylene (Fabelinsky *et al.*, 1977), with steadily increasing resolution. Spectral resolution of 10^{-3} cm^{-1} is now typical in cw high-resolution CARS experiments. For many light molecules the CARS resolution is now limited by the Doppler width of the Raman

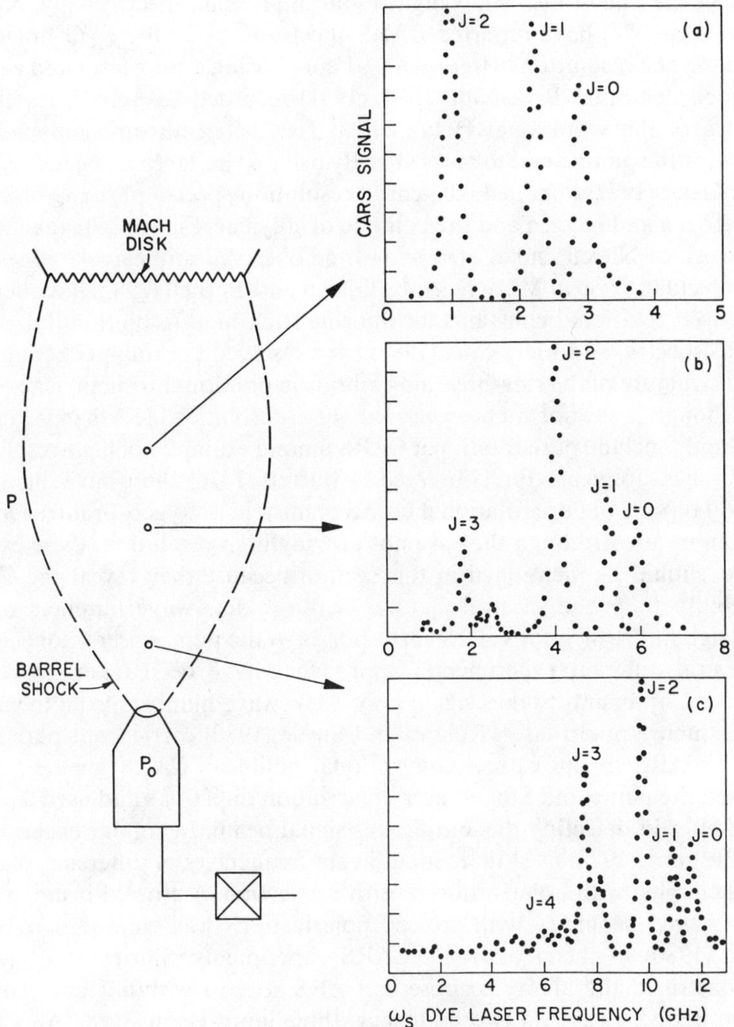

FIG. 1.19. High-resolution CARS spectra of methane in a supersonic jet: (a) $T = 34$ K, (b) $T = 44$ K, and (c) $T = 94$ K. Spectra taken at three different locations in the jet. [From Gustafson *et al.* (1982).]

transition. In this case the effective resolution can be improved by cooling the sample in a supersonic jet, as demonstrated by the work of Gustafson *et al.*(1982). Spectra of methane taken in a supersonic jet by Gustafson *et al.* at 0.001-cm^{-1} resolution are shown in Fig. 1.19. The residual linewidths of ~0.007 cm^{-1} are due to Doppler, pressure, and transit-time broadening.

Although cw CARS spectroscopy affords the highest resolution, pulsed CARS experiments also allow high-resolution Raman spectroscopy. Boquillon *et al.* (1977) have reported CARS spectroscopy of the ν_1 Q branch of methane at a resolution better than 0.01 cm^{-1} using a ruby laser and a ruby-pumped dye laser. Beckmann *et al.* (1981) recorded 0.05-cm^{-1} resolution spectra of the vibrational Q branch of NO, using nitrogen-pumped dye lasers for the pump and Stokes beams. By using a similar laser system, Nitsch and Kiefer (1977) obtained 0.03-cm^{-1}-resolution spectra of the Q branches of nitrogen and oxygen and the ν_2 mode of ethylene. Figure 1.20, taken from the work of Nitsch and Kiefer, shows the observed and calculated spectra of molecular oxygen. More recently, Gilson and Purnell (1982) have derived improved rotational constants for fluorine from high-resolution (0.1-cm^{-1}) CARS spectra, and Fietz *et al.* (1982) have resolved the ring-puckering hot-band structure of the ring-breathing vibration of normal trimethylene oxide.

Although it has not yet been carried out at resolutions less than 0.1 cm^{-1}, we should include pure rotational CARS among examples of high-resolution CARS measurements. First observed by Barrett (1976), there have since been several reports of pure rotational CARS of nitrogen, oxygen, or nitrogen and oxygen in air. Although they are not of truly high resolution, these experiments should be mentioned in this section because they reveal the CARS capability to probe spectral features within a few wave numbers of the Rayleigh line, which for CARS corresponds to the pump-laser frequency.

Several different experimental approaches have been taken to permit detection of an anti-Stokes signal only a few wave numbers from the much more intense pump laser. Roland and Steele (1980) carried out pure rotational CARS in air with a conventional collinear CARS geometry, but crossed the pump and Stokes laser polarization directions and used a polarizing filter in detecting the anti-Stokes signal beam. In similar experiments Beattie *et al.* (1978) used three input beam frequencies of different polarizations coupled with polarization-sensitive detection. A crossed-beam, phase-mismatched geometry with crossed polarizations was employed by Goss *et al.* (1980) in their rotational CARS experiments. Shirley *et al.* (1980) demonstrated the ability to observe CARS spectra within 7 cm^{-1} of the pump frequency with a two-frequency, three-input-beam BOXCARS technique, which has $\mathbf{k}_2$ and $\mathbf{k}_3$ in a plane orthogonal to the plane containing the two $\mathbf{k}_1$ wave vectors. A rotational spectrum of nitrogen obtained by Shirley *et al.* is shown in Fig. 1.21.

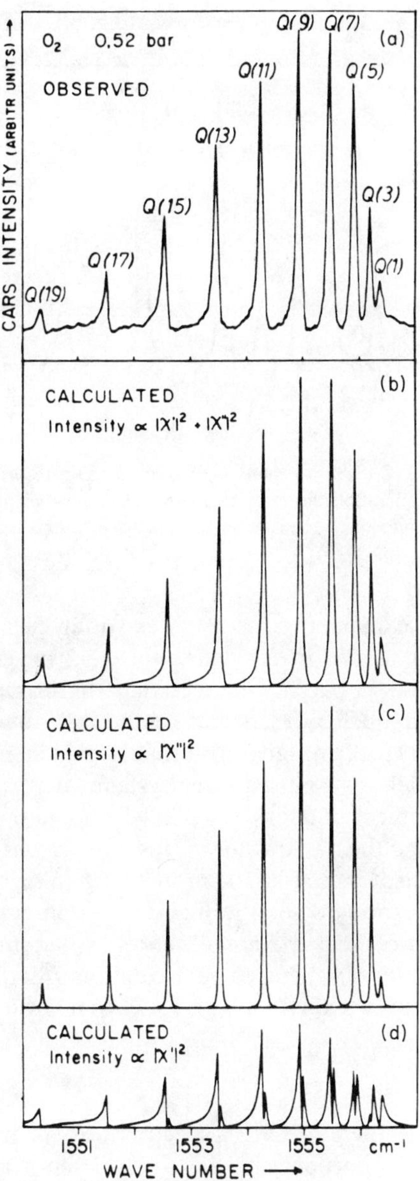

FIG. 1.20. High-resolution CARS spectrum of oxygen: (a) observed spectrum at 0.03-cm^{-1} resolution, (b) calculated spectrum, (c) square of the imaginary component of the third-order dielectric susceptibility, (d) square of the real component of the third-order dielectric susceptibility. [From Nitsch and Kiefer (1977). © North-Holland Publishing Company, Amsterdam, 1977.]

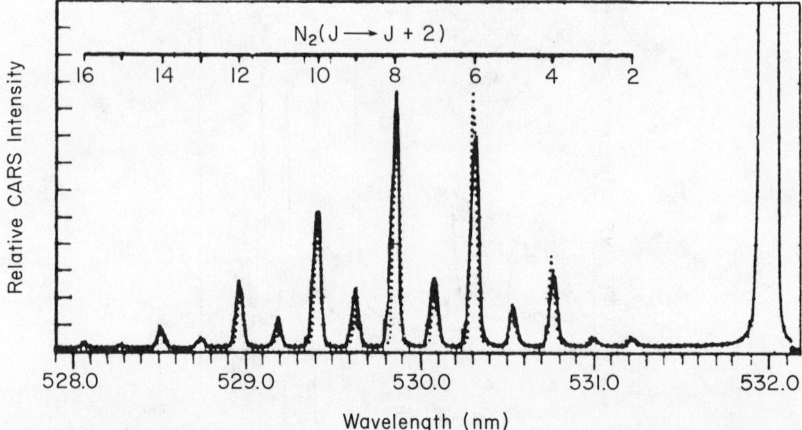

FIG. 1.21. Rotational CARS spectrum of nitrogen at STP recorded with a BOXCARS technique. The pump and Stokes laser polarizations are perpendicular. The solid curve gives the observed spectrum and the dotted curve the calculated spectrum. The pump laser is at 532 nm. [From Shirley *et al.* (1980).]

High-resolution Raman spectroscopy has so far been limited largely to the intense Raman modes in methane, nitrogen, oxygen, and hydrogen. This situation is due in part to the fact that the highest resolution laser sources, cw single-frequency lasers, have quite low power outputs and, as noted in Subsection 1.3.B, produce anti-Stokes signal intensities many orders of magnitude smaller than pulsed laser systems, despite the narrower cw linewidths. Development of quasi-cw laser systems, described in Subsection 1.3.B, which combine the narrow linewidths of cw single-frequency sources with the high power of pulsed lasers, promises to mitigate this problem. In the future we can expect to see the high-resolution capabilities of CARS exploited in studies of weaker Raman modes in diatomic and polyatomic molecules. Further development of pure rotational CARS techniques also should contribute to the growth of high-resolution CARS spectroscopy.

F. Combustion Diagnostics

The potential usefulness of CARS spectroscopy for making gas concentration measurements, particularly spatially and temporarlly resolved concentration measurements, was perceived even before the development of tunable laser sources made such measurements generally feasible. Regnier and Taran (1973), using a ruby laser for the CARS pump and a ruby-pumped hydrogen-stimulated Raman scattering oscillator to generate the Stokes

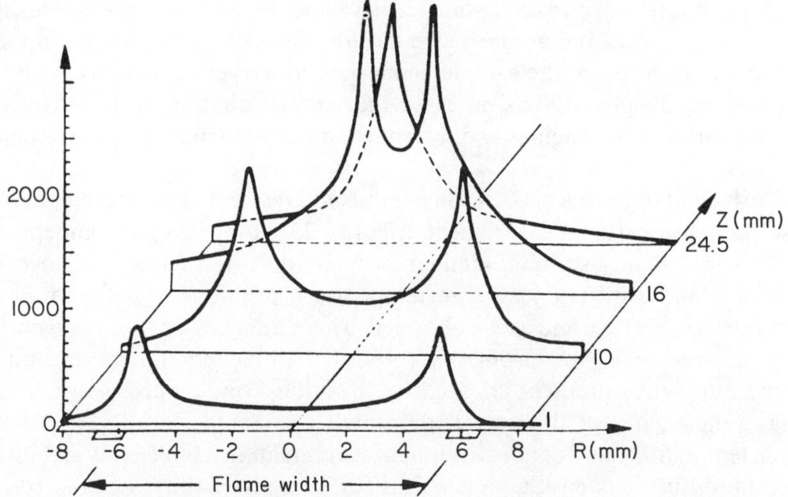

FIG. 1.22. Hydrogen concentration distribution in a horizontal natural gas flame measured by CARS. Coordinate R is the distance from the burner axis; Z is the distance along the axis; R is vertical, pointing downward. [From Regnier and Taran (1973).]

beam, demonstrated the detection of hydrogen at 100 ppm in nitrogen. Their measurement of the spatially resolved hydrogen density distribution in a premixed natural gas/air flame, illustrated in Fig. 1.22, showed how significant the potential of CARS was for mixture diagnostics, particularly in combustion. Note that the experimental points in Fig. 1.22 represent averages over only 5–10 laser shots.

Today this potential has been realized to a large extent and combustion research is probably the major application of CARS spectroscopy. The importance of this application of CARS is testified to by the review by Eckbreth and Schreiber (1981) devoted solely to CARS combustion diagnostics. Almost all the desirable features of CARS can be used to advantage in combustion studies. The sensitivity facilitates single-laser-pulse measurements, particularly in the multiplex configuration (cf. Subsection 1.3.B). The sensitivity and short pulse duration possible with pulsed lasers permits highly time-resolved analysis of transient combustion phenomena. The coherent, diffraction-limited character of the CARS signal beam makes remote detection, which is necessary with many real combustors, simple. The large discrimination against sample luminescence, made possible by the small signal beam divergence, eliminates many problems encountered in doing spectroscopy in large-scale, high-temperature combustion environments. The high spatial resolution that is possible with crossed-beam CARS techniques (cf. Subsection 1.3.B) makes point density and temperature measurements fairly routine. And the nonintrusive nature of CARS precludes any appreciable modification of the sample being probed. Development of CARS for combustion diagnostics has proceeded far enough that applications to real combustors, e.g., jet engines and internal combustion engines, are now being reported.

A principal objective of CARS in combustion research is accurate, spatially resolved temperature measurement. Figure 1.23 shows nitrogen temperature profiles in a highly sooting, laminar propane diffusion flame, obtained by Eckbreth and Hall (1979). These temperature profiles are believed to be accurate to ± 50 K, and were obtained by an analysis of the nitrogen Q-branch rotational band profile. Eckbreth (1980) has demonstrated similar temperature measurement capabilities, including single-pulse temperature measurement, in two different real combustors. Switzer *et al.* (1979) have made temperature and concentration measurements in a bluff-body stabilized propane diffusion flame. Stenhouse *et al.* (1979) reported the first nonintrusive species and temperature measurements in a firing propane- or gasoline-fueled internal combustion engine with CARS. Klick *et al.* (1981) have made the first broadband, single-pulse measurements of temperature and species concentration in a firing internal combustion engine. Some of their

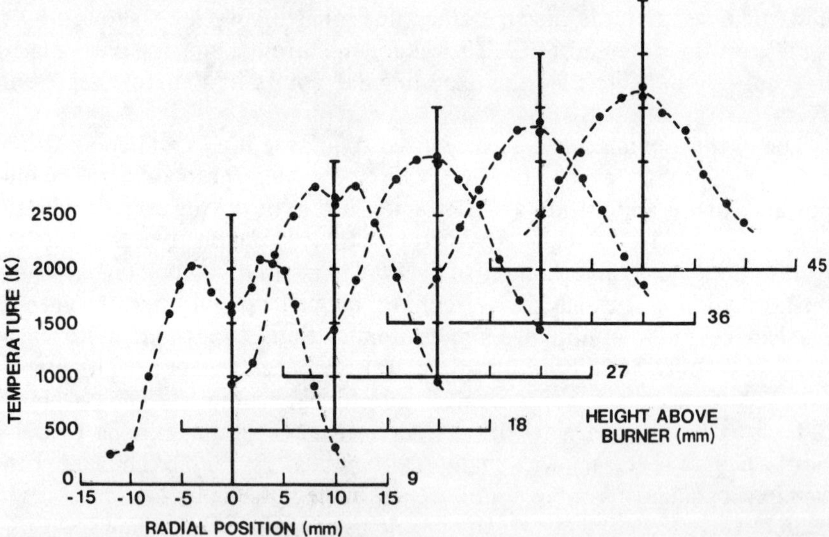

FIG. 1.23. Radial temperature profiles in a highly sooting, laminar propane diffusion flame. Temperatures determined from the nitrogen CARS Q-branch rotational band profile. [From Eckbreth and Hall (1979).]

nitrogen temperature results are shown in Fig. 1.10. All the measurements were made with 1-mm^3 spatial resolution, and the single-pulse results have 10-ns temporal resolution.

Extension of CARS measurements to a wider variety of chemical species in flames and combustors is now being pursued actively. Hall *et al.* (1979) have carried out CARS thermometry on water in a methane/air flame, and Eckbreth *et al.* (1979) have detected CO_2 in CO/O_2 flames. Also, Teets and Bechtel (1981) have reported detection of oxygen atoms and oxygen molecules in hydrogen/oxygen and methane/oxygen flames.

The need for high spatial resolution in combustion applications has been the primary impetus for the development of crossed-beam, phase-matched CARS techniques (Eckbreth, 1978; Shirley *et al.*, 1980; Marko and Rimai, 1979). Similarly, the desire to extend CARS measurements to minor species in combustion environments has spurred development and application of nonresonant background suppression techniques (cf. Subsection 1.3.C) like coherent anti-Stokes Raman ellipsometry (Rahn *et al.*, 1979). Most CARS combustion applications have been for measurement of temperature, using the CARS spectrum of nitrogen as a thermometer. Since nitrogen is the major chemical constituent in air-fed combustion, spectra of this species are not plagued with nonresonant background interference. As Fig. 1.14 shows, however, minor species detection is made difficult by the nonresonant background. The potential of CARE and other polarization techniques in making minor-species CARS measurements, as illustrated in Fig. 1.16, is quite promising, and we are sure to see more applications of polarization CARS to combustion environments in the future. Resonance CARS (cf. Subsection 1.3.D) should also prove useful in expanding the scope of CARS combustion applications. The electronic-resonance-enhanced measurement of C_2 at ~ 1 ppm in an acetylene welding torch (Attal *et al.*, 1982) demonstrates the sensitivity possible here.

G. Time-Resolved Spectroscopy

There are many situations in the physical and biological sciences in which the experimentalist needs to use a spectroscopic probe to investigate some transient species or temporally varying phenomena, e.g., in measurement of vibrational relaxation, in determination of the structure of electronic excited states of molecules, or in detection of photochemical intermediates. In order to be useful for any such investigation a spectroscopic method must have high sensitivity and high temporal resolution. High sensitivity and high temporal resolution are two of the principal attributes of CARS, and as a result this spectroscopic method is finding considerable use in time-resolved spectroscopy. Coherent anti-Stokes Raman spectroscopy is particularly useful in

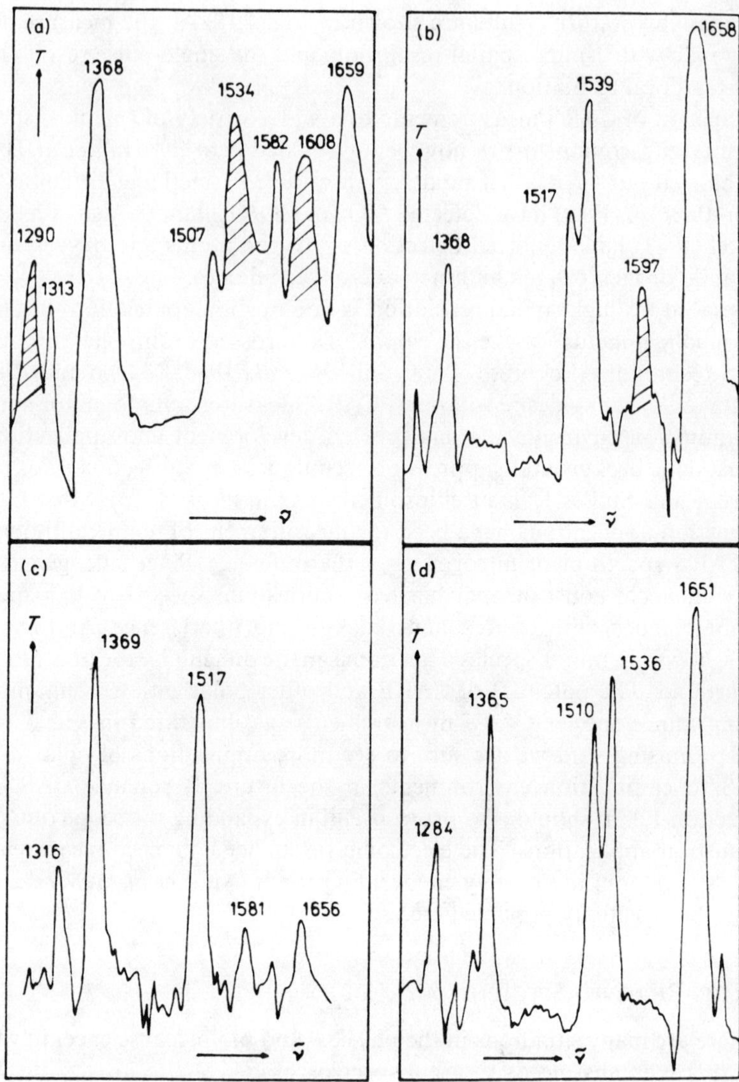

FIG. 1.24. CARS spectra of the ground electronic state (upper spectra; $\lambda_p = 541$ nm) and excited electronic state (lower spectra; $\lambda_p = 588$ nm) of (a and c) rhodamine 6G and (b and d) rhodamine B. [From König *et al.* (1980). © North-Holland Publishing Company, Amsterdam, 1980.]

the investigation of time-dependent phenomena and transient chemical species because as a light-scattering technique its temporal resolution is determined solely by the time width of the laser pulse used to effect it. This gives the experimentalist convenient control of the temporal resolution.

Included among the examples of CARS time-resolved spectroscopy are the picosecond experiments of Zinth *et al.* (1978) on the vibrational dephasing time of carbon tetrachloride in cyclohexane, and the similar experiments of Kamga and Sceats (1980) on vibrational dephasing of carbon disulfide in toluene. Brodnikovsky *et al.* (1982) have used CARS to follow the collisional relaxation of CO_2 following population of excited vibrational states via coherent Raman excitation.

König *et al.* (1980) have been able to record CARS spectra of both the ground and first excited electronic states of rhodamine laser dyes by using resonance CARS to study the dyes at 10^{-3} to 10^{-4} M in ethanol. Their results, some of which are shown in Fig. 1.24, illustrate the powerful combination of sensitivity and fluorescence rejection in the CARS process, since these fluorescent compounds have very short radiative lifetimes and high

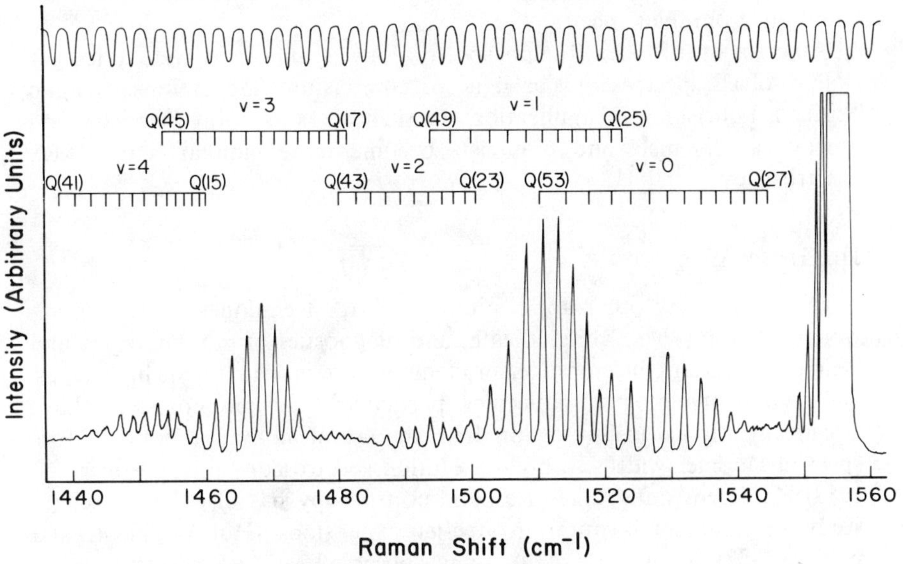

FIG. 1.25. Collision-free CARS spectrum of the Q branch of oxygen formed in the visible photodissociation of ozone. Spectral features between 1545 and 1560 cm^{-1} are due to oxygen impurity in the ozone. Stokes laser étalon fringes (2.892-cm^{-1} free spectral range) are shown at the top of the figure along with vibrational and rotational state identification of the Raman transitions. [From Valentini *et al.* (1981). © North-Holland Publishing Company, Amsterdam, 1981.]

fluorescence quantum yields. Decola *et al.* (1980) have observed simultaneously the Raman spectra of the excited and ground electronic states of pentacene in benzoic acid crystal at 77 K. The photoisomerization of cyclohexatriene has been studied by Luther and Wieters (1980), who used CARS to detect a transient molecular state upon excitation into S_1 at 266 nm.

Detection of molecular photofragments produced upon single- or multiple-photon photodissociation has been demonstrated. Gross *et al.* (1979) detected a CARS spectrum that they believed to be due to C_2 upon 266-nm photolysis of benzene. By using a picosecond CARS technique, Hetherington *et al.* (1981) showed that C_2 was indeed produced in the UV multiphoton photodissociation of benzene, and that the C_2 fragment appeared within the 25-ps width of the UV laser excitation pulse. Valentini *et al.* (1981) carried CARS photofragment spectroscopy a significant step further in determining not only the identity, but also the vibrational and rotational state distributions of the molecular photofragments. They observed the molecular oxygen produced in the visible photodissociation of ozone. A spectrum taken from their work is shown in Fig. 1.25. The time resolution in these experiments was sufficient to ensure that the spectra were collision-free, so Valentini *et al.* could extract the nascent photofragment rovibrational quantum state distributions from their spectra.

Coherent anti-Stokes Raman spectroscopy is almost as well suited for time-resolved spectroscopy as it is for combustion applications. We can expect a flourishing of applications to such areas as photochemistry and kinetics as chemists and biologists become more familiar with CARS spectroscopy.

H. Other Applications

There are many other applications of CARS techniques that are noteworthy. Among these are studies in and diagnostics of molecular jets and beams, molecular concentration and temperature measurements in plasmas, and studies of biological molecules, particularly chromophores. We have already mentioned in Subsection 1.3.E the use of molecular jets to reduce spectral Doppler widths in high-resolution spectroscopy (Gustafson *et al.*, 1982). Coherent anti-Stokes Raman spectroscopy has also been used to study molecular relaxation in free-jet expansions (Huber-Wälchli and Nibler, 1982). König *et al.* (1982) have observed a CARS spectrum in an argon/ethylene jet, which they attribute to large ethylene–argon van der Waals clusters.

Coherent anti-Stokes Raman spectroscopy also can be used as a diagnostic for molecular jets. In one of the earliest applications of CARS spectroscopy Regnier *et al.* (1974) visualized the flow of a hydrogen supersonic jet by using unfocused CARS beams of up to 10-cm diameter and photographic detection. Murphy *et al.* (1979) obtained time-averaged concentration profiles, spatially resolved along a line across a methane jet by using a BOXCARS technique, and Hirth and Vollrath (1976) measured number density fluctuations in real time in a turbulent jet. Gustafson *et al.* have (1981) used high-resolution cw CARS to carry out velocimetry in a methane supersonic jet. Their results, which are shown in Fig. 1.26, indicate an accuracy of ±4% for a flow velocity of 960 m/s.

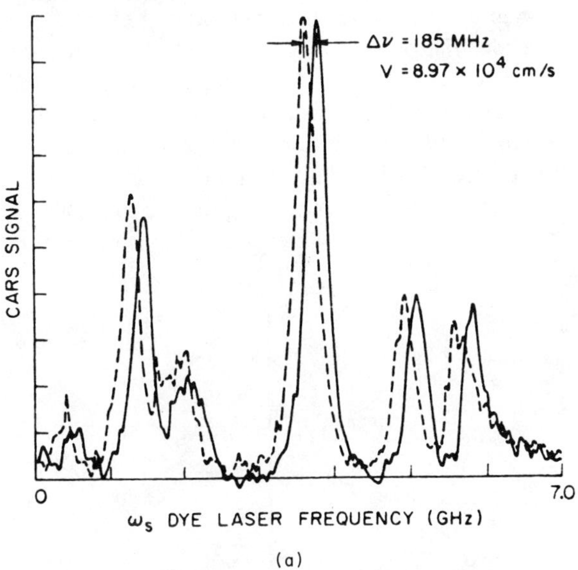

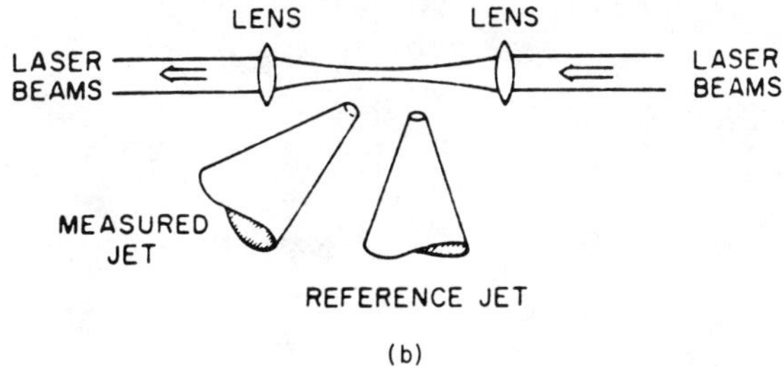

FIG. 1.26. CARS velocimetry in a methane supersonic jet: (a) spectra from the reference jet (dashed line) and from the measured jet (solid line); (b) jet apparatus diagram showing that the measured jet has a velocity component in the direction of the CARS beams, while the reference jet has no velocity component in this direction. [From Gustafson *et al.* (1981). © 1981 IEEE.]

Nibler *et al.* (1976) showed that the CARS sensitivity and discrimination against sample luminescence could be capitalized upon in making molecular temperature and concentration measurements in electric discharges. By assuming a Boltzmann distribution over vibrational states, they found the vibrational temperature in a deuterium discharge to be 1050 K, although the rotational temperature was nearly ambient. In subsequent work with nitrogen discharges Shaub *et al.* (1977b) found non-Boltzmann vibrational level populations. Pealat *et al.* (1981) measured a rotational distribution with a temperature of 475 K for a low-pressure hydrogen plasma, but a non-Boltzmann vibrational state distribution was evident. CARS spectra of hydrogen in a plasma, obtained by Pealat *et al.*, are reproduced in Fig. 1.27.

Application of CARS to biological molecules generally involves use of electronic resonance enhancement. Tretzel and Schneider (1979) have obtained CARS spectra of light-adapted and dark-adapted bacteriorhodopsin. As Fig. 1.11 from their work shows, it is possible to get a sufficient signal-to-noise ratio to distinguish the two forms in only a single 1.0-ns laser pulse.

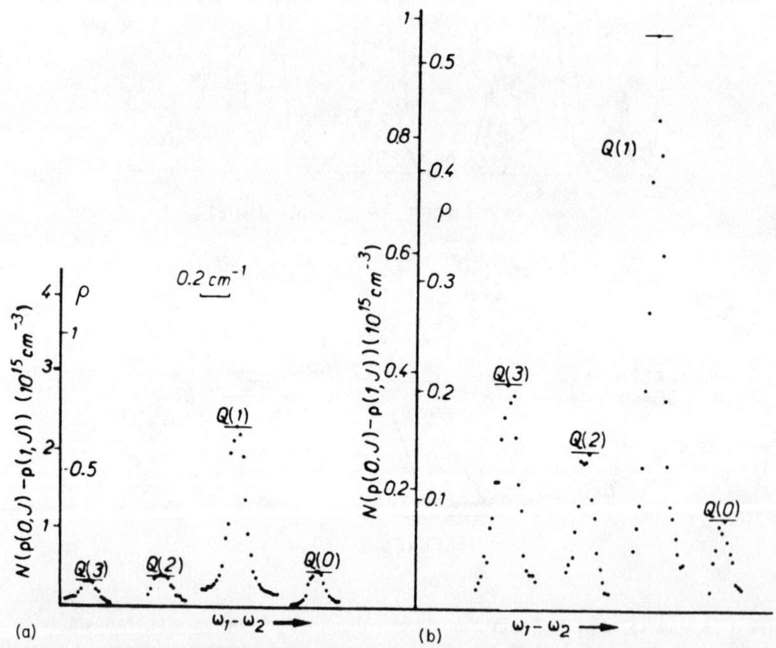

FIG. 1.27. Profiles of the Q(0) through Q(4) lines in the $v = 0 \rightarrow v = 1$ fundamental transition of neutral hydrogen recorded by CARS spectroscopy: (a) in static hydrogen gas, and (b) in a low-pressure hydrogen plasma. [From Pealat *et al.* (1981).]

Dutta *et al.* (1977) have used resonance CARS to study the structure and dynamics of flavin adenine dinucleotide and glucose oxidase. Nestor *et al.* (1976) recorded resonance CARS spectra of ferrocytochrome c and cyanocobalamin, and Igarashi *et al.* (1980) studied porphyrins.

Among other uses of CARS we must note the work of Roland and Steele (1981), who used CARS spectra of carbon dioxide at near-critical density to determine orientational and vibrational collision cross sections. Duncan *et al.* (1982) have reported a novel use of CARS for cell microscopy, and Shen *et al.* (1979) have demonstrated that picosecond CARS of submonolayers of adsorbed species appears feasible.

1.4. Conclusion

As we hope the preceding sections have shown, CARS is a powerful, versatile, and widely useful spectroscopic technique. As yet only a small fraction of the potential of the technique has been realized. Although CARS has been applied to many spectroscopic problems, only in the area of combustion diagnostics have the applications gone very far beyond the proof-of-principle stage. As CARS techniques become more widely accepted as standard laboratory spectroscopic tools by scientists in physics, chemistry, biology, and engineering the application of CARS will continue to grow. I hope that this review will play some part in encouraging that growth.

Acknowledgments

I gratefully acknowledge Professor R. L. Byer for encouraging me to write this review and Dr. A. Owyoung for many helpful discussions. I am particularly indebted to Dr. K. Veirs for a very careful, critical reading of the manuscript, and to Evelyn Cone for her expeditious and accurate typing of the manuscript.

References

Akhmanov, S. A., Bunkin, A. F., Ivanov, S. G., and Koroteev, N. I. (1978). *Sov. Phys.—JETP* (*Engl. Transl.*) **47,** 667.

Aliev, M. R., Kozlov, D. N., and Smirnov, V. V. (1977). *JETP Lett.* (*Engl. Transl.*) **26,** 27.

Armstrong, J. A., Bloembergen, N., Ducuing, J., and Pershan, P. S. (1962). *Phys. Rev.* **127,** 1918.

Attal, B., Schnepp, O. O., and Taran, J.-P. E. (1978). *Opt. Commun.* **24,** 77.

Attal, B., Débarre, D., Müller-Dethlefs, K., and Taran, J. P. E. (1983). *Rev. Phys. Appl.* **18,** 39.

Barrett, J. J. (1976). *Appl. Phys. Lett.* **29,** 722.

Barrett, J. J., and Begley, R. F. (1975). *Appl. Phys. Lett.* **27,** 129.

Beattie, I. R., Gilson, T. R., and Greenhalgh, D. A. (1978). *Nature* **276,** 378.

Beckmann, A., Fietz, H., Kiefer, W., and Laane, J. (1981). *Phys. Rev. A* **24,** 2518.

Beckmann, A., Fietz, H., Baierl, P., and Kiefer, W. (1982). *Chem. Phys. Lett.* **86,** 140.
Begley, R. F., Harvey, A. B., Byer, R. L., and Hudson, B. S. (1974). *J. Chem. Phys.* **61,** 2466.
Bjorklund, G. C. (1975). *IEEE J. Quantum Elec.* **QE-11,** 287.
Bloembergen, N. (1965). "Nonlinear Optics." Benjamin, Reading, Massachusetts.
Bloembergen, N., and Shen, Y. R. (1964). *Phys. Rev. Lett.* **12,** 504.
Bogaard, M. P., and Orr, B. J. (1975). *In* "International Review of Science: Physical Chemistry" (A. D. Buckingham, ed.), Series 2, Volume 2. Butterworths, London.
Boquillon, J. P., Moret-Bailly, J., and Chaux, R. (1977). *C. R. Acad. Sci. Ser. B* **284,** 205.
Brodnikovsky, A. M., Gladkov, S. M., and Korateev, N. I. (1982). *Opt. Commun.* **40,** 312.
Bulatov, E. D., Kazlov, D. N., Otlivanchik, E. A., Pashinin, P. P., Prokhorov, A. M., Sisakyan, I. N., and Smirnov, V. V. (1980). *Sov. J. Quantum Electron.* **10,** 740.
Butcher, P. N. (1965). "Nonlinear Optical Phenomena." Bulletin 200, Eng. Exp. Station, Ohio State University, Columbus.
Carreira, L. A., Maguire, T. C., and Malloy, T. B., Jr. (1977). *J. Chem. Phys.* **66,** 2621.
Chabay, I., Klauminzer, G. K., and Hudson, B. S. (1976). *Appl. Phys. Lett.* **28,** 27.
Christie, J. H., and Lockwood, D. J. (1971). *J. Chem. Phys.* **54,** 1141.
Campaan, A., and Chandra, S. (1979). *Opt. Lett.* **4,** 170.
Decola, P. L., Andrews, J. R., Hochstrasser, R. M., and Trommsdorff, H. P. (1980). *J. Chem. Phys.* **73,** 4695.
Druet, S. A. J., Attal, B., Gustafson, T. K., and Taran, J. P. (1978). *Phys. Rev. A* **18,** 1529.
Druet, S. A. J., and Taran, J.-P. E. (1981). *In* "Progress in Quantum Electronics," Vol. 7, pp. 1–72. Pergamon, Oxford.
Duncan, M. D., Oesterlin, P., König, F., and Byer, R. L. (1981). *Chem. Phys. Lett.* **80,** 253.
Duncan, M. D., Reintjes, J., and Manuccia, T. J. (1982). *Opt. Lett.* **7,** 350.
Dutta, P. K., Nestor, J. R., and Spiro, T. G. (1977). *Proc. Nat. Acad. Sci. USA* **74,** 4146.
Eckbreth, A. C. (1978). *Appl. Phys. Lett.* **32,** 421.
Eckbreth, A. C. (1980). *Combust. Flame* **39,** 133.
Eckbreth, A. C., and Hall, R. J. (1979). *Combust. Flame* **36,** 87.
Eckbreth, A. C., Hall, R. J., and Shirley, J. A. (1979). AIAA Pap. 79-0083. AIAA, New York.
Eckbreth, A. C., and Schreiber, P. (1981). *In* "Coherent Applications of Nonlinear Raman Spectroscopy" (A. B. Harvey, ed.), Chapter 2.. Academic Press, New York.
Eesley, G. L. (1981). "Coherent Raman Spectroscopy." Pergamon, Oxford.
Esherick, P., and Owyoung, A. (1982). *In* "Advances in Infrared and Raman Spectroscopy" (R. J. H. Clark and R. E. Hestor, eds.), Vol. 10. Heyden, London.
Fabelinsky, V. I., Krynetsky, B. B., Kulevsky, L. A., Mishin, V. A., Prokhorov, A. M., Savel'ev, A. D., and Smirnov, V. V. (1977). *Optics Commun.* **20,** 389.
Fenner, W. R., Hyatt, H. A., Kellam, J. M., and Porto, S. P. S. (1973). *J. Opt. Soc. Am.* **63,** 73.
Fietz, H., Beckmann, A., Kiefer, W., and Wieser, H. (1982). *Chem. Phys. Lett.* **87,** 491.
Gilson, T. R., and Purnell, M. R. (1982). *J. Raman Spec.* **12,** 222.
Goss, L. P., Fleming, J. W., and Harvey, A. B. (1980). *Opt. Lett.* **5,** 345.
Gross, K. P., Guthals, D. M., and Nibler, J. W. (1979). *J. Chem. Phys.* **70,** 4673.
Guha, S., and Falk, J. (1981). *J. Chem. Phys.* **75,** 2599.
Gustafson, E. K., McDaniel, J. C., and Byer, R. L. (1981). *IEEE J. Quantum Elec.* **QE-17,** 2258.
Gustafson, E. K., McDaniel, J. C., and Byer, R. L. (1982). *Opt. Lett.* **7,** 434.
Guthals, D. M., Gross, K. P., and Nibler, J. W. (1979). *J. Chem. Phys.* **70,** 2393.
Hall, R. J. (1979). *Combust. Flame* **35,** 47.
Hall, R. J., Shirley, J. A., and Eckbreth, A. C. (1979). *Opt. Lett.* **4,** 87.
Harvey, A. B., ed. (1981). "Chemical Applications of Nonlinear Raman Spectroscopy." Academic Press, New York.
Hauchecorne, G., Kerherve, F., and Mayer, G. (1971). *J. Phys.* (*Orsay*, *Fr.*) **32,** 47.

Henesian, M. A., Kulevskii, L., and Byer, R. L. (1976). *J. Chem. Phys.* **65,** 5530.
Henesian, M. A., Duncan, M. D., Byer, R. L., and May, A. D. (1977). *Opt. Lett.* **1,** 149.
Herrmann, J., and Landmann, M. (1979). *Opt. Commun.* **29,** 172.
Herzberg, G. (1945). "Molecular Spectra and Molecular Structure." Van Nostrand, Princeton, New Jersey.
Hetherington, W. M., III, Korenowski, G. M., and Eisenthal, K. B. (1981). *Chem. Phys. Lett.* **77,** 275.
Hirth, A., and Vollrath, K. (1976). *Opt. Commun.* **18,** 213.
Huber-Wälchli, P., and Nibler, J. W. (1982). *J. Chem. Phys.* **76,** 273.
Hudson, B. (1974). *J. Chem. Phys.* **61,** 5460.
Hudson, B., Hetherington, W., III, Cramer, S., Chabay, I., and Klauminzer, G. K. (1976). *Proc. Nat. Acad. Sci. USA* **73,** 3798.
Igarashi, R., Adachi, Y., and Maeda, S. (1980). *J. Chem. Phys.* **72,** 4308.
Itzkan, I., and Leonard, D. A. (1975). *Appl. Phys. Lett.* **26,** 106.
Kamga, F. M., and Sceats, M. G. (1980). *Opt. Lett.* **5,** 126.
Kittel, C. (1971). "Introduction to Solid State Physics." Wiley, New York.
Kleinman, D. A. (1962). *Phys. Rev.* **26,** 1977.
Klick, D., Marko, K. A., and Rimai, L. (1981). *Appl. Opt.* **20,** 1178.
Kogelnik, H., and Li, T. (1966). *Appl. Opt.* **5,** 1550.
König, F., Österlin, P., and Byer, R. L. (1982). *Chem. Phys. Lett.* **88,** 477.
König, R., Lau, A., and Weigmann, H. J. (1980). *Chem. Phys. Lett.* **69,** 87.
Krynetsky, B. B., Kulevsky, L. A., Mishin, V. A., Prokhorov, A. M., Savel'ev, A. D., and Smirnov, V. V. (1977). *Opt. Commun.* **21,** 225.
Landsberg, G. S., and Mandelstam, L. I. (1928). *Naturwissenschaften* **16,** 557.
Lau, W., Werncke, W., Klein, J., and Pfeiffer, M. (1977). *Opt. Commun.* **21,** 309.
Laufer, G., Miles, R. B., and Santavicca, D. (1979). *Opt. Commun.* **31,** 242.
Levenson, M. D., and Bloembergen, N. (1974). *Phys. Rev. B* **10,** 4447.
Levenson, M. D., and Song, J. J. (1980). *In* "Coherent Nonlinear Optics" (M. S. Feld and V. S. Letokhov, eds.), Chapter 7. Springer-Verlag, Berlin.
Long, D. A. (1977). "Raman Spectroscopy." McGraw-Hill, New York.
Lotem, H., Lynch, R. T., Jr., and Bloembergen, N. (1976). *Phys. Rev. A* **14,** 1748.
Luther, K., and Wieters, W. (1980). *J. Chem. Phys.* **73,** 4131.
Lynch, R. T., Jr., Kramer, S. D., Lotem, H., and Bloembergen, N. (1976). *Opt. Commun.* **16,** 372.
McIlwain, M. E., and Hindman, J. C. (1980). *J. Chem. Phys.* **73,** 68.
Maker, P. D., and Terhune, R. W. (1965). *Phys. Rev.* **137,** A801.
Marko, K. A., and Rimai, L. (1979). *Opt. Lett.* **4,** 211.
Moya, F., Druet, S. A. J., Taran, J. P. E. (1975). *Opt. Commun.* **13,** 169.
Murphy, D. V., Long, M. B., Chang, R. K., and Eckbreth, A. C. (1979). *Opt. Lett.* **4,** 167.
Nestor, J., Spiro, T. G., and Klauminzer, G. (1976). *Proc. Nat. Acad. Sci. USA* **73,** 3329.
Nibler, J. W., and Knighten, G. V. (1977). *In* "Raman Spectroscopy of Gases and Liquids" (A. Weber, ed.), Chapter 7. Springer-Verlag, Berlin.
Nibler, J. W., McDonald, J. R., and Harvey, A. B. (1976). *Opt. Commun.* **18,** 371.
Nitsch, W., and Kiefer, W. (1977). *Opt. Commun.* **23,** 240.
Orr, B. J., and Ward, J. F. (1971). *Mol. Phys.* **20,** 513.
Oudar, J.-L., Smith, R. W., and Shen, Y. R. (1979). *Appl. Phys. Lett.* **34,** 758.
Owyoung, A. (1981). *In* "Coherent Applications of Nonlinear Raman Spectroscopy" (A. B. Harvey, ed.), Chapter 7. Academic Press, New York.
Pantell, R., and Puthoff, H. (1969). "Fundamentals of Quantum Electronics." Wiley, New York.
Pealat, M., Taran, J. P. E., Taillet, J., Bacal, M., and Bruneteau, A. M. (1981). *J. Appl. Phys.* **52,** 2687.

Placzek, G. (1934). "Handbuch der Radiologie." Akademische Verlagsgesellschaft, Leipzig.
Rado, W. G. (1967). *Appl. Phys. Lett.* **11,** 123.
Rahn, L. A., Zych, L. J., and Mattern, P. L. (1979). *Opt. Commun.* **30,** 249.
Rahn, L. A., Farrow, R. L., Koszykowski, M. L., and Mattern, P. L. (1980). *Phys. Rev. Lett.* **45,** 620.
Raman, C. V. (1928). *Ind. J. Phys.* **2,** 387.
Regnier, P. R., and Taran, J.-P. E. (1973). *Appl. Phys. Lett.* **23,** 240.
Regnier, P. R., Moya, F., and Taran, J. P. E. (1974). *AIAA J.* **12,** 826.
Roh, W. B., Schreiber, P. W., and Taran, J.-P. E. (1976). *Appl. Phys. Lett.* **29,** 174.
Roland, C. M., and Steele, W. A. (1980). *J. Chem. Phys.* **73,** 5919.
Roland, C. M., and Steele, W. A. (1981). *J. Chem. Phys.* **74,** 2733.
Shaub, W. M., Harvey, A. B., and Bjorklund, G. C. (1977a). *J. Chem. Phys.* **67,** 2547.
Shaub, W. M., Nibler, J. W., and Harvey, A. B. (1977b). *J. Chem. Phys.* **67,** 1883.
Shen, C. K., de Castro, A. R. B., and Shen, Y. R. (1979). *Phys. Rev. Lett.* **43,** 946.
Shirley, J. A., Hall, R. J., and Eckbreth, A. C. (1980). *Opt. Lett.* **5,** 380.
Smith, D. C., and Meyerand, R. G., Jr. (1974). *In* "Principles of Laser Plasmas" (G. Bekefi, ed.), Chapter 11. Wiley (Interscience), New York.
Song, J. J., Eesley, G. L., and Levenson, M. D. (1976). *Appl. Phys. Lett.* **29,** 567.
Stenhouse, I. A., Williams, D. R., Cole, J. B., and Swords, M. D. (1979). *Appl. Opt.* **18,** 3819.
Switzer, G. L., Roquemore, W. M., Bradley, R. B., Schreiber, P. W., and Roh, W. B. (1979). *Appl. Opt.* **18,** 2343.
Teets, R. E., and Bechtel, J. H. (1981). *Opt. Lett.* **6,** 458.
Terhune, R. W. (1963). *Bull. Am. Phys. Soc.* **8,** 359.
Tolles, W. M., Nibler, J. W., McDonald, J. R., and Harvey, A. B. (1977). *Appl. Spectrosc.* **31,** 253.
Tretzel, J., and Schneider, F. W. (1979). *Chem. Phys. Lett.* **66,** 475.
Valentini, J. J., Moore, D. S., and Bomse, D. S. (1981). *Chem. Phys. Lett.* **83,** 217.
Weber, A., ed. (1979). "Raman Spectroscopy of Gases and Liquids." Springer-Verlag, Berlin.
Weil, H., and Schreiber, P. W. (1982). *Appl. Opt.* **21,** 941.
Wilson-Gordon, A. D., Klimovsky-Barid, R., and Friedmann, H. (1982). *Phys. Rev. A* **25,** 1580.
Yajima, T., and Takatsuji, M. (1964). *J. Phys. Soc. Jpn.* **19,** 2343.
Yuratich, M. A., and Hanna, D. C. (1977). *Mol. Phys.* **33,** 671.
Zinth, W., Laubereau, A., and Kaiser, W. (1978). *Opt. Commun.* **26,** 457.

Chapter 2

Diffraction Gratings and Mountings for the Vacuum Ultraviolet Spectral Region

*W. R. HUNTER**

NAVAL RESEARCH LABORATORY
WASHINGTON, D.C.

2.1. Introduction	63
2.2. Diffraction Gratings	65
A. General Considerations	65
B. Manufacturing Methods for Gratings	71
C. Focal Properties of Gratings	91
D. Grating Efficiencies	102
2.3. Grating Mountings	146
A. Plane Grating Mountings	148
B. Concave Grating Mountings	166
C. Transmission Grating Mountings	174
References	175

2.1. Introduction

The unique aspect of vacuum ultraviolet (VUV) research is exemplified by the modifier—vacuum. All the research must be conducted *in vacuo* because of the absorption of VUV radiation by the atmospheric gases nitrogen and oxygen. Another major feature of this spectral region concerns the optical properties of dielectric materials. In the near UV, visible, and infrared regions, dielectrics are available for making prisms and lenses commonly used in spectrographs. As the wavelength decreases and the VUV is approached, however, there comes a wavelength beyond which no transmitting materials

* Present address: Sachs/Freeman Associates, Inc., Bowie, Maryland.

ISBN 0-12-710404-6

are available. The optical properties of dielectrics change character to resemble those of metals in that their absorption coefficients become quite large, 10^4 cm^{-1} or more. Although prisms and lenses can be used in restricted portions of the VUV, it is usually more convenient to use reflecting diffraction gratings as dispersing elements and mirrors for focusing, especially if the wavelength range to be covered extends beyond the transmittance limit of the dielectric intended for the prism or lens. Dispersing and focusing properties are combined in the concave diffraction grating that is the mainstay of VUV spectroscopy. Plane gratings are also useful; however, they are usually used in connection with focusing or collimating mirrors.

This chapter contains two main sections. The first is about diffraction gratings. Much has been done to improve gratings in the past two decades. Improvements in ruling techniques, such as interferometric control, have reduced the number and intensity of ghosts, and blaze characteristics have been improved. Ruling on aspheric surfaces reduces aberrations, in particular astigmatism. Perhaps the most significant development in recent years has been the interference, sometimes called holographic, grating. These gratings are made by recording the interference field produced by two light beams in a light-sensitive medium. The flexibility of the recording system provides the ability to form nonuniformly spaced grooves in a controlled manner that can be used to reduce aberrations as well as modify spectrographic focal surfaces. The radical changes in the properties of holographic gratings from those of the earlier gratings suggest the sobriquet classical for the latter. We shall use this term when referring to any grating with uniformly spaced grooves. We will also refer to gratings produced via ruling engines as conventional. Further reductions in aberrations can be achieved by recording holographic gratings on aspheric surfaces, thus combining the benefits of both types of correction. Finally, a new generation of ruling engine has been developed that can rule nonuniformly spaced grooves.

The second section is concerned with mountings for gratings. One might be inclined to relabel the section "Grating Instruments." Some of the mountings, however, have never been made into instruments, but are of interest because of their potential for future applications. Then, too, descriptions of grating instruments abound and to redescribe those that are well known is to waste time and space. Therefore, the second section will be restricted to mountings the author feels have a future potential and unusual instruments that have not been widely discussed.

In closing this introduction it seems reasonable to make a plea for some standardization and consolidation of nomenclature. The VUV came by its name honestly—because of the necessity for conducting research *in vacuo.* However, it is also referred to as the extreme ultraviolet (EUV or XUV) and occasionally as the far UV. Once spectroscopy from rockets and satellites had become widespread, astronomers subdivided the region into the EUV and XUV, the former being the spectral region wherein gratings, mirrors, etc. were used in normal incidence, and the latter in grazing incidence. The fact that normal incidence can be used to wavelengths as short as 300 Å and grazing incidence is sometimes used to wavelengths as long as 1200 Å appears to have had no significance. A much more reasonable division, in this writer's opinion, occurs at about 1050 Å. To longer wavelengths LiF and other dielectrics transmit and can be used as windows, lenses, or prisms because the absorption coefficient α is small ($\alpha \approx 10\ \text{cm}^{-1}$). To shorter wavelengths there are no transmitting materials and $\alpha = 10^4\ \text{cm}^{-1}$; therefore, one relies almost entirely on reflection. In this chapter the entire region will be referred to as the VUV because the author does not want to be responsible for further proliferation of nomenclature and fragmentation of the VUV.

2.2. Diffraction Gratings

A. General Considerations

The theory of gratings has been given elsewhere (Rowland, 1883a,b; Beutler, 1945; Namioka, 1959; Werner, 1967,1970; Sai *et al.*, 1968; Ishiguro *et al.*, 1979) in great detail, so only the salient points necessary for this article will be given here. The grating equation can be written in vector form (Spencer and Murty, 1962) as

$$\mathbf{S}' \times \mathbf{y} = \mathbf{S} \times \mathbf{y} + (n\lambda/d)\mathbf{y}, \tag{2.1}$$

where $\mathbf{S}$ and $\mathbf{S}'$ are unit vectors in the directions of the incident wave and the diffracted wave, respectively, and n, λ, and d are the order number, wavelength, and grating spacing, respectively. Vector $\mathbf{S}$ has direction cosines, with respect to $\mathbf{x}$, $\mathbf{y}$, and $\mathbf{z}$, of $\cos\delta$, $\cos\theta$, and $\cos\gamma$. Those of $\mathbf{S}'$ are $\cos\delta'$, $\cos\theta'$, and $\cos\gamma'$. $\mathbf{x}$, $\mathbf{y}$, and $\mathbf{z}$ are unit vectors of a right-handed set oriented with respect to the grating as shown in Fig. 2.1. The plane defined by the $\mathbf{x}$ and $\mathbf{y}$ unit vectors will be called the reference plane.

The $\mathbf{x}$ and $\mathbf{z}$ components of Eq. (2.1) are

$$-y\cos\gamma' = -y\cos\gamma,$$

$$y\cos\delta' = -y\cos\delta + (n\lambda/d)y.$$

Since y is the modulus of a unit vector, the equations become

$$\cos\gamma' = \cos\gamma, \tag{2.2a}$$

$$\cos\delta' = -\cos\delta + n\lambda/d. \tag{2.2b}$$

If the grating is used in the usual manner with the wave vector of the incident light perpendicular to the rulings, i.e., lying in the reference plane, $\gamma' = \gamma = \pi/2$. Angles δ and δ' are the complements of the angle of incidence α and the diffraction angle β, respectively. Then Eq. (2.2b) becomes

$$\pm n\lambda = d(\sin\alpha + \sin\beta). \tag{2.3a}$$

It is also convenient to use the equation in the following form:

$$\pm nG\lambda = \sin\alpha + \sin\beta, \tag{2.3b}$$

where G is the groove density in grooves per centimeter (g/cm), because manufacturers of gratings invariably give the groove density rather than the line spacing.

The signs of the angles and the order numbers depend on the convention used. The convention to be used here, taken from Sawyer (1963), is shown in Fig. 2.2. The incident wave vector makes an angle α with the grating normal N. The zeroth order, sometimes called the direct beam or central image, is the specular reflection of the incident beam for a reflecting grating, and continues, undeviated, for a transmitting grating. The zeroth order divides the diffracted orders into positive and negative orders. If one defines α as being positive, then the signs of the orders n and of the values of β will

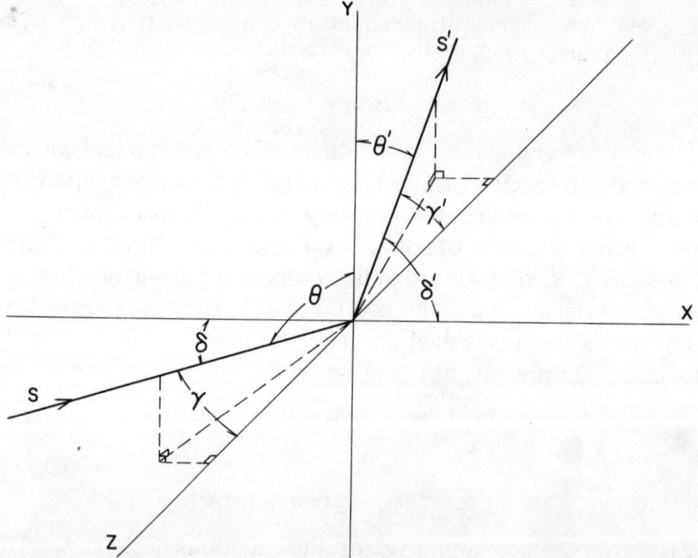

FIG. 2.1. The coordinate system associated with a grating and the direction angles of the incident and diffracted wave vectors. The grating grooves lie in the x, z plane and are parallel to z; y is the grating normal N.

be positive if measured in the same sense as α for a reflecting grating (clockwise for Fig. 2.2). For a transmitting grating the opposite is true. In fact, the arrangement of orders for a transmitting grating is the mirror image of the arrangement for a reflecting grating. Note that β is measured from the grating normal and n from the zeroth order.

The orders lying between the incident beam and the zeroth order are sometimes referred to as inside orders. Using this convention, inside orders are positive.

Any sign convention is permissible, of course, as long as it is used consistently. Occasionally problems arise in determining the sign of the order number when ray tracing. Wilson (1982) has published guidelines on this subject and has compared sign conventions of some of the commercial ray-tracing programs.

Equation (2.3a) or (2.3b) can be used to find the direction in which a particular n is diffracted. It is also of interest to know the rate at which the direction changes with wavelength, i.e., the angular dispersion. Differentiating Eq. (2.3a) or Eq. (2.3b) with respect to λ, one has

$$d\beta/d\lambda = \pm nG/\cos\beta \tag{2.4}$$

in radians per unit wavelength, or radians per centimeter if G is in grooves per centimeter. It is also of interest to know how rapidly the wavelength changes with distance along the focal surface parallel to the direction of dispersion. This rate of change is given by

$$d\lambda/dL = d\lambda/d\beta\, d\beta/dL = (\cos\beta/nG)\, d\beta/dL\,,$$

where the form of $d\beta/dL$ depends on the form of the focal surface. For a

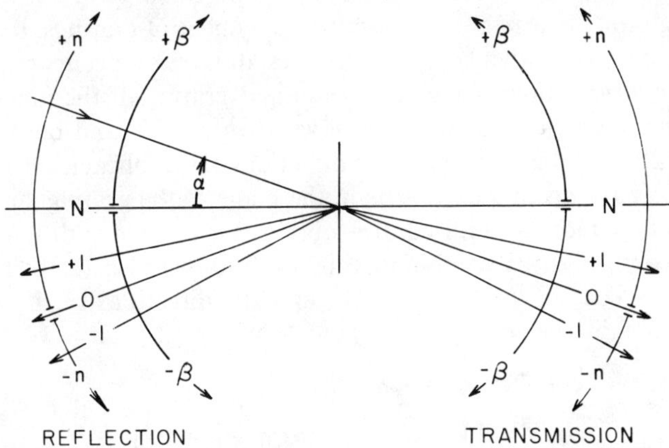

FIG. 2.2. Illustration of the grating convention (Sawyer, 1963) for ascertaining the sign of different orders.

plane grating with a focusing lens, $\Delta L = f\,\Delta\beta$, where f is the focal length of the lens. Then

$$d\lambda/dL = \cos\beta/nGf \times 10^8\ \text{cm}^{-1},$$

which is the expression for the rate of change of wavelength with distance along the focal curve. This is also known as the reciprocal dispersion. If $f = 100$ cm and $G = 6000$ g/cm, $d\lambda/dL = 166.6666\ldots$ Å/cm. In terms of angstroms per millimeter, the usual specification, the rate of change for $\beta = 0$ is 16 Å/mm.

Using Rayleigh's criterion, the smallest wavelength difference that can be resolved occurs when $\lambda + \Delta\lambda$ has its central maximum at the position of the first minimum of λ. Now the first diffraction minimum for a rectangular aperture of width A makes an angle with respect to the central maximum of λ/A rad. If $A = W\cos\beta$, where W is the ruled width of the grating and β is the angle of diffraction, then for a rectangular grating of width W the first maximum occurs at $\Delta\beta = 1/W\cos\beta$. But $\Delta\beta = (d\beta/dL)\,\Delta\lambda$ and, from Eq. (2.4), $d\beta/d\lambda = Gn/\cos\beta$. Therefore $\lambda/W\cos\beta = Gn\,\Delta\lambda/\cos\beta$ and

$$\lambda/\Delta\lambda = WGn.$$

This is the well-known formula for the resolving power. The product WG is the total number of grooves, and the resolving power depends on the *product* of the total number of grooves and the order number. This means that the same resolving power can be obtained with few grooves and large n as with many grooves and small n. However, the free spectral range, which is the largest wavelength span, in a given order, that does not overlap the same span in adjacent orders, is inversely proportional to n.

Although for the usual, or classical, employment of gratings, the incident wave vector is perpendicular to the grooves, diffraction occurs regardless of the relative orientation of incident beam and grating. If the incident wave vector is *not* perpendicular to the grooves then $\gamma \neq 90°$ and both Eq. (2.2a) and Eq. (2.2b) must be used to find the directions of the diffracted wavelengths. Since these wave vectors do not lie in the plane of the grating, an equation relating θ' to δ and γ is required. It is obtained from the condition $\cos^2\delta' + \cos^2\theta' + \cos^2\gamma' = 1$. By combining this condition and Eq. (2.2), one obtains $\cos^2\theta' = 1 - \cos^2\gamma - (n\lambda/d + \cos^2\delta)^2$, and the directions of the diffracted waves are obtained from

$$\cos\delta' = \cos\delta + n\lambda/d, \tag{2.5a}$$

$$\cos\theta' = [1 - \cos 2\gamma - (n\lambda/d + \cos\lambda)^2]^{1/2}, \tag{2.5b}$$

$$\cos\gamma' = \cos\gamma. \tag{2.5c}$$

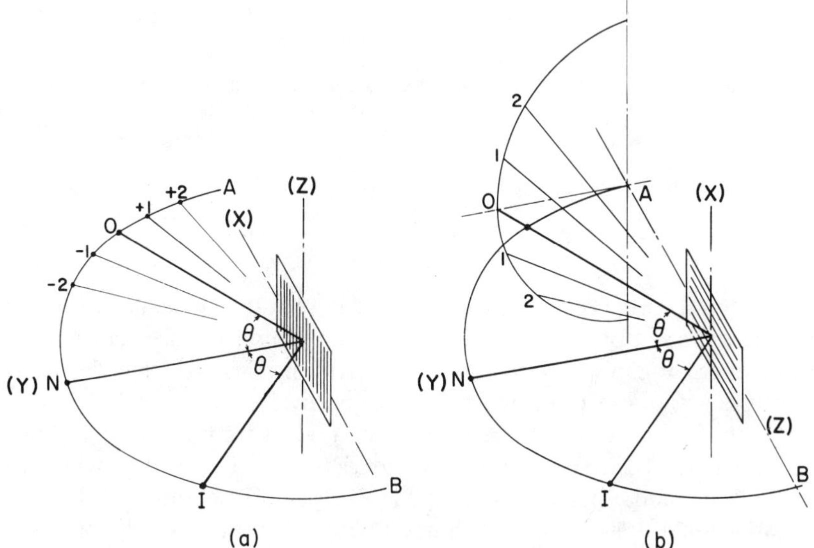

FIG. 2.3. Illustration of (a) classical and (b) conical diffraction. [From Hunter (1980). © North-Holland Physics Publishing, Amsterdam, 1980.]

Note that the z components of the vectors are all equal and that $\cos^2 \delta' + \cos^2 \theta' = 1 - \cos^2 \gamma$. Therefore the diffracted wavelengths lie on a cone with axis parallel to the z direction and half-angle equal to γ. Because the spectrum lies on a cone, the phenomenon is referred to as conical diffraction. When the projection of the incident beam on the grating is parallel to the grooves the cone half-angle is at its minimum. We shall refer to this condition as minimum conical diffraction (MCD). Figure 2.3 compares the classical (a) and MCD (b) grating mountings and shows some of the diffracted wavelengths. If the grating is rotated about its normal so that the angle between the groove direction and the projection of the incident beam increases, the cone half-angle increases until, when the incident beam and grooves are perpendicular, the diffracted orders lie on a plane, a cone with half-angle $\pi/2$.

Cash (1982) has shown that the grating equation can be put in a slightly different form that is convenient to use at grazing incidence and is easy to visualize. Referring to the spherical coordinate system in Fig. 2.4, where φ is the azimuth and γ the colatitude, one calculates A,

$$A = r(1 - \sin^2 \gamma \cos^2 \varphi)^{1/2}.$$

Then, by the sine law,

$$A/\sin \delta = r/\sin 90^\circ,$$

from which

$$\cos\delta = \sin\gamma\sin\varphi.$$

The same calculation can be done by using spherical coordinates for the diffracted ray, and the result is

$$\cos\delta' = \sin\gamma'\sin\varphi'.$$

However, $\gamma = \gamma'$, so Eq. (2.3b) becomes

$$nG\lambda = \sin\gamma(\sin\varphi + \sin\varphi'),$$

where γ has its usual meaning of the angle between the incident wave vector and the direction of the grooves z; φ is the azimuth of the incident wave vector in the x–y plane. It is defined as zero if it coincides with the y axis. Cash uses α and β in place of φ and φ', respectively.

The physical meaning of Cash's equation is clear from a consideration of the half-circle in Fig. 2.4 that is the intersection of the cone on which the spectrum lies and a plane parallel to the x–y plane. The radius of the circle is proportional to sin γ, and the horizontal lines drawn from the points on the circle where the zeroth order and diffracted wavelength intersect it are proportional to $\sin\gamma\sin\varphi$ for the zeroth order and $\sin\gamma\sin\varphi'$ for the diffracted wavelength. Their sum is $n\lambda/d$, which is just Cash's equation.

Mountings employing conical diffraction are not yet widely used. Experi-

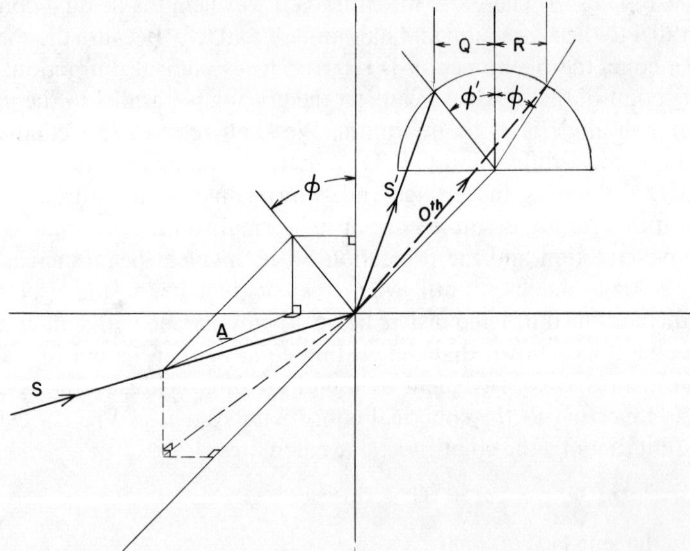

FIG. 2.4. The coordinate system associated with a grating and the spherical coordinates used by Cash (1982). [From Cash (1982).]

ment has shown, however, that conical diffraction is more efficient in the VUV at wavelengths less than 500 Å than classical diffraction (Neviere *et al.*, 1978). Werner (1977a) has shown the same for the soft x-ray region. For this reason we expect conical diffraction to come into much more common use in the short-wavelength part of the VUV and in the soft x-ray region.

The free spectral range (FSR) of a grating is conveniently defined as the wavelength interval (range) from a given wavelength in order n to the same wavelength in order $n + \lambda$. The rate of change of wavelength with n can be found by differentiating Eq. (2.3a) to obtain $\Delta\lambda\, n + \Delta n\, \lambda = 0$. Therefore $\Delta\lambda/\lambda = \Delta n/n$, and if $\Delta n = 1$, then $\Delta\lambda = \lambda/n$. For large n the FSR can be quite small. For example, an echelle grating used in order 100 in the spectral range around 3000 Å would have an FSR of approximately 30 Å. If the spectrum covers more than 30 Å there will be some ambiguity as to the actual wavelength being measured. This situation is usually referred to as overlapping of orders and is quite severe when n is large.

By using a grating with small order number and a greater groove density, the FSR can be increased, under certain conditions, and confusion due to overlapping orders diminished. Increased groove densities, however, do not help very much if the spectrum extends over a very wide range, e.g., synchrotron radiation. For such a source there is usually a continuum of wavelengths that are shorter than the spectral range of interest and that appear because of large values of n.

Since order overlap is a fundamental property of gratings some other agency must be used to sort orders, such as filters, detectors with limited wavelength range sensitivity, cross-dispersion, etc.

B. Manufacturing Methods for Gratings

Heretofore diffraction gratings have been considered only as a collection of lines on a surface—a sort of physical abstraction that ensures uniform groove spacing and straightness. In fact, the methods for manufacturing gratings impart some sort of shape, or profile, as well as crookedness and nonuniform spacing to the grooves. In the early days of grating ruling, very little attention was given to the groove profile. As experience accumulated, however, the realization of the importance of the groove profile began to take hold. Wood (1910) developed the so-called blazed reflection grating with a "sawtooth" profile, which was capable of throwing most of the diffracted energy into a given order. Two other groove profiles have come into general use; the sinusoidal and laminar profiles. The first resembles a sine wave and the second a square wave. Each has its own peculiar characteristics. The following sections will discuss the methods of manufacture; the spectral characteristics will be presented in the section on efficiency.

1. *Conventional Ruled Gratings*

Ideal conventional diffraction gratings are ruled so that the grooves are parallel, uniformly spaced, straight lines. If the substrate is spherical, the grooves are uniformly spaced on the chordal surface, which means that they are not uniformly spaced on the spherical surface. In practice, grooves are formed by drawing a diamond stylus across the surface of a grating blank. The stylus and its carriage are part of a ruling engine, a very precise mechanism, that controls the relative positions of stylus and blank with great accuracy. Detailed accounts of the principles, construction, and operation of ruling engines have been given by Harrison (1949a), Stroke (1967), Palmer *et al.* (1975), and Hutley (1982).

In the past, reflecting gratings were ruled on speculum metal blanks, and some, intended for x-ray work, were ruled directly on glass. Speculum metal is no longer used to make reflecting optics, and ruling in soft metal films, vacuum-deposited onto suitable substrates, has supplanted ruling in glass, mainly because the grooves can be shaped by shaping the ruling edge of the diamond stylus. In addition, diamond wear is greatly reduced so that the groove profile changes only slowly, if at all, as ruling progresses. Rulings are usually done in an aluminum or gold coating that has been deposited on a glass, fused silica, etc., blank. Hunter and Hass (1980) have described coatings in which gratings are ruled.

The thickness of the coating depends, to a certain extent, on the groove density and the groove profile desired. For gratings with medium to large groove densities (200–2000 g/mm), a coating of about 5000-Å thickness is sufficient. At the other extreme, a grating with only tens of grooves per millimeter may require a coating some micrometers in thickness.

The properties of the surface to be ruled that allow it to be deformed and burnished by the diamond stylus appear to be more important than its optical properties. If the optical properties of the surface are not suitable for the intended application, then after the grating has been completed a coating with suitable optical properties can be applied. Both aluminum and gold are suitable for ruling, as is silver. Silver may cause problems, however, because of the tarnish that forms during storage. Gold may be a better choice than aluminum because it has no appreciable oxide. Aluminum oxide, although not as hard as diamond, will cause diamond wear in the course of a long ruling and may cause a significant change in groove profile. An example of diamond wear was observed during ruling of a plane grating coated with a vacuum-deposited aluminum film (Loewen, 1983). The ruled area was 20.3 cm square, the desired blaze angle was 4°, and the groove density was 1200 g/mm. Measurements showed that the blaze angle changed during ruling by about 1° because of wear of the diamond caused by the aluminum oxide. A simple calculation showed that the diamond point effectively traveled 49.5 km during the ruling.

Not all soft metals are useful for ruling. For example, indium is very soft but tends to stick to the diamond during ruling, thus creating streaks on the grating surface (Bach, 1983). Table 2.1 lists a number of materials that have about the same hardness as silver and gold (Weast, 1968). Perhaps some of these materials would be suitable for ruling. Very little has been done in the way of a systematic study of materials in which to rule because most institutions with ruling engines are commercial and are unwilling to support, or financially incapable of supporting, the required research.

In the thickness required for ruling, the surface of the coating will be rougher than a 1000–2000-Å-thick film intended only as a mirror. The grating manufacturer depends on the burnishing action of the diamond to produce smooth groove facets; however, some of the surface roughness may remain. Figure 2.5 (Bach, 1983) shows an electron micrograph of a ruling in

TABLE 2.1

SOFT MATERIALS THAT ARE, OR MIGHT BE, SUITABLE FOR GRATING RULING

Material	Hardness (mohs)
Al	2–2.9
Ag	2.5
Au	2.5–3
Bi	2.5
C (graphite)[b]	0.5–1
Cd	2.0
Cu	2.5–3
In	1.2
Mg	2.0
Pb	1.5
Sb	3–3.3
Se	2.0
Sn	1.5–1.8
Sr	1.5–2.5
Te	2.3
Wood's metal[b,c]	3.0
Zn[b]	2.5

[a] Data from Weast, 1968.

[b] Preparing vacuum-deposited coatings of these materials suitable for ruling may be difficult.

[c] Wood's metal: Bi (50%), Pb (25%), Sn (12.5%), Cd (12.5%).

gold. The groove density is 313 g/mm and the blaze angle is 1°20′. Remnants of the surface roughness can be seen at one side of the large facets. Apparently the diamond did not completely burnish those facets. Such roughness will undoubtedly contribute to stray light, but to what extent is impossible to predict.

In principle, the groove profile can have any shape that can be produced on the ruling edge of the diamond stylus. Perhaps the most common profile is triangular with an apex angle of approximately 90°. Figure 2.6 illustrates the profile of such a grating. Of the two sides, one is usually inclined at a small angle to the surface, thus producing a large facet, whereas the other, smaller, side is inclined at a large angle to the surface. Such a profile is said to be blazed. The blaze condition occurs when the incident wave vector and

FIG. 2.5. Electron micrograph of a conventional ruling in gold. The groove density is 313 g/mm and the blaze angle is 1°20′. Remnants of the surface roughness can be seen at the left side of each groove. [From Hunter and Hass (1980).]

that of a particular diffracted wavelength make equal angles with a *facet* normal, i.e., when the direction of diffraction coincides with the direction of specular reflection from the facet. Under these conditions the "blaze" wavelength contains most of the diffracted energy; however, blaze may not be well defined when the groove spacing is comparable to the wavelength. The angle between the facet and the grating surface is the blaze angle. In Fig. 2.6, N_g is the normal to the average grating surface and N_f is the normal to the large facet. The incident wave vector INC is inclined at an angle of incidence α with respect to N_g and the diffracted blaze wavelength, 1st, is inclined with respect to N_g at the angle of diffraction β. Both INC and 1st are inclined at the same angle σ with respect to the large facets to fulfill the blaze requirement.

The grating Eq. (2.3b) can take a slightly different form if given in terms of the blaze angle. In Fig. 2.6 the grating is used in classical diffraction. $\alpha + \beta$ is the deviation angle 2θ. Then the bisector of 2θ is N_f, which is inclined to N_g by the blaze angle θ_B. Now $\theta_B = \alpha - \beta$. Substituting in Eq. (2.3b),

$$n\lambda G = 2d \sin\theta_B \cos\theta,$$

or using the complement of θ, which is σ,

$$n\lambda G = 2d \sin\theta_B \sin\sigma.$$

The latter equation brings out the similarity between Bragg diffraction from crystal planes of spacing d and operation of a grating at blaze, because $d \sin\theta_B$ is equivalent to the crystal plane spacing.

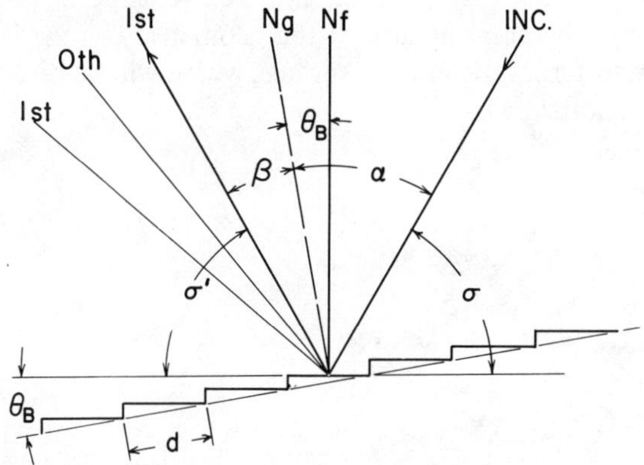

FIG. 2.6. Illustration of the blaze condition for a plane grating. 1st is the blaze wavelength, INC is the incident wave vector, α and β are the angles of incidence and diffraction, respectively, and θ_B is the blaze angle. N_g is the grating normal, and N_f is the facet normal. [From Hunter *et al.* (1982). © North-Holland Physics Publishing, Amsterdam, 1982.]

It should be noted that the blaze condition is a general condition and occurs whether or not the grating is used in classical or conical diffraction. If INC and N_f are fixed relative to each other and the grating is rotated about N_f from the classical to the MCD position, the orders that originally lay in a plane are now on a cone. However, the direction of 1st remains fixed, i.e., its direction is invariant under a rotation about N_f. A proof is given in a paper by Neviere *et al.* (1978) for the inside first order, which they refer to as the negative first order, but can be generalized to any inside order. Therefore, 1st remains the direction of the blaze wavelength regardless of the amount of rotation about N_f.

The blaze condition can also occur when the small facet is illuminated. This is the usual condition under which an echelle grating is used. These gratings have only hundreds, sometimes tens, of grooves per millimeter. They are used in high orders, perhaps 100 or so, and have practically no free spectral range. Cross-dispersion using another grating, or prism, is required to separate overlapping orders (see Subsection 2.3.A.5).

If the grating is plane, ignoring diamond wear during ruling, the groove profiles will be the same across the grating surface. If, however, the grating is spherical, the fixed orientation of the diamond gives rise to a change in blaze characteristic across the spherical surface. Usually the diamond is set for the correct blaze angle at the apex of the sphere. As it departs from the apex, the blaze triangle changes. On one side of the apex the large facet becomes larger and is inclined at less of an angle with respect to the grating surface, and the small facet becomes smaller and is inclined at a larger angle with respect to the grating surface. The opposite happens on the other side of the apex. Figure 2.7 illustrates the apparent change in profile across a concave grating. The consequence of the geometric change is a change in grating efficiency across the grating surface, which will be discussed in some detail in Subsection 2.2.D.

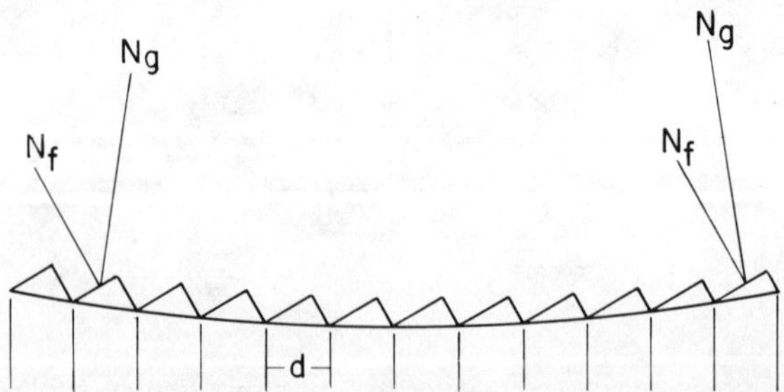

FIG. 2.7. Illustration of how the blaze changes across the surface of a spherical concave grating.

For small blaze angles, or a small radius of curvature, the large groove facet could be parallel to the spherical surface at some location, in which case the blaze would coincide with the zeroth order, an undesirable condition. This condition can be avoided by ruling *multipartite* gratings, that is, by ruling the grating in equally sized smaller areas, or panels, and reorienting the diamond to the proper blaze at the center of each panel. This procedure increases the average efficiency across the surface but reduces the resolving power to that of one of the panels. Gratings with a 1-m radius of curvature and small blaze angles are frequently ruled in three parts; a tripartite ruling.

2. *Holographic Gratings*

The intensity maxima and minima produced when two coherent light beams intersect can be recorded in a suitable medium. Thus a substrate coated with a recording medium can be exposed to recombining beams and, after the appropriate "development" process, will have a grating on its surface. A detailed description of the technique has been given by Hutley (1982).

The idea is not new. It was first proposed by Michelson (1927) to produce gratings on photographic plates. Burch (1960) and Burch and Palmer (1961) reported gratings made by this method. It was not until the advent of the laser, however, that the technique could be developed to the present level. Rudolph and Schmahl (1967a,b) and Labeyrie and Flamand (1969) produced gratings by recording recombining light beams in photoresist.

The groove density is determined by the wavelength of the recording light, the angle at which the recombining beams intersect, and the orientation of the recording surface with the interference region. A formula giving the groove spacing is

$$d = \lambda/(2n \sin \theta \sin \varphi),$$

where 2θ is the angle of intersection of the two beams, φ is the angle at which the recording surface is inclined to the interference fringes, and n is the index of refraction of the medium containing the fringe pattern. Figure 2.8 shows the orientation of the interference field and substrate. The smallest spacing occurs when $\theta = \varphi = 90^\circ$ and is $\lambda/2n$. If the recording is made in air, $d_{min} = \lambda/2$. If smaller spacings are required, the fringe pattern must be formed in a medium of index >1.

If the recombining light beams are collimated the fringes are straight. Collimation is not a prerequisite, however, and recording fringe patterns of noncollimated beams gives rise to gratings with interesting focal properties, sometimes called corrected gratings. A discussion of this subject will be deferred to the section on concave gratings.

The most commonly used medium in which the interference field is recorded is photoresist, a light-sensitive organic polymer that has large solubility changes on exposure to light, usually ultraviolet light. If the solubility is increased on exposure, the resist is known as a positive resist. If the solubility is decreased, it is a negative resist. A number of photoresists have been described by Clark (1971).

Photoresist is applied to the substrate in liquid form by "spinning." An appropriate amount of photoresist is placed at the center of the grating blank. The blank is then rotated rapidly (3000–5000 rpm) about its center to spread the resist in a uniform layer over the blank's surface. Layer thicknesses range from hundreds of angstroms to micrometers, depending on the spinning rate and the viscosity of the resist. The thickness must also be controlled for the particular type of grating desired. Coatings of resist applied to circular blanks generally are uniform in thickness, but square or rectangular blanks show edge effects, nonuniform thickness at straight edges and corners, caused by the flow of resist along these edges during spinning. Edge effects may cause efficiency variations in the finished grating that make shadowing, or masking, of the grating perimeter desirable when the grating is being used. Dust particles trapped on the substrate during or before spinning also cause perturbations in the flow of photoresist and leave parabolalike patterns in the finished photoresist surface.

In a plane perpendicular to the fringes formed by the recombining beams, the fringe intensity has a $\cos^2$ distribution. Therefore, one would expect the

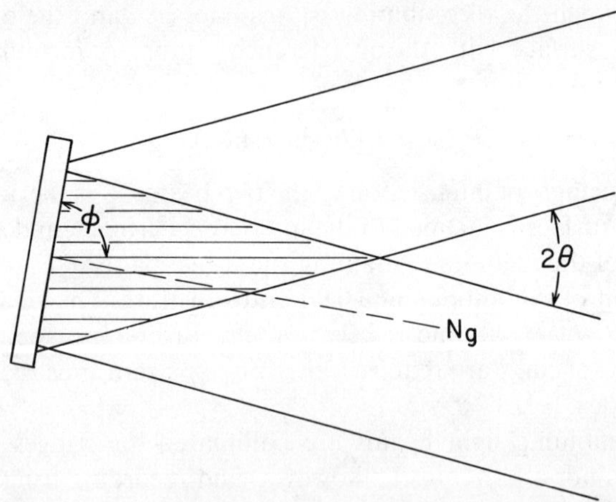

FIG. 2.8. Orientation of the interference field and substrate when recording a holographic grating.

same sort of distribution in the recording medium; i.e., after exposure and etching (developing) the grooves should have a sinusoidal or at least symmetrical shape. Light-recording media, however, are notorious for having a nonlinear response on exposure to light. Furthermore, the developing, or etching, process has its own peculiarities so that some investigation of the system is required to determine the optimum procedure for obtaining the desired groove profile.

The properties of photoresist as a recording medium have been investigated by a number of authors (Beesley and Casteldyne, 1970; Brandes and Curran, 1971; McPhedran *et al.*, 1973; Dill *et al.*, 1974,1975; Neureuther and Dill, 1974; Neureuther and Hagouel, 1974; Austin and Stone, 1976; Wilson and Brown, 1976; Brown and Wilson, 1977). It was found that the depth to which a photoresist layer could be etched is a nonlinear function of the exposure (in millijoules per square centimeter) and is similar to the H–D curves characteristic of photographic film. In contrast, the etch depth is a linear function of the development time. Once the relation between etch depth and exposure is established, a large variety of symmetric profiles can be generated with a suitable combination of initial photoresist thickness, exposure, and development time.

A symmetrical groove profile means that a grating illuminated at normal incidence will diffract equal intensities into both positive and negative orders. Namioka and Hunter (1973) have measured the efficiency of such gratings and found equal energy distributions in the positive and negative orders. Illuminating such a grating at oblique incidence introduces a false blaze in that the inside orders contain more energy than the outside orders. This effect is caused solely by unequal illumination of the groove profile. Reversing the direction of illumination also reverses the false blaze so that the inside orders are still the most intense.

A true blaze requires an asymmetric groove profile, which can be obtained through the so-called developing process applied to the photoresist or by illuminating the photoresist layer in a certain manner during exposure. Most successful attempts at blazing holographic gratings are done by tricks of illumination, so the development process will not be discussed further. The Sheridon technique (Sheridon, 1968) is perhaps the easiest to use and is readily applicable to plane gratings. Figure 2.9 illustrates how the technique works. The substrate is inclined to the fringes so that the fringe pattern *inside* the photoresist is inclined at an angle θ_B, the blaze angle, to the substrate. Then the Littrow blaze wavelength is given by $\lambda/2n$ where λ is the recording wavelength. According to Hutley (1982), the actual Littrow blaze wavelength is always shorter than that calculated because of the manner in which the solvent etches the photoresist.

The value of the blaze angle may be too large to be useful in the VUV. It can be made smaller by ion etching through the photoresist into the substrate (Hutley, 1982). Generally the resist etches faster than the substrate; consequently, the depth of the groove is reduced by the ratio of the etching rates if etching is continued until all photoresist is removed.

A modified version of the Sheridon technique can be used to produce asymmetric groove profiles on spherical concave gratings (Hutley and Hunter, 1981). Figure 2.10 illustrates how this is done. A convergent laser beam enters the back of the grating blank, the point of convergence being a point on the Rowland circle. A convex mirror whose center of curvature lies at the same point on the Rowland circle reflects the radiation back through the grating blank, producing spherical standing waves in the photoresist layer. After development, the groove facet normals all coincide at the same point on the Rowland circle. Thus, if a source is put at that point, the grating is perfectly blazed for use in a Littrow mount. If the source and detector are at different points on the Rowland circle, the blaze is no longer perfect; however, the departure from blaze is considerably less than for a conventional ruled grating. Gratings formed in this manner are uncorrected, that is, they are equivalent to type I holographic gratings or uncorrected conventional gratings.

Fourier synthesis can also be used to provide asymmetric groove profiles on plane gratings. In effect, the photoresist coating is exposed to more than one wavelength during recording. The recording wavelength ratio and fringe spacing must be chosen such that the recorded fringe patterns combine to produce a sawtooth (asymmetric) groove profile, hence the name Fourier

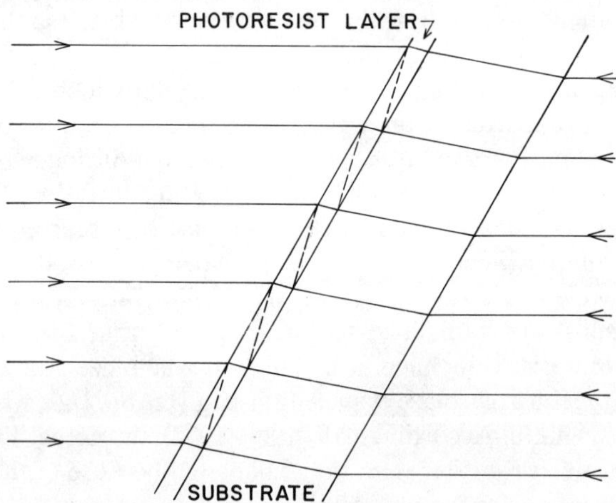

FIG. 2.9. The Sheridon technique for producing blazed, holographic plane gratings.

synthesis. In principle only two wavelengths are necessary, in the ratio of 1:2, to produce a fairly good sawtooth profile. In practice more than two would be extremely difficult to use. There are a number of ways of implementing Fourier synthesis (Bryngdahl, 1970; Schmahl, 1974) and small blazed gratings have been produced, but the technique appears to be more difficult than that of Sheridon.

Aoyagi and Namba (1976) have produced asymmetric groove profiles from sinusoidal profiles on plane gratings by ion etching. The stream of ions is directed at an angle to the plane of the sinusoidal grating and etching of the resist occurs most rapidly the closer the resist surface and ion beam are to normal incidence.

Holographic gratings would appear to have advantages over conventional gratings in that they can be recorded rapidly on plane or spherical surfaces. For example, the conventional grating used in the Apollo Telescope Mount (ATM) slitless spectrograph (Tousey *et al.*, 1977) of the SKYLAB experiment had a groove density of 3600 g/mm, a groove length of 12.4 cm, and a grating width of 12 cm. Four weeks of ruling time was required during which the ruling engine was isolated, except through electrical power lines. The same grating could be produced by recording an interference pattern in perhaps $\frac{1}{2}$h. In addition to fast recording there is also the ability to record on highly aspheric surfaces. Speer *et al.* (1974) have recorded holographic gratings on toroidal blanks with a major radius of 2 m and a minor radius of 5.56 mm.

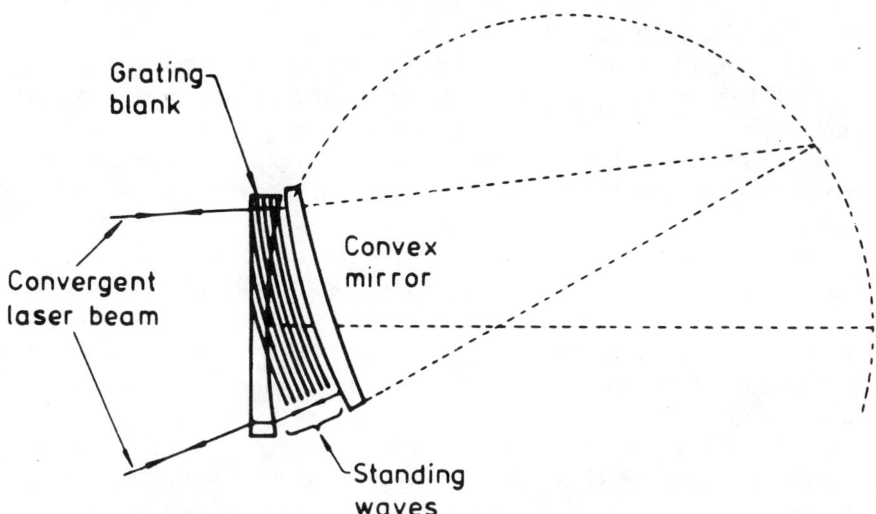

FIG. 2.10. A modification of the Sheridon technique for producing blazed holographic concave spherical gratings. [From Hutley and Hunter (1981).]

One must not assume that holographic gratings can be recorded without any problems. Vibrations in the recording system reduce the recorded contrast and must be eliminated. Small changes in temperature or atmospheric pressure can cause the interference fringes to shift position. Uniformity in the recording beams is a critical feature in manufacture of holographic gratings. Because the laser beam has a Gaussian distribution of intensity, the recording beams must be greatly expanded to render them approximately uniform. Nonuniformity causes the amplitude, or profile, of the grooves to vary and changes the efficiency from point to point on the grating surface.

Scattered and diffracted radiation from supports and from the edges of lenses of mirrors used in the recording system is also recorded in the hologram that eventually becomes the grating surface. Such spurious recorded signals give rise to stray light when the surface is used as a grating.

3. *Corrected Conventional Gratings*

In essence, the technique for ruling corrected conventional gratings is the same as that described in Subsection 2.2.B.1. The correction is done by ruling curved grooves that are spaced according to a design. The design is calculated in the same manner as for a holographic grating, that is, choosing the groove spacing and curvature to minimize aberrations. To realize this design, however, the ruling engine must be altered to permit ruling curved, nonuniformly spaced, grooves. Harada and his associates (Harada *et al.*, 1975, 1980; Kita *et al.*, 1983) in Japan have developed a numerically controlled ruling engine capable of meeting the requirements stated above.

To accomplish the planned nonuniform spacing, the grating blank is translated continuously beneath the reciprocating diamond and its speed is controlled numerically. A laser interferometer is used to monitor the carriage position, and the translation of the blank is modulated by a pulsed motor that provides a slight additional rotation of the screw driving the carriage. The spacing does not vary continuously as with a holographic grating, but in steps. That is, a number of grooves will be ruled with a fixed spacing; adjoining sets of grooves will have slightly different spacings.

Groove curvature is obtained by guiding the diamond stylus in a plane inclined to the apex normal of the blank. Thus the grooves are loci of the intersections of planes tilted with respect to the grating sphere radius and the spherical surface.

According to Harada *et al.*, the modified ruling engine has distinct advantages over the holographic method of producing gratings. The groove spacing can be varied over a much wider range than can be done holographically, and a wider range of groove curvatures can also be selected. Thus the corrected conventional grating can be more strongly corrected than its holographic counterpart. Furthermore, the grooves can be blazed, which is not easily done with a corrected holographic grating.

4. *Anisotropically Etched Gratings*

Microlithography has long been a tool in making chips for microprocessors. Improvements in pattern writing, resist exposure, and selective material removal (anisotropic etching) have enabled this technique to be applied to the manufacture of grating couplers used in integrated optics and to plane gratings. The gratings are made on single crystals and the essential feature of the technique is the fact that etching rates are not the same in different crystal directions.

Shams *et al.* (1979) made blazed gratings on the (110) surface of single-crystal GaAs. For this orientation the (111) plane makes an angle of 35°16′ with the surface and the (001) plane is perpendicular to the surface. Thus the blaze angle will be 35°16′. After suitable cleaning of the surface, a photoresist layer was "spun" on to produce a film less than 2500 Å thick. The 4579-Å line of an Ar-ion laser was used to create a holographic grating in the photoresist film. Groove spacings of 3000 to 5000 Å (3333 to 2000 g/mm) were used. After exposure, the photoresist was etched away so that strips of the GaAs surface were exposed alternating with strips protected by photoresist. Preferential chemical etching was then used to obtain the grooves in the GaAs surface. Etch rates were controlled by cooling the etchant.

Blaze angles smaller than 35° can be made if the surface is cut at the proper angle with respect to the crystal planes. Muller *et al.* (1979) and Roszhart (1984) have done this with single-crystal silicon. The following process is that described by Roszhart. A grating of the desired groove density is ruled in the conventional manner and then treated so as to provide a transmission grating with narrow opaque strips. The ratio of the opening to the line spacing is the complement of the "duty cycle." If the opening is 10% of the line spacing, the duty cycle is 90%. The fabrication sequence for a chemically etched Si grating is shown in Figs. 2.11–2.13. A single crystal of

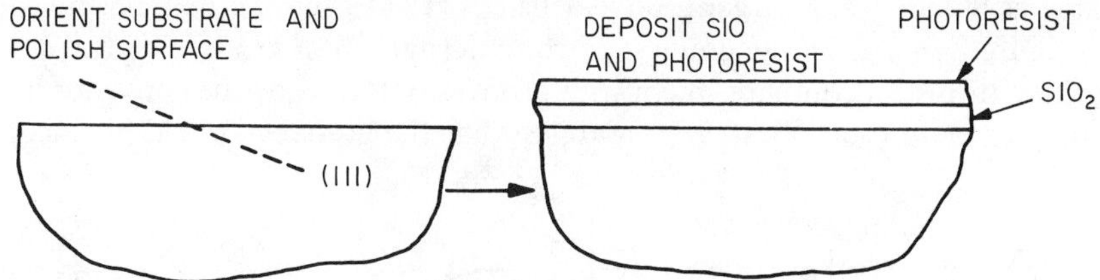

FIG. 2.11. Part of the sequence of anisotropic etching of gratings in single-crystal silicon: orienting the surface with respect to the 111 planes, and coating it with SiO_2 and photoresist. [From Roszhart (1984).]

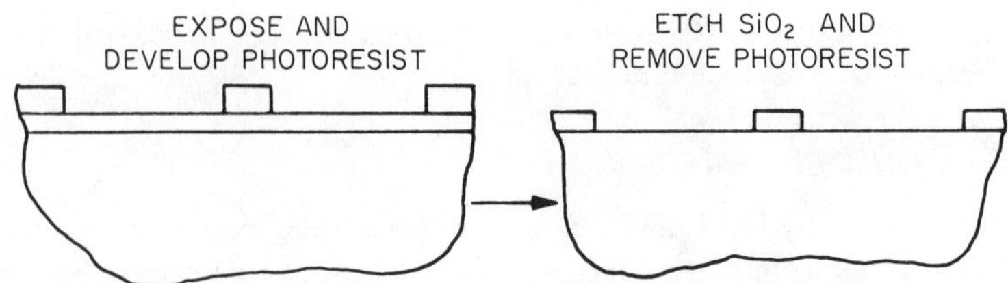

FIG. 2.12. Exposure and development of photoresist layer to replicate the master grating, and subsequent removal of the unprotected SiO_2 layer and photoresist. [From Roszhart (1984).]

Si is cut, ground, and polished such that the polished surface makes an angle with the (111) planes that is equal to the blaze angle desired. After cleaning, a layer of SiO_2 is thermally grown on the surface and photoresist is spun on in the usual manner. The original ruled transmission grating is then placed in contact with the photoresist layer and the photoresist exposed through the transmission grating, using high-intensity UV radiation. A three-step development process is used. The first step is to replicate the transmission grating into the photoresist, as shown at the left in Fig. 2.12. The second step is to remove those portions of the SiO_2 layer not protected by the photoresist strips, as shown to the right of Fig. 2.12. The third step, shown to the left of Figure 2.13 shows how the Si is etched preferentially, using a solution of KOH in deionized water. Those parts of the Si surface not covered by the SiO_2 begin to etch while the protected portions do not. Etching continues into the crystal but is bounded by the two (111) planes that intersect adjacent SiO_2 strips on the surface. When the etchant reaches the intersection of the two (111) planes, the etching of that particular groove is complete. Because the etch rate perpendicular to the (111) planes is very small, the process is easily controlled and a precise profile is easily obtained for all grooves. After etching, the SiO_2 mask can be removed with a hydrofluoric acid solution and the grating has been completed.

Figure 2.13 (right) also shows how the duty cycle appears in the completed grating. If the groove density is small (300 g/mm), the duty cycle can be as large as 90–95%. For larger groove densities (1200 g/mm), it may be 50%.

Figure 2.14 shows a scanning electron micrograph of grooves of a silicon grating (top) and compares them with grooves obtained by the conventional ruling method (bottom). It is easy to see that the grooves formed in silicon

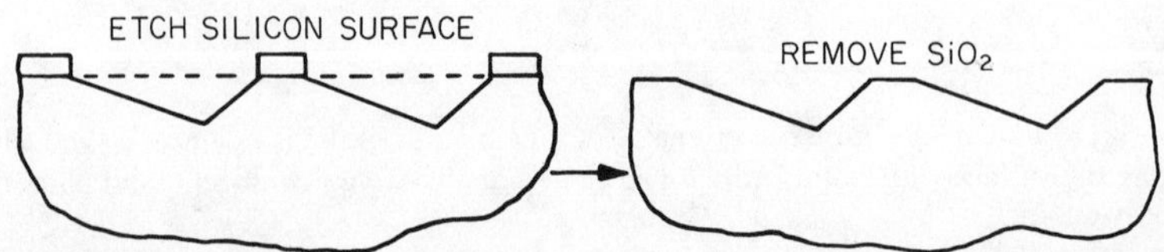

FIG. 2.13. Anisotropic etching followed by removal of the SiO_2 strip. [From Roszhart (1984).]

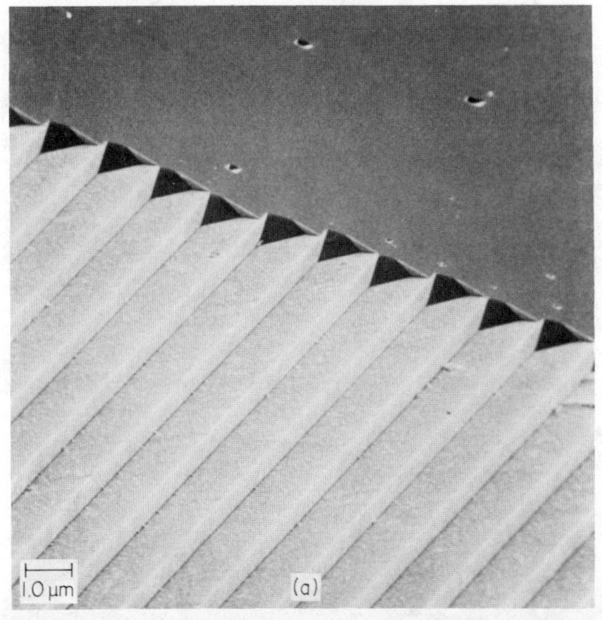

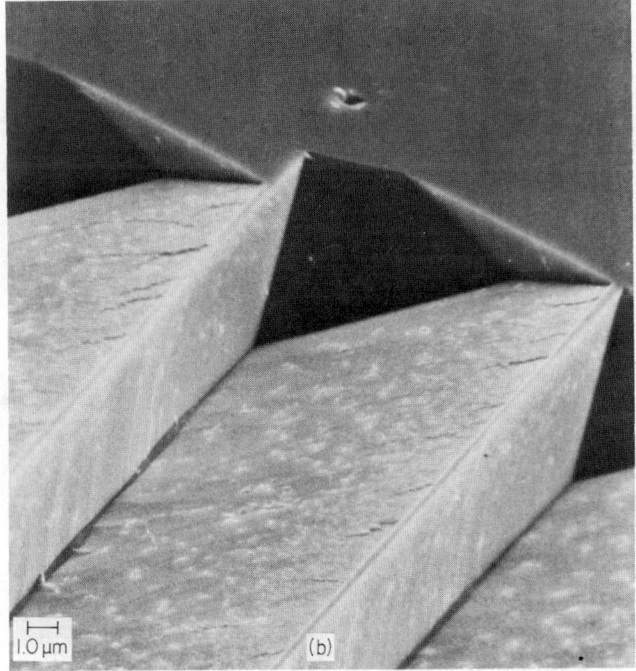

FIG. 2.14. (a) and (b) Scanning electron micrographs of a grating etched in single-crystal silicon with a groove density of 75 g/mm (*continued*). [From Roszhart (1984).]

FIG. 2.14 (*continued*). Conventionally ruled grating grooves are shown (c and d) to compare the groove straightness and smoothness of the two methods. [From Roszhart (1984).]

are much smoother than those formed by the ruling diamond. Roszhart has made gratings with blaze angles as small as 10°. Presumably even smaller blaze angles are possible, depending on how accurately the polished surface can be oriented with respect to the (111) planes. Other groove profiles, triangular and rectangular, can also be made by suitable orientation of the polished surface with respect to the crystalline structure.

As with most processes, groove defects can occur. Roszhart discusses three possible causes. First, if the original grating is misaligned with the intersections of the (111) planes the groove walls can take on a layered, or steplike, appearance. Second, defects in the master grating will be transmitted to the silicon grating, and third, if slip planes are present in the crystal they will be seen in the grating.

The gratings made by Roszhart covered a 3 × 3-cm area on 5-cm-diameter crystal substrates. He points out that boules with diameters of 27 cm and lengths of 50 cm have been grown and that chemically etched silicon gratings of these dimensions can, in principle, be made.

5. *Laminar Gratings*

The groove profile associated with laminar gratings, also known as lamellar gratings, resembles a square wave. Such gratings can be ruled with a diamond, although subsequent operations are necessary to produce the finished square-wave profile. Sayce and Franks (1964) reported a technique that allows the diamond to rule through an aluminum layer almost to the substrate. The metal is then etched to the extent that it is completely removed from the groove bottoms, leaving straight, parallel, strips of metal. The tops of these strips, or lands, are not necessarily flat and may have raised areas at their edges that are the remains of burrs thrown up by the ruling diamond. If the grating is to be used as a mask these burrs are probably not important. If, however, the grating is to be used in grazing incidence for the VUV or soft x-ray region, the burrs may cause shadowing that can reduce the grating efficiency and increase scattering. The substrate surface, however, is smooth, and what Sayce and Franks sought was a method for reproducing the smoothness of the substrate on the grooves of the grating. They do this by replicating. The grating with alternate strips of metal and exposed substrate material is overcoated with gold. This surface is then cemented to a "backing plate," i.e., another substrate, with epoxy cement. After the cement has cured the two plates are separated. The tops of the grooves of the replica have the smoothness of the original substrate surface and the grating can be used in grazing incidence as long as the bottoms of the grooves are not required to have a smooth, flat, shape.

An alternative method is to coat the original etched grating with chromium of whatever thickness desired. The grating is then treated with an alcoholic solution of potassium hydroxide, which permeates through the chromium cladding on the aluminum strips and dissolves the aluminum. Gentle rubbing with cotton removes the remnants of the aluminum–chromium strips and leaves thin strips of chromium on the substrate. Such a grating can be used as is, or with a coating of a suitable metal, or it can be replicated.

The etched grating described above can be used as a mask to generate another laminar grating with the same groove density. If a thin coating of photoresist is spun on the surface of a blank, it can be exposed to light through the mask and then etched to produce a photoresist mask on the substrate, that is, strips of photoresist alternating with strips of the exposed substrate. The photoresist mask is then coated with a layer of metal of controlled thickness and the photoresist etch is once again applied. Usually the metal overlying the photoresist strips has sufficient discontinuities to permit the underlying photoresist to be dissolved away, taking with it the overlying metal but leaving behind the metal strips deposited on the substrate. Overcoating the entire surface then results in a laminar grating with a predetermined step height.

The photoresist mask can also be produced by a holographic technique. After exposure the photoresist is etched away so as to produce the desired land-to-groove ratio. Thereafter the procedure is the same as described in the paragraph above. The holographic technique permits production of corrected laminar gratings if desired.

6. *Replica Gratings*

Ruling conventional gratings is an expensive process, mainly because of the time consumed in ruling. Because of this expense, most spectrographs use replica gratings unless the environment is so severe that the replica cannot survive. According to Meyer (1949), replica gratings were made as long ago as 1872. Lord Rayleigh (1899a–d, 1903) and Quincke (1872) appear to have been the first to have made replicas from glass gratings. Lord Rayleigh made photographic contact prints, but he also tried casting, i.e., pouring gelatin on the grating and removing it after it was dry. Quincke deposited silver chemically on the grating, then electroplated to produce a thick layer. Finally, the layer was stripped off the grating to produce a reflection replica grating.

Present-day replicas are made by using epoxy in a modification of the casting process. The original grating is first coated with a parting agent and then a coating of the metal desired on the replica surface. The parting agent ensures poor adherence of the replica surface metal coating to the original grating and allows the original and replica to be parted. A small amount of epoxy is then poured onto the coated grating and a substrate, which will be the body of the replica grating, is placed on top. The substrate must be worked around to ensure that the epoxy layer spreads over the entire interface, has no air bubbles, and is on the order of a few micrometers thick. Because there is some shrinkage as the epoxy cures, it is important that the epoxy layer have a uniform thickness to minimize and equalize the shrinkage. After the epoxy has set, the original and replica are separated.

In order to have an epoxy layer of uniform thickness, the shape of the substrate must match that of the original fairly closely. Usually original grating blanks have a surface accurate to one-tenth of a wave (6329 Å), and blanks intended for replicas are accurate to one-quarter wave. If the grating is spherical, the original can be ruled on a convex blank for replication onto a concave blank. If the original is concave, a convex submaster must be made from which concave replicas can be obtained. A good original can be the progenitor of a rather large family of replicas. There are sometimes first- and second-generation submasters from which replicas for consumption are taken.

Some spectroscopists prefer to use first-generation replicas. In these replicas the burr at the top of the groove on the original grating, caused by the ruling diamond, is at the bottom of the groove of the replica. Since the bottom of the groove of the original grating is, in all probability, smoother than the top, where the burr is located, the argument for inverting the ruling to get best performance appears convincing. If the grating is to be used in grazing incidence, the presence of a burr can shadow the groove facet, thus reducing the efficiency, or can scatter radiation. In normal incidence the condition of the groove top is perhaps not so important. If the original grating is concave, inverting of the ruling cannot be done because only even-generation replicas can be used.

Almost any type of grating can be replicated. The author has measured the efficiency of replicated holographic gratings, those with laminar groove profiles, and blazed gratings.

7. *Transmission Gratings*

For years transmission gratings were used for introducing students to the idea of diffraction gratings and for training in the laboratory. Coarse transmission gratings are still widely used in testing optical surfaces: the Ronchi test. There appeared to be little use for transmission gratings in the VUV because of the absorption of the substrate supporting the grating. If, however, the absorbing substrate could be eliminated, transmission gratings would have an advantage over gratings used at grazing incidence in that the aperture could be greatly increased. Astronomers have long been interested in soft x-ray spectrographs for space applications and have developed techniques for producing freestanding transmission gratings with slit densities of up to 1000 slits/mm. Dijkstra and Lantward (1975) appear to be the first to have reported this technique. They started with a nickel-coated substrate onto which a layer of photoresist was added. Three methods were investigated for producing the gratings: (1) contact printing of a standard fullsized transmission grating, (2) a step-and-repeat method using a small transmission grating to produce a full-size grating, and (3) recording a holographic grating on the prepared substrate. The first method was suitable for slit densities of 200 g/mm or less, the second for densities up to 500 g/mm, and the third for larger slit densities.

After exposure, the exposed photoresist is etched away, leaving strips of nickel alternating with the remaining unexposed photoresist strips. This surface is then gold coated. Finally, the remaining photoresist is removed and the gold transmission grating detached from the glass substrate by selective etching of the nickel. Because the slits are open, a coarse supporting structure in the form of an auxiliary grid is required. In order to reduce diffraction effects caused by the supporting grid it is given a somewhat random shape similar to a "flagstone pattern as used by landscape gardeners" (Dijkstra and Lantward, 1975).

Further research into transmission gratings for the soft x-ray region has been carried out by Kallne *et al.* (1978), Delvaille *et al.* (1980), Arakawa and Caldwell (1980), and Kallne (1982). With the exception of Arakawa and Caldwell, these researchers studied open-slit gratings only. Arakawa and Caldwell used a much simpler scheme to produce the grating, although the simplicity limits the applicability of the grating. They formed a holographic grating with symmetrical groove profiles on a substrate in the usual manner. The grating is first completely coated with a metal that has transmission windows in the spectral region of interest. Then the grating is partially coated with another metal such that only one side of each groove is coated. The transmission windows of the second metal should not coincide with those of the first. The completed grating is then removed from the substrate and placed over an aperture. Arakawa and Caldwell used silver to coat the sides of the grooves of an aluminum-coated grating and placed the finished grating over a 9-mm-diameter aperture. Because aluminum has a window region in the VUV extending from about 600 to 170 Å, and silver does not, the resulting grating can be used from 600 to 170 Å. It has the further advantage that visible and UV radiation is not transmitted through the grating; hence stray light that might arise from these wavelengths is eliminated.

Although the motive for producing transmission gratings for the soft x-ray region has been improvement in speed of soft x-ray spectrometers, there is no reason why they should not be used in the VUV should the application arise.

8. *Electron-Beam Lithography*

One apparently promising but as yet undeveloped method for manufacturing gratings is electron lithography. Fujita *et al.* (1982) have reported making blazed transmission gratings and Fresnel lenses by this method. An electron-beam resist, polymethyl methacrylate (PMMA), was used rather than a photoresist because the etching rate of the resist depends on the electron dose. By tailoring the dose, the sawtooth profile can be obtained on etching. The first step is to spin the resist on the blank. Then it is coated with about 200 Å of gold to prevent charging during bombardment by the electrons. Next the grating pattern is drawn on the resist, using a computer-controlled electron beam. The required electron dose distribution is obtained by using a different number of scans for the same location of the beam. In forming one groove, the dose can vary from 1.7×10^{-4} C at the deep part of the groove to 0.3×10^{-4} C at the shallow part. Gratings with 100 to 200 g/mm have been produced. There is some roughness on the groove surface, the cause of which is unknown.

The authors did not give the dimensions of the grating, but usually gratings formed by electron-beam lithography are too small to be of much use in spectroscopy. Also, the groove densities are limited because if the grooves are too close together, the electrons may be scattered within the resist and change the dose in adjoining grooves, which would change the finished groove profile.

C. Focal Properties of Gratings

The great contribution to spectroscopy introduced by Rowland in the form of the concave spherical grating was the combination, in one optical element, of the ability to focus and disperse radiation. Inevitably, the aberrations associated with concave spherical surfaces, plus optical behavior peculiar to gratings, are also incorporated in the concave grating. Rowland explained the optical characteristics of the concave grating, as have a number of others listed in Subsection 2.2.A. Rather than go through the analysis yet again, only the pertinent results will be given, as obtained by Namioka (1959). Using Fermat's principle, one calculates the light path, from entrance slit to grating to exit slit, using a coordinate system with origin at the grating apex (x along the normal, y perpendicular to the grooves, and z parallel to the grooves), and expresses the path as a function of w, the grating width, and l, the length of the grooves. If the partial derivatives of the light path function with respect to w and l equal zero, the path is an extremum and the coefficients of the w and l terms can be used to obtain the grating equation, the optimum focusing conditions, and an insight into the aberrations.

1. *Uncorrected Concave Gratings*

For a grating of radius R, as w and l approach the grating center, the coordinate origin, one has the equations governing the central ray:

$$(1 + z^2/r^2)^{1/2}(\sin\alpha + \sin\beta) = nG\lambda \tag{2.6a}$$

and

$$z/r = z'/r'. \tag{2.6b}$$

Equation (2.6a) is the grating equation with α, β, n, G, and λ defined as before. Since the entrance slit and its images extend above and below the Rowland circle plane, the coefficient $(1 + z^2/r^2)^{1/2}$ is used to correct the grating equation, which is valid only in the Rowland circle plane, i.e., the meridional plane; z is the distance along the entrance slit above or below the Rowland circle plane; and r is the distance from the entrance slit center to the grating apex; that is, $r = R\cos\alpha$. Equation (2.6b) represents the geometric relation between object points on the entrance slit and their images. Here z' is the distance above or below the Rowland circle plane in the slit image, and $r' = R\cos\beta$.

The focusing condition is expressed by

$$(\cos^2\alpha)/r = (\cos\alpha)/R + (\cos^2\beta)/r' - (\cos\beta)/R = 0. \tag{2.7}$$

A solution is

$$r = R\cos\alpha \qquad \text{and} \qquad r' = R\cos\beta, \tag{2.8}$$

which is the equation of a circle, the Rowland circle, and gives the location of the diffracted images of the slit on the circle. If $r = \infty$, there is another solution given by

$$r = \infty \qquad \text{and} \qquad r' = R\cos^2\beta/(\cos\alpha + \cos\beta). \tag{2.9}$$

This is the focal condition for the Wadsworth mounting, which requires the incident radiation to be collimated. Equations (2.8) and (2.9) are for the horizontal, or tangential, foci. The vertical, or sagittal, foci are obtained from

$$1/r - (\cos\alpha)/R + 1/r' - (\cos\beta)/R = 0, \tag{2.10}$$

the solutions of which are

$$r = R/\cos\alpha \qquad \text{and} \qquad r' = R/\cos\beta \tag{2.11}$$

and

$$r = \infty \quad \text{and} \quad r' = R/(\cos\alpha + \cos\beta). \tag{2.12}$$

Equations (2.11) are equations of a straight line tangent to the Rowland circle at the normal to the grating apex. Any point on this tangent will be imaged as a vertical line (horizontal focus) at the position $r' = R/\cos\beta$. One can find the location of the vertical, sometimes called the secondary, foci by solving Eq. (2.10) for r'. By using $r = R\cos\alpha$ from Eq. (2.8), we find

$$r' = R/(\cos\beta - \sin\alpha\tan\alpha). \tag{2.13}$$

If α is taken as a constant, the equation defines r' as a function of β. If $\alpha = 0$, the equation reduces to the second Eq. (2.8), and the secondary focal line and the Rowland circle osculate at $\alpha = \beta = 0$. If $\alpha = 0$, the curve is a parabola that does not intersect the Rowland circle; hence the vertical and horizontal foci never coincide and the spherical grating in a Rowland circle mount always has astigmatism except for $\alpha = \beta = 0$. Because of astigmatism, a point source for the Rowland circle mounting is imaged vertically as a line of length

$$l(\text{ps}) = L(\sin^2\beta + \sin\alpha\tan\alpha\cos\beta), \tag{2.14}$$

and the length of the slit image is given by

$$l(\text{si}) = B(\cos\beta/\cos\alpha) + l(\text{ps})$$

where B is the length of the slit and L is the illuminated length of the rulings.

Equations (2.12) refer to the Wadsworth mounting. Both foci coincide for β equal to zero. Thus the Wadsworth mount provides an easily available stigmatic image.

The focal conditions derived above are predicated on grooves equally spaced on the chord of a concave grating. But if the grating aperture becomes very wide, the constant groove spacing is no longer sufficient for good focusing and the rays diffracted from the outer regions of the grating are no longer focused on the Rowland circle; the grating has spherical aberration. One can infer that there is an optimum grating width for obtaining maximum resolution from a concave grating. The theory was worked out by Mack *et al.* (1932), and the formula for optimum width, as given by Namioka (1961), is,

$$W_{\text{opt}} = 2.36[(4\lambda R^3\cos\alpha\cos\beta)/(\pi A)]^{0.25},$$

where $A = \sin^2\alpha\cos\beta + \cos\alpha\sin^2\beta$, and R is the radius of curvature of the grating.

It is possible to reduce the astigmatism encountered when using the Rowland circle mounting with a concave spherical grating by changing the shape of the grating surface. Haber (1950) has investigated the toroidal grating and found a considerable reduction in astigmatism. A torus is generated by rotating a circle about any straight line, except a diameter, lying in the plane of the circle. The radius of the circle is taken as ρ, and the distance from the center of the circle to the axis of rotation is $R - \rho$, where R is the radius of the toroid. If $\rho = R$, a circle is generated by the rotation, so the sphere may be considered a special case of the torus. If the axis of rotation lies within the circle, there will be two possible concave surfaces as shown in Fig. 2.15. The inner surface resembles a football; the outer surface is the surface of interest. The location of the section that is the grating is shown by the rectanglelike figure centered at the origin of the coordinate system. The rulings are the intersection of equally spaced planes parallel to the axis of revolution and perpendicular to the grating tangent plane, just as with the spherical grating.

Haber's analysis was performed by obtaining an expression for the light path and applying Fermat's principle. He obtains the general grating equation (2.6a) and the equation representing the geometric relation between object and image points (2.6b). The condition for the vertical focus is also the same as Eq. (2.7), which shows that the toroidal grating can be used in a Rowland circle mount. However, the equation for the horizontal foci is different from Eq. (2.10). It is

$$1/r - (\cos\alpha)/\rho + 1/r' - (\cos\beta)/\rho = 0.$$

Unlike Eq. (2.10), for which the only stigmatic solution is $\alpha = \beta = 0$, this equation can be solved for other values of α and β because there is still a free choice for the parameter ρ.

Introducing the values for r and r', obtained from Eq. (2.8), one obtains

$$\rho/R = \cos\alpha\cos\beta.$$

The equation for the secondary foci is obtained in the same manner as for the spherical concave grating. The result is

$$r' = \rho\cos\alpha/\{\cos^2\alpha - [(\rho/R) - \cos\alpha\cos\beta]\}.$$

The curves of ρ as a function of β, for different values of α, are parabolas that intersect the Rowland circle in two points except for the value of α for which $\beta = 0$, for which the two points coincide. Therefore the toroidal grating has two distinct values of β for which the image is stigmatic. These stigmatic points can be selected by choosing ρ, R, and the grating spacing.

Tousey *et al.* (1964) have used a toroidal grating in a rocket spectrograph used to record the solar spectrum from about 1200 to 2000 Å. Their spectrograph used two gratings in crossed dispersion (see Subsection 2.3.A.5). The first grating was a sphere but the second was a sphere distorted into approximately a toroidal shape. The distortion was accomplished by pressing at diametrically opposed points on the circumference of the grating with two screws.

Huber *et al.* (1981) have designed an elastic substrate for a toroidal grating. The substrate is circular with a graded thickness given by $H^3 = A(1 - p^2)$, where A is a constant and $p = r/r_0$, the radius in units of the substrate radius r_0. Martensitic stainless steel is the substrate material. Distortion is accomplished by four "bridges," each spanning $\pi/6$ of the circumference, and each driven by a screw. A comparison of the measured and calculated spatial blur circles showed that, as a mirror, the toroid performance was satisfactory.

The toroids described by Tousey *et al.* and Huber *et al.* cannot have a large difference in radii of curvature, and can only be used effectively in normal-incidence instruments. Toroids with large differences in radii must be fabricated.

Speer *et al.* (1974) have investigated the case where $R > 2\rho$; i.e., the circle is rotated about an external axis. They designed and constructed a toroidal grating for the soft x-ray region. For the design parameters they selected an angle of incidence of 2°, the wavelength of minimum astigmatism to be 44 Å, and the grating to be used in the inside first order. For the major radius they chose $R = 2$ m. Thus the small radius was calculated to be 5.65 mm. The

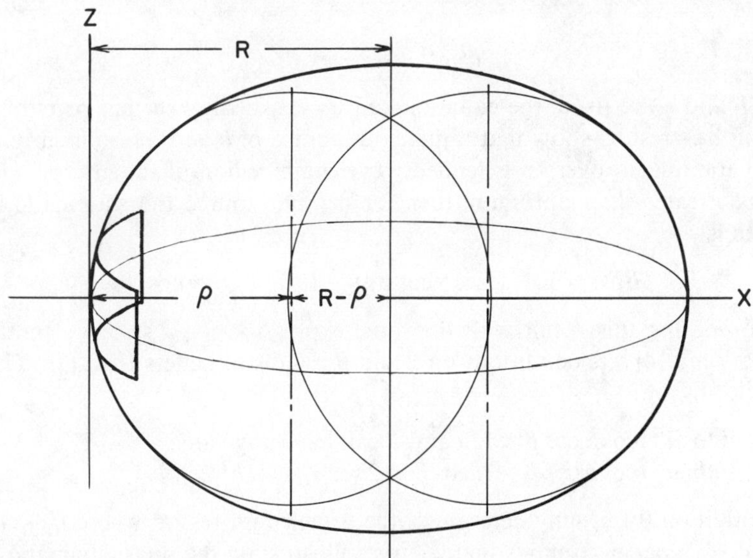

FIG. 2.15. A toroid. That portion of the surface used for a toroidal grating of the type described by Haber (1950) is outlined by solid lines at the left.

grooves were formed holographically with a density of 600 g/mm. In their paper they show both white light and soft-x-ray (44 Å) images to demonstrate that the performance was as calculated. Speer *et al.* (1979) have also fabricated and tested toroidal gratings with $R = 5$ m and $\rho = 25$ mm.

Ellipsoids and toroids are somewhat similar surfaces and one might expect similar performance in the reduction of aberrations found in spherical gratings. Namioka (1961) has studied the ellipsoidal grating and found that astigmatism can be reduced over an extended wavelength range but not reduced to zero. He chose an ellipsoid with minor axes a, b, c along the coordinate axes x, y, z, respectively. As might be expected, his analysis produced Eqs. (2.6a) and (2.6b). The focusing conditions, however, differ from Eqs. (2.7) and (2.10). The horizontal focal condition is

$$(\cos^2 \alpha)/r - (a/b^2) \cos \alpha + \cos^2 \beta/r' - (a/b^2) \cos \beta = 0,$$

and the vertical focal condition is

$$1/r - (a/c^2) \cos \alpha + 1/r' - (a/c^2) \cos \beta = 0$$

One obtains

$$r = (b^2/a) \cos \alpha \qquad \text{and} \qquad r' = (b^2/a) \cos \beta$$

as a solution of the horizontal focal equation. If these values are substituted in the vertical focal equation, one obtains the conditions for a stigmatic image:

$$b^2/c^2 = \sec \alpha \sec \beta.$$

If b and c are fixed, the equation can be satisfied by certain pairs of $\alpha\beta$. Namioka's results show that a judicious choice of b and c results in quasi-stigmatic images over an extended wavelength region. If the grating width is not greater than optimum, then for a point source the astigmatic line length is

$$l(\text{ps}) = L(1 + \sec \alpha \cos \beta)|1 - (b^2/c^2) \cos \alpha \cos \beta|.$$

Comparing this result with the same expression for a spherical grating (equation 2.14) sets conditions on α and β if l_{ell} is to be less than l_{sph}. These conditions are:

(a) If $(b^2/c^2) \cos \alpha \cos \beta < 1$, α and β can have any value.
(b) If $(b^2/c^2) \cos \alpha \cos \beta \geq 1$, $\cos \beta < 2 \sec \alpha/(1 + b^2/c^2)$.

Condition (b) usually determines the wavelength region where $l_{\text{ell}} < l_{\text{sph}}$. Namioka's paper contains many curves illustrating the quasi-stigmatic behavior to be expected from ellipsoidal gratings.

Singh and Majumder (1969) have studied cylindrical gratings with circular grooves for use in Rowland circle mountings. Figure 2.16 shows the two cases they consider. In case 1 the axis of the cylinder is perpendicular to the Rowland circle, and in case (b) it is parallel to the circle. In both cases the rulings, when projected onto a plane tangent to the Rowland circle, are concentric circles with centers located at O. The distance from O to the grating center is ρ_0. If the radius of a particular groove is ρ, then one has $\rho - \rho_0 = \pm nd$, where d is the grating spacing. On forming the light path function and applying Fermat's principle, they obtain Eqs. (2.6a), (2.6b), and (2.7) and a fourth equation,

$$1/r + 1/r' + (\sin\alpha + \sin\beta)/\rho_0 = 0, \tag{2.15}$$

which is related to astigmatism. This equation is different from the corresponding equation for a concave spherical grating, Eq. (2.10). From Eq. (2.7) it is evident that a cylindrical grating (case 1) can be used in a Rowland circle mounting. The focal conditions for a Rowland circle mount are given in Eq. (2.8). If they are substituted into the equation above, one obtains the stigmatic conditions if a cylindrical grating with curved grooves is used,

$$R/\rho_0 = -\sec\alpha\sec\beta\cot[(\alpha+\beta)/2],$$

where R is the radius of the cylinder. If one substitutes $r = R\cos\alpha$ and $r' = r_h$ in Eq. (2.15), an equation for the secondary focal curves is obtained:

$$r_h = -R\cos\alpha/\{1 + [(\sin\alpha + \sin\beta)R\cos\alpha]/\rho_0\},$$

where r_h is the distance of the horizontal focal lines from the center of the grating. Figure 2.17 shows the Rowland circle with two of the secondary focal curves corresponding to $\alpha = 0°$ and $20°$, and for $R/\rho_0 = 6$.

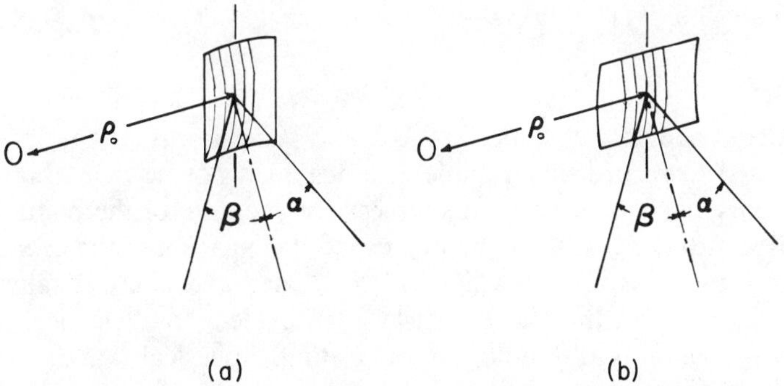

FIG. 2.16. The two cases of curved grooves on cylindrical grating blanks described by Singh and Majumder (1969). (a) Cylinder axis is perpendicular to the Rowland circle; (b) cylinder axis is parallel to the Rowland circle.

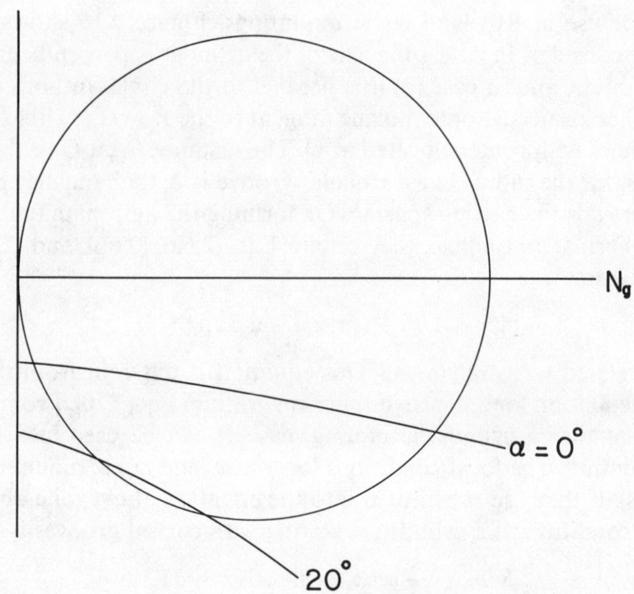

FIG. 2.17. Secondary focal curves for the cylindrical grating of Fig. 2.16a.

The authors find that the astigmatism is much greater if the rulings are straight lines parallel to the cylinder axis rather than concentric circles.

For case (b) they find that the focal properties of the cylindrical grating are similar to those of a plane grating but with considerably less astigmatism than found in a plane grating. Once again, the astigmatism is less if the grooves are circular, but even with straight grooves there are some stigmatic points. Apparently no investigations have been made for corrected holographic gratings formed on cylinders.

2. *Concave Holographic Gratings*

As mentioned in Subsection 2.2.B.2, the wave fronts of the interfering beams used to record holographic gratings need not be plane but can be spherical, i.e., originate at point sources. The location of the point sources with respect to the grating blank determines the spacing of the grooves as a function of position on the grating surface. Plane waves cause equally spaced straight grooves on the chordal surface, equivalent to a classical grating, also known as a type I holographic grating. Spherical waves cause the grooves to be curved and the curvature changes with position on the grating surface. Varying the groove spacing and curvature causes the diffracted wave fronts to be nonspherical in nature, which gives rise to aberrations. If the aspheric nature of the wave front can be made to cancel the aspheric

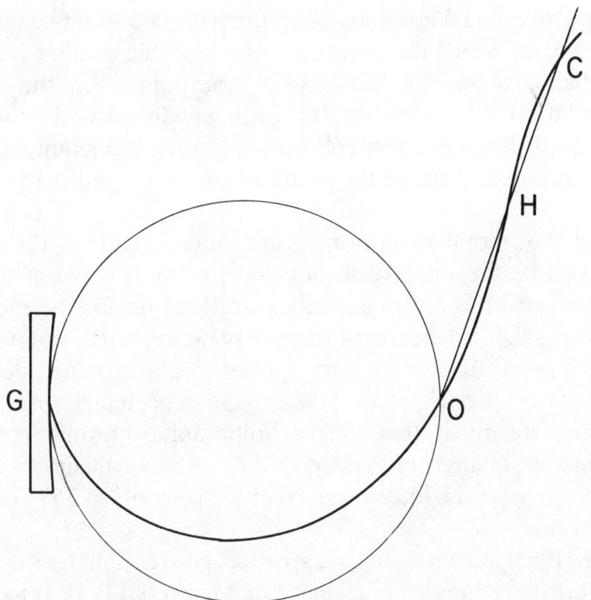

FIG. 2.18. Focal curve of a type III spherical holographic grating.

wave front caused by the spherical grating blank, then the aberrations of the concave grating can, in principle, be canceled. In practice, holographic gratings can be designed to reduce aberrations and even cancel them at certain wavelengths. In doing so, however, the shape of the focal curve may be changed.

The calculations involved in the process of designing a holographic grating are quite similar to those used to calculate the focal curve of the classical grating. The dissimilarity lies in the nonuniform spacing of the grooves, which arises from the spherical waves used to generate the curved grooves. In fact, terms in the light path function must include the coordinates of the recording points to obtain the local groove spacing. A series of articles by Noda *et al.* (1974a–c) cover theory, ray tracing, and design of holographic gratings. If the recording points are at infinity, i.e., plane waves, the focal curve is the Rowland circle. If both recording points are on the Rowland circle, the focal curve is also the Rowland circle because the grooves are equally spaced on the chordal surface *in* the meridional plane. At other points on the chordal surface, however, the spacing is different. The interfering beams form a series of confocal hyperbolas on the chordal surface. If one of the sources is at the center of curvature of the grating blank, the grating is a type II holographic grating, and some correction of astigmatism is obtained.

There are also type III gratings, which are recorded with two point sources, one inside and one outside the sphere of which the grating is a part, and lying on a diametral line. The distances of these points from the origin have a harmonic relation with respect to the grating radius; i.e., the radius is their geometric mean. The focal curve for such a grating is a lemniscate as shown in Fig. 2.18. It passes through the center of curvature and the two recording points.

By careful choice of the recording point source locations, the shape of the lemniscate can be arranged such that that part of it between the two stigmatic points A and B is approximately a straight line. Furthermore, this line is at near-normal incidence with respect to wavelengths coming from the grating. Such corrections have been applied to gratings intended for use in grazing incidence. Fonck *et al.* (1982) have reported a spectrometer for plasma purity diagnosis that uses a holographic grating recorded on a toroidal blank at an angle of incidence of 71°. The focal curve is flat and the angle of incidence on the focal plane changes from 19° to 25° over the useful wavelength range.

Kita *et al.* (1983) have reported a corrected, conventionally ruled, spherical grating for use at 87° angle of incidence that has a flat field. It has been used in spectrograph to record soft x-ray spectra from 50 to 250 Å.

3. *Plane Gratings*

Although plane gratings with straight, uniformly spaced grooves have no focusing properties in the sense of concave gratings, they are capable of altering the geometry of an incident radiation beam. Easiest to visualize is their anamorphic property. The beam dimension parallel to the rulings remains unchanged on diffraction but that perpendicular to the rulings can be

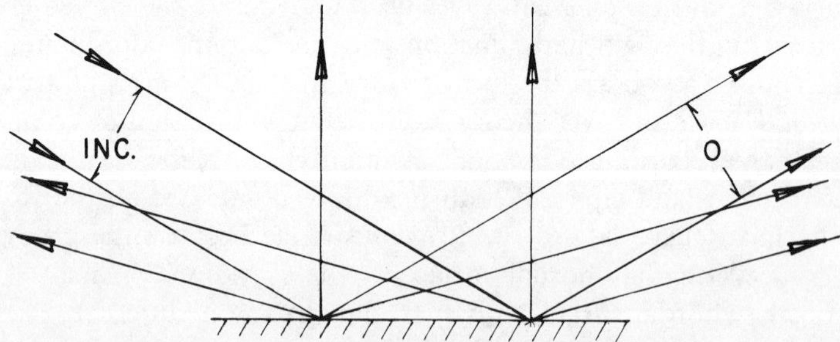

FIG. 2.19. Illustration of the anamorphic property of plane gratings. The grooves are perpendicular to the plane of the figure.

either larger or smaller than the incident beam. Inside orders, between the zeroth order and the incident beam, have a larger dimension perpendicular to the rulings than the other orders. This effect is illustrated in Fig. 2.19 for a collimated, monochromatic beam.

If, also, the indicent beam is converging or diverging, there are two additional effects to consider. The larger of the two is the change in dispersion with angle of incidence. Figure 2.20 shows this effect for a beam of monochromatic radiation diverging from a point source. Because the deviation of the diffracted rays is not uniform in angle and depends on the angle of incidence, the virtual image of the source shows the characteristics associated with coma. Thus the diffracted beam has a nonuniform intensity, and a real image formed by optics in the diffracted beam will have an aberration resembling coma unless compensating aberrations are introduced. For a given divergence, this effect is augmented as the angle of incidence increases.

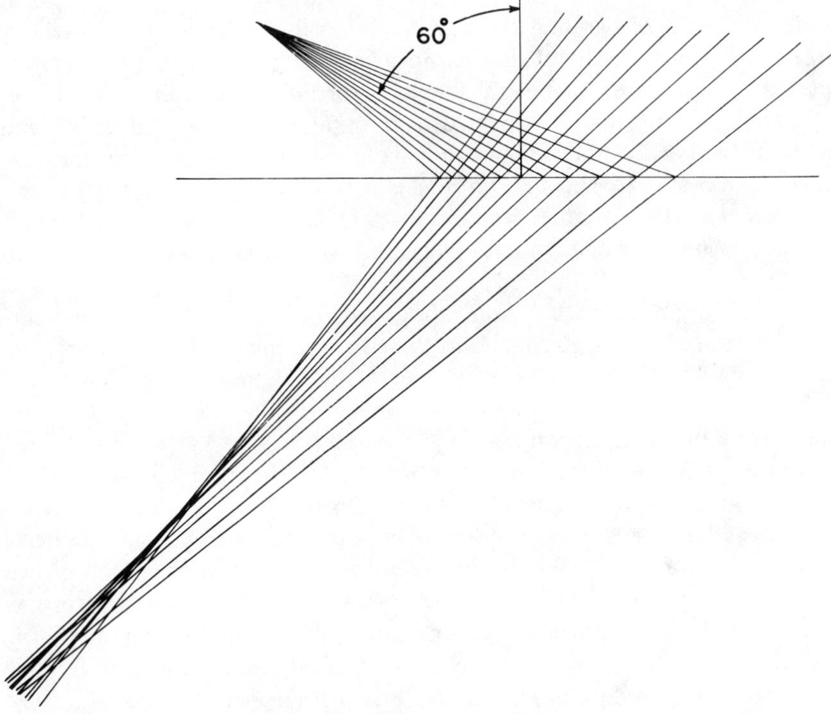

FIG. 2.20. Illustration of defocusing caused by the change in dispersion when a plane grating is illustrated by diverging radiation. The grating grooves are perpendicular to the plane of the figure. The incident rays are 2° apart.

The second, smaller, effect is that of conical diffraction, which arises because only the meridional plane of rays is perpendicular to the rulings. Conical diffraction causes the diffracted beam to expand in the direction parallel to the rulings as the angle of incidence is increased.

In principle, plane gratings can also be made capable of imaging by holographic means. For example, a Fresnel zone plate, a grating with concentric circular grooves nonuniformly spaced, will image a point source on its axis at other axial points corresponding to the different wavelengths emitted by the source. A portion of the zone plate, not on axis, does the same thing. If used at wavelengths other than that for which the plate was designed, the aberrations are large enough to make such gratings impractical (Hutley, 1982).

D. Grating Efficiencies

1. *Measurement*

The efficiency of a grating at a given $n\lambda$ is the ratio of the diffracted intensity to the incident intensity at that $n\lambda$. In principle, grating efficiencies can be measured in the same manner as plane mirror reflectance values. A beam of monochromatic radiation, directed to the grating, is measured before and after diffraction. In practice, a great deal of care must be used to ensure good photometry and to account for the effects of polarization if necessary. Michels *et al.* (1974) and Hunter and Prinz (1977) have discussed techniques for measuring efficiencies of both plane and concave gratings at all angles of incidence.

The optimum technique requires that small portions of the grating surface be measured in a given $n\lambda$ and these measurements later assembled to form a monochromatic efficiency map of the grating surface. The main reason for adopting this scanning technique is to eliminate the effect of nonuniformity of the radiation from the monochromator that illuminates the test grating. As mentioned in Subsection 2.2.B.1, the blaze change across a concave grating surface causes efficiency changes across that surface. In addition, the efficiency may change for other reasons; crossing from one panel to another of a multipartite grating, a sequence of incompletely burnished grooves, etc. Consequently, a monochromatic beam from a grating instrument used to illuminate the test grating will, in all probability, be nonuniform. By stopping down the beam, the effect of nonuniform illumination is made negligible compared to the changes in efficiency across the surface of the test grating. A second reason for using this technique is that the f-number of VUV monochromators, especially grazing incidence monochromators, is so large that the test grating cannot be filled.

The simplest way to measure small areas is to move the grating with respect to the illuminating beam at a uniform rate and record the diffracted intensity as a function of position, thus providing a "scan" of the grating surface. For example, the dimensions of the radiation beam at the grating surface might be 1 cm parallel to the grooves and 1 mm perpendicular to them. If the grating is moved perpendicular to its groove direction and a continuous recording made of the diffracted intensity, the recording shows how the efficiency varies in a strip 1 cm wide across the grating surface. If the groove length is greater than 1 cm, the grating must be raised or lowered and the scans repeated until the entire surface is mapped.

The angle of incidence should be that at which the grating will eventually be used. If the grating is to be illuminated by an entrance slit, it can be moved on a circle with a radius equal to that of the grating. This arrangement has an advantage in that the angles of incidence and diffraction remain constant during the scan, and the detector need not be moved. If the illumination is done with collimated radiation, the grating can be moved along a straight line. Because the angles of incidence and diffraction will be constantly changing during the scan, however, the detector must be moved during the scan to collect all the diffracted radiation in $n\lambda$ unless the grating is being measured *in focus*, i.e., in a simulated instrument. Concave grating efficiencies are not usually measured in an in focus condition because of the difficulty and expense of simulating the many mountings that would be required. It is much more convenient to measure efficiencies in a geometry resembling that used for measuring the reflection of plane mirrors, as described by Michels *et al.* It is true that the angles of incidence on the grating may differ from those encountered in the actual spectroscope, the difference being greater the smaller the f-number. However, the f-numbers for most normal-incidence spectroscopes are not small: $f/4$ or larger. For an $f/4$ grating used at normal incidence, the angle of incidence changes from 0° at the center to approximately 7° at the periphery, if illuminated by collimated radiation. The reflectances of coating materials do not change much from 0° to 7°, nor do grating efficiencies unless strong anomalies are present, which is unlikely (see Subsection 2.2.D.3). Consequently, the reflectometer technique described by Michels *et al.* can be relied on to give results whose accuracies are commensurate with reflectance measurements, which are, at best, about 3%.

Once an efficiency map has been obtained in the manner described above, the average efficiency over the surface can be calculated and the result will be valid for the conditions under which the grating was measured. This average is the value of most interest to spectroscopists, and is one of the numbers required to calibrate a spectroscope.

In the discussions that follow, the radiation from the monochromator, used to measure grating efficiencies, is not polarized unless stated otherwise.

It has been the author's experience that the polarization caused by a normal-incidence monochromator is usually negligible, especially for wavelengths longer than 1000 Å. The same is true for grazing incidence monochromators at wavelengths shorter than about 400 Å. Not many efficiency measurements using polarized VUV radiation have been reported because (1) the polarizers are generally reflecting polarizers and they do not have a large throughput, (2) the efficiencies of gratings are not very large, and (3) the number of photons obtained from conventional light sources is also not large. These conditions combine to provide experimenters with rather small signal/noise ratios, which make the measurements difficult. Hanson and Arakawa (1966) have measured grating efficiencies with a reflecting polarizer and Caruso *et al.* (1981) have measured grating efficiencies with polarized radiation obtained by reflection from an LiF plate set approximately at the Brewster angle. A grating measuring device using synchrotron radiation would be most useful.

An example of an efficiency map for a concave ruled grating is shown in Fig. 2.21 (Hunter, 1980). The grating has a 1-m radius of curvature, 600 g/mm, is coated with Al + MgF_2, where the MgF_2 thickness T is 250 Å, and was measured at 1608 Å in the strong second order at near-normal incidence. The blaze angle given by the manufacturer is 4°45′, corresponding to a Littrow blaze wavelength of 2760 Å. The ruling is 50 mm wide and monopartite. The efficiency changes from almost zero at the left to approximately 43% at the

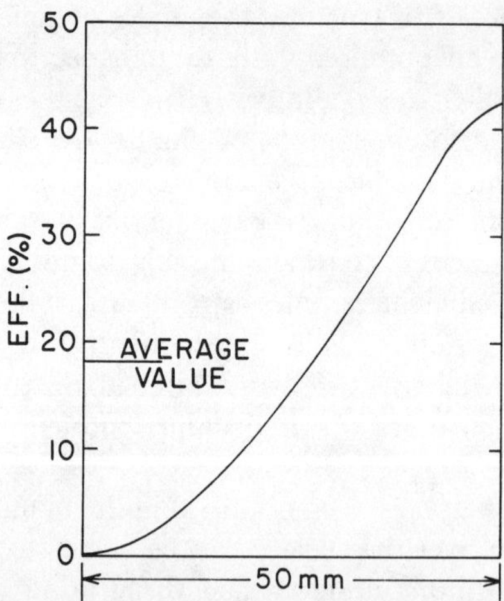

FIG. 2.21. Measured grating efficiency map in the second order of a concave, monopartite, conventional grating with 600 g/mm at 1608 Å. Angle of incidence is 0°, radius of curvature is 1 m, blaze angle is 4°45′, and coating is Al + MgF_2. [From Hunter (1980). © North-Holland Physics Publishing, Amsterdam, 1980.]

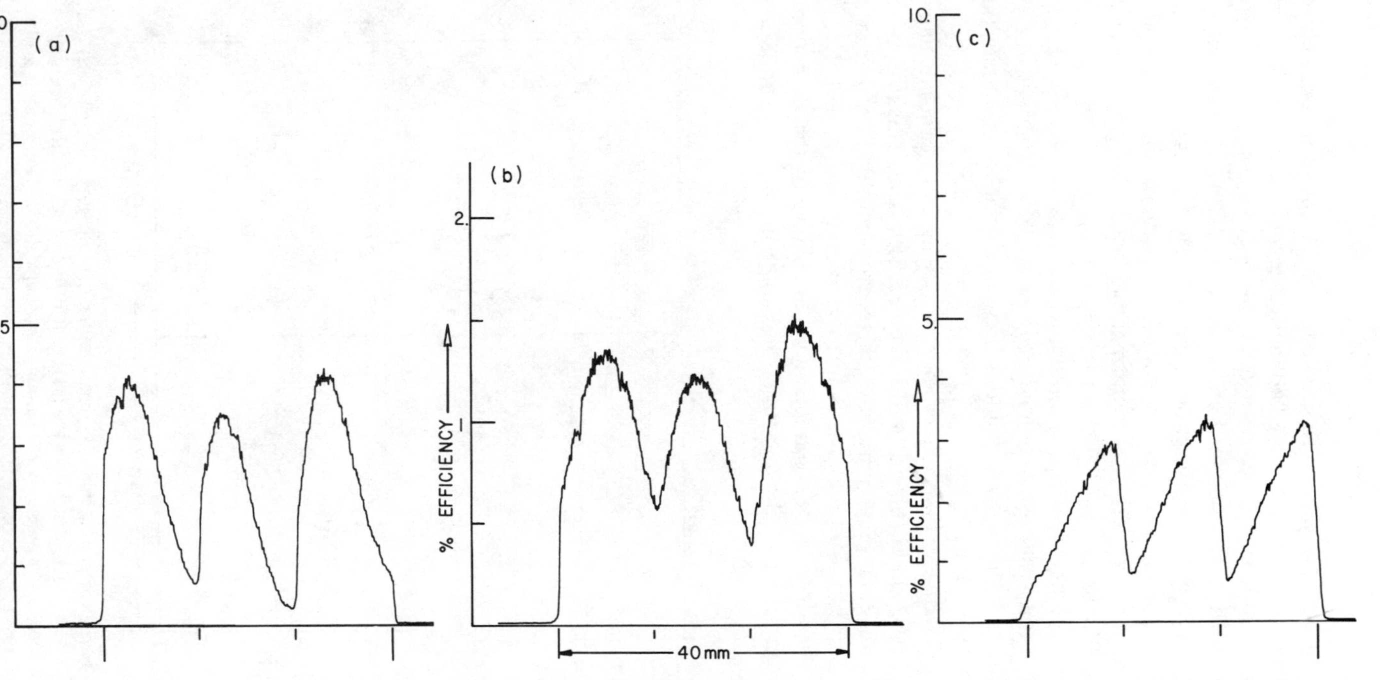

FIG. 2.22. Measured grating efficiency maps at three wavelengths, in the first order, of a concave, tripartite, conventional spherical grating at near-normal incidence. (a) $\lambda = 584$ Å, (b) $\lambda = 736$ Å, and (c) $\lambda = 1216$ Å. Radius of curvature is 40 cm, coating is aluminum. The blaze angle is set for 736 Å in (b). [From Michels (1974).]

right with an average value of 18%. The reason for the pronounced nonuniform efficiency is the discrepancy between blaze and measuring wavelength.

In order to avoid such large changes in efficiency across gratings, they are sometimes ruled in sections, or panels, wherein the blaze angle is set correctly at the center of each section. Figure 2.22 (Michels, 1974) shows an efficiency map of a 40-cm radius-of-curvature grating at 584, 736, and 1216 Å in the strong first orders at near-normal incidence. This grating was ruled in three parts (tripartite), with 600 g/mm, and was intended to have a Littrow blaze wavelength of 800 Å. Apparently the diamond was set very close to the correct blaze angle because the efficiency appears to be symmetrical about the center of each panel at 736 Å and is skewed in opposite directions for the other two wavelengths.

Figure 2.23 (Hunter, 1980) shows an efficiency map of a concave, tripartite grating at 1216 Å in both zeroth and strong first orders. This grating has a blaze angle of 2°45′ (800-Å Littrow blaze wavelength), 1200 g/mm, a Pt coating, a 1-m radius of curvature, and was measured with a 10° angle of incidence. The divisions between the panels are shown by the almost vertical lines. The central panel shows a smooth change in efficiency, undoubtedly

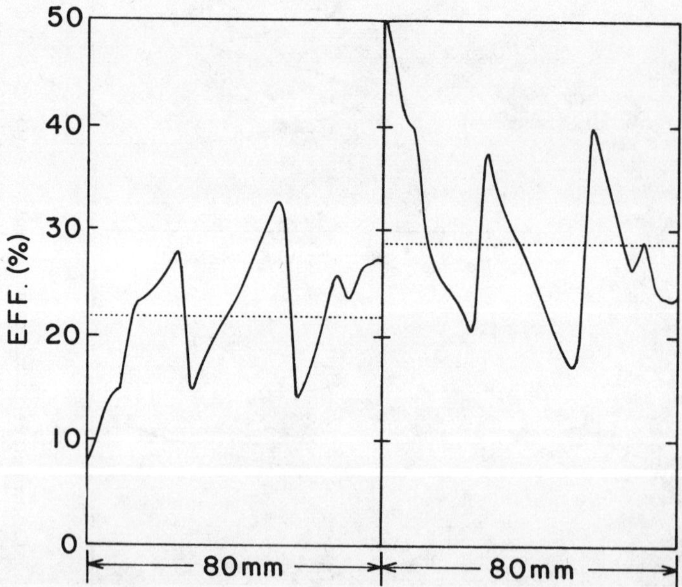

FIG. 2.23. Measured grating efficiency maps in the zeroth (right) and first (left) orders of a concave, tripartite, conventional spherical grating at 1216 Å. Angle of incidence is 10°, radius of curvature is 1 m, groove density is 1200 g/mm, blaze angle is 2°45′, and coating is platinum. [From Hunter (1980). © North-Holland Physics Publishing, Amsterdam, 1980.]

caused by a change in blaze angle, but that cannot be explained by the simple change in diamond orientation described in Subsection 2.2.B.1. Possibly these anomalous changes are caused by the "target pattern" shown in Fig. 2.24 (Hunter, 1980). This is a photograph in white light of the ruled area of the grating of Fig. 2.23. The crescents in the outer panels are referred to as a target pattern because of their resemblance to a target. They correspond to changes of efficiency in the visible and there is no reason to suspect that they do not give rise to efficiency changes in the VUV as well. They have not been positively identified with efficiency changes in the VUV because the probe beam is usually large enough to blur any distinctive pattern. The origin of the target pattern is controversial. According to some it is a visual indication of the locus of constant diamond stylus orientation on the surface of the grating sphere, which would be circles around the apex. Others claim it is caused by problems in the bearings supporting the diamond stylus. The target pattern occurs only on conventionally ruled gratings if it occurs at all.

Blazed concave holographic gratings show some change in blaze across the ruled area but to a lesser extent than ruled gratings because the standing wave fronts used to record the grating are formed from spherical waves (see Subsection 2.2.B.2). Figure 2.25 (Hunter, 1974) compares the ruled tripartite grating of Fig. 2.23 with a concave holographic blazed grating. The holographic grating is gold coated and has 1200 g/mm and a 1-m radius of curvature. The zeroth and strong and weak first orders are shown. On either side of the zeroth orders are very sharp efficiency maxima, which are actually specular reflections from the unruled portion of the grating.

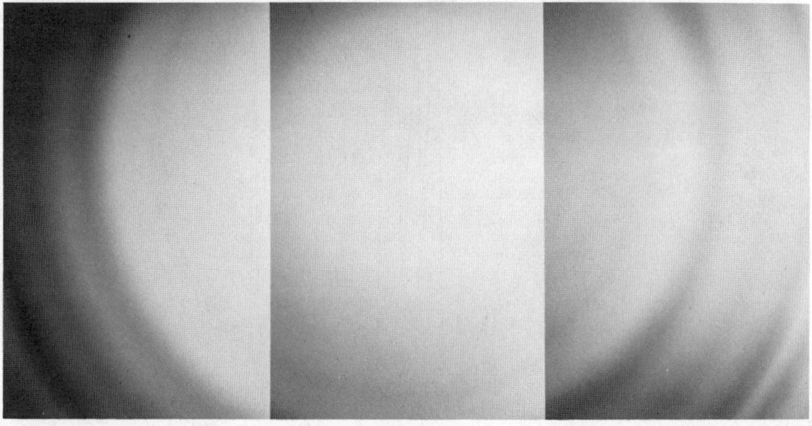

FIG. 2.24. Photograph of the surface of the grating of Fig. 2.23 in white light, showing the presence of "target pattern." [From Hunter (1980). © North-Holland Physics Publishing, Amsterdam, 1980.]

Concave holographic gratings with sinusoidal groove profiles have an even more uniform efficiency across the surface than holographic blazed concave gratings. Figure 2.26 (Hunter, 1974) shows the two first orders of a large, concave holographic grating, measured at 1440 Å and at an angle of incidence of 0°. This grating has 2400 g/mm, a radius of curvature of 85 cm, and a width of 26.8 cm, a bit more than three times the width of the ruled

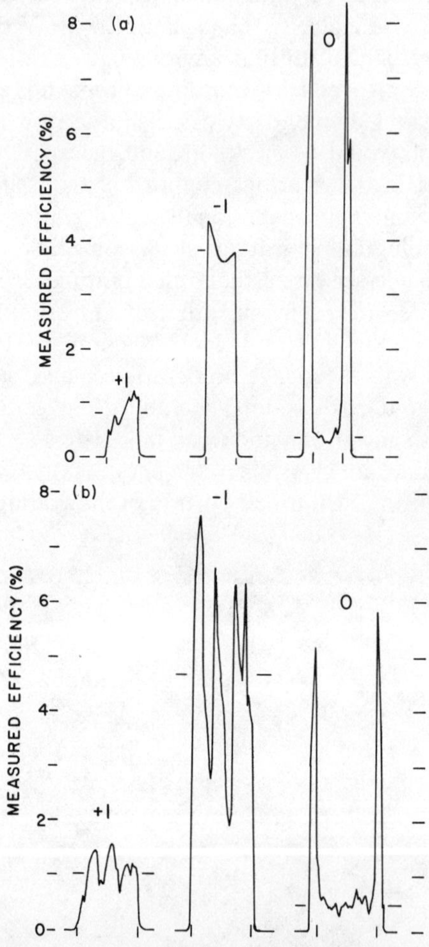

FIG. 2.25. Comparison of the efficiency map of the grating of Fig. 2.23 (562 Å) (b) with the efficiency map of a concave, blazed, holographic grating (412 Å) (a). The holographic grating was made by using the modified Sheridon technique shown in Fig. 2.10, and it has a radius of curvature of 1 m, a groove density of 1200 g/mm, and was coated with gold. [From Hunter (1980). © North-Holland Physics Publishing, Amsterdam, 1980.]

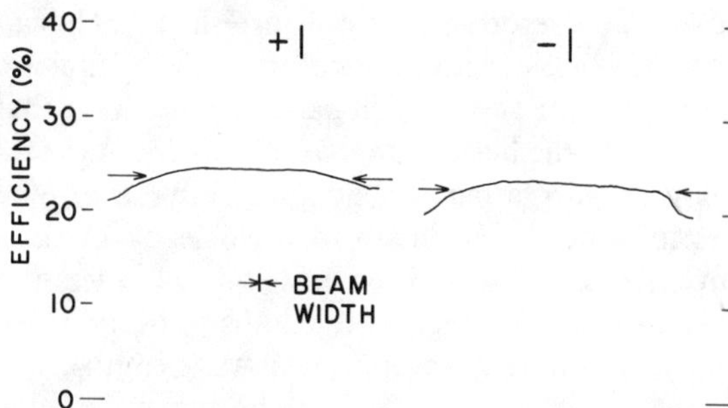

FIG. 2.26. Efficiency maps at 1440 Å of a large, spherical holographic grating with sinusoidal groove profiles. The radius of curvature is 85 cm, the groove density is 2400 g/mm, the coating is Al + MgF_2, and the grating width is 26.8 cm. The small vertical line labeled "beam width" shows the width of the probe beam. The efficiency is remarkably uniform for such a large aperture. [From Hunter (1974).]

grating shown in Fig. 2.23. The horizontal arrows show the average values of the efficiencies. They are within 4% of being equal.

To obtain the grating efficiency as a function of wavelength, the average value of efficiency across the surface is plotted as a function of wavelength. Figure 2.27 (Hunter, 1980) compares the efficiency versus wavelength curves for the two gratings of Fig. 2.25, both measured at 10° angle of incidence.

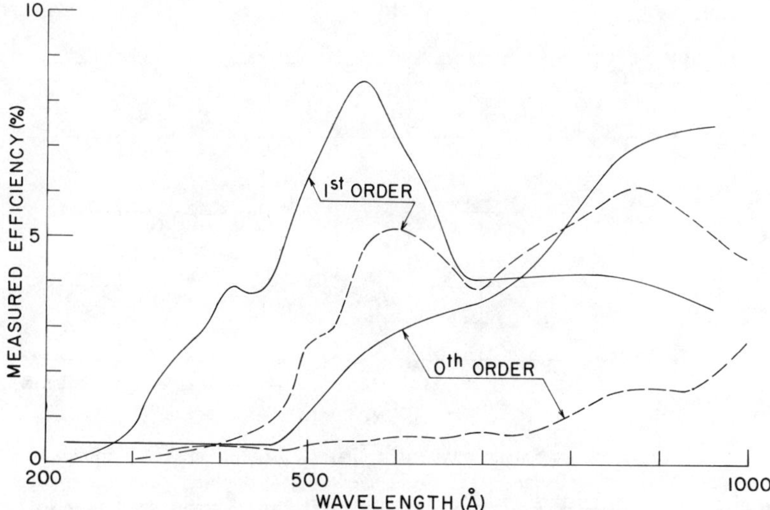

FIG. 2.27. Comparison of the efficiency versus wavelength characteristics of the holographic grating of Fig. 2.25 with the conventional grating of Fig. 2.23. Only the first and zeroth orders are shown. [From Hunter (1980). © North-Holland Physics Publishing, Amsterdam, 1980.]

The two strong first and zeroth orders only are shown. The large maximum at about 550 Å for the first order of the holographic grating is caused by the reflectance spectrum of the gold, which has a maximum at that wavelength, and also by the fact that the blaze is approximately 550 Å. At the short wavelengths the holographic grating has an unusually large efficiency, about 0.7% at 300 Å. In contrast the first-order efficiency of the conventional grating is about 0.1% at 300 Å and remains somewhat less than that of the holographic grating toward longer wavelengths until, at about 700 Å, they are approximately the same. To even longer wavelengths the conventional grating shows larger efficiency values. Both zeroth orders are small at the short wavelengths but that of the holographic grating begins to increase at about 500 Å and continues to increase toward longer wavelengths. This "anomalous" increase is not expected in blazed gratings and is not understood.

Figure 2.28 (Hunter, 1980) shows the measured efficiency of the holographic grating of Fig. 2.26, which has sinusoidal groove profiles, as a function of wavelength from 1180 to 2000 Å. The angle of incidence is 15° and the coating is Al + MgF_2, where the thickness of the MgF_2 is 250 Å. The strong first order has a very uniform efficiency with wavelength which begins to decrease only at wavelengths less than 1300 Å. This loss in efficiency is caused by the characteristics of the coating rather than the groove form. The zeroth order is suppressed by use of a quarter-wave groove depth at about 1200 Å. The predominance of one first order over the other is strictly

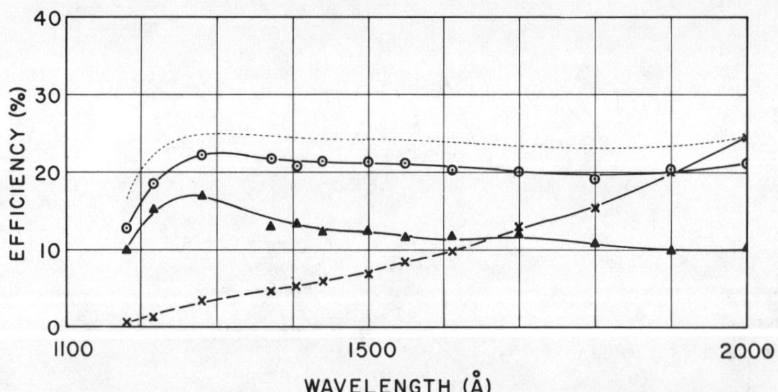

FIG. 2.28. The efficiency versus wavelength characteristic of the holographic grating of Fig. 2.26 at 15° angle of incidence. The circles shown the strong first order, the triangles the weak first order, and the × marks the zeroth order. The zeroth order was suppressed at the shorter wavelengths by choosing a groove depth of approximately 0.25 times the wavelength. [From Hunter (1974).]

a function of angle of incidence. If the measurement had been made at normal incidence, the two first-order intensities would have been practically equal.

All of the foregoing conclusions and results also apply to gratings used in grazing incidence. Figure 2.29 (Hunter, 1980) shows efficiency maps at 192 Å of a conventional grating and a holographic grating with sinusoidal groove profiles at an angle of incidence of 80°. Each was coated with gold. The ruled grating is monopartite. The average value of the first order of the ruled grating is 18% with a maximum value of about 24%. The average value of the second order is about a factor of 10 less. In contrast, the first and second orders of the holographic grating are about the same and are nonuniform, to an extent surprising for symmetrical groove profiles. The nonuniformity is caused by a change in amplitude of the grooves of a factor of 2 from one side of the grating to the other, the shallower grooves occurring to the right of the efficiency maps. The change in profile amplitude was caused by nonuniform illumination during recording of the grating. Figure 2.30 (Hunter, 1980) shows the efficiency versus wavelength curve of the holographic grating of Fig. 2.29. The two sets of data points for each order were obtained by measuring the grating efficiency on both sides of the grating normal to determine whether or not the groove profiles were symmetrical, and the conclusion is that they are. Only the first three orders, aside from the zeroth order, are shown, but the fourth and fifth orders could also be measured.

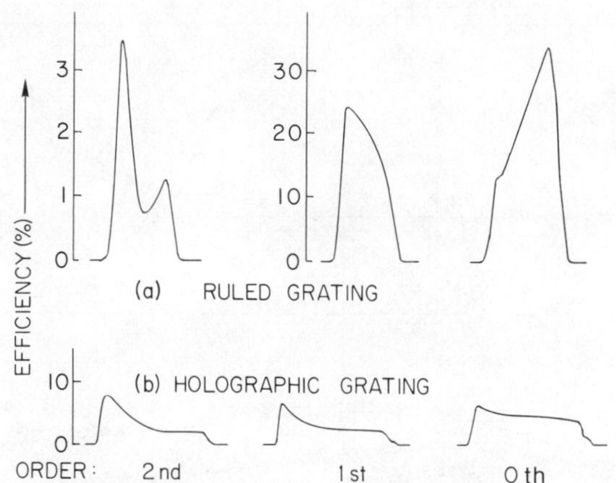

FIG. 2.29. Comparison of efficiency maps of a spherical concave, conventional, monopartite grating (a) and a holographic grating (b) with a sinusoidal groove profile in different orders at 192 Å. The radius of curvature is 1 m, the groove density is 2400 g/mm, the coating is gold, and the angle of incidence is 80°. [From Hunter (1980). © North-Holland Physics Publishing, Amsterdam, 1980.]

Figure 2.31 (Hunter, 1980) shows the efficiency versus wavelength of the conventional grating of Fig. 2.29 and compares it with that of the holographic grating of Fig. 2.30. For this conventional grating the blaze can be clearly seen at about 200 Å. The second order, where shown, is always less than 10% of the first order and is increasing toward shorter wavelengths as would be expected.

The clearly defined blaze wavelength of the conventional concave grating shown in Fig. 2.31 is unusual. There are two factors that tend to obscure the location of the blaze wavelength. They are the reflectance spectrum of the coating material and the change in efficiency (blaze) across the grating surface. In this case the reflectance spectrum of gold at large angles of incidence is fairly uniform and, perhaps more important, the grating is monopartite and does not have the very large changes in blaze across the surface that are shown for the tripartite grating of Fig. 2.23. Consequently, the blaze wavelength is easily identified. If the grating has a gradual blaze change across its surface, as would be expected with a grating of large radius (3 or 4 m), or if it is plane, the only factor to cause confusion in location of the blaze wavelength is the coating reflectance spectrum. If the efficiency of the grating is divided by the reflectance of the coating, one obtains the "groove

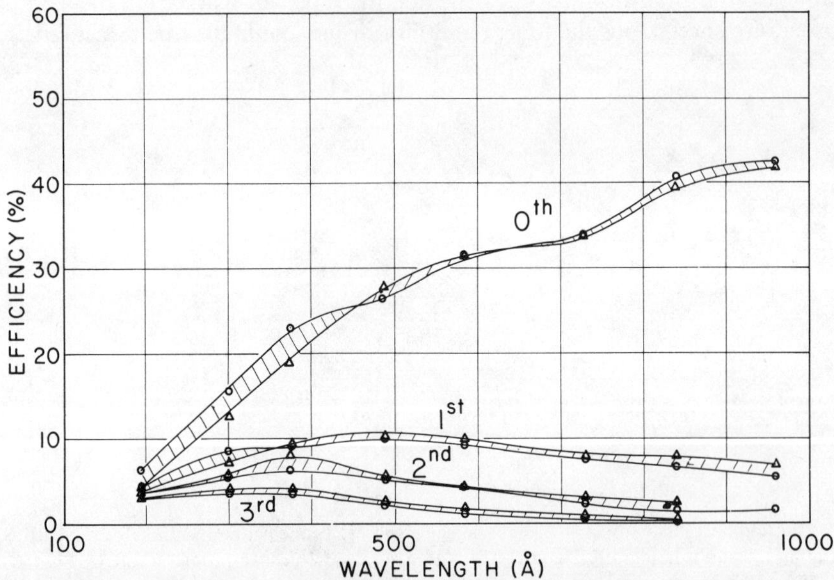

FIG. 2.30. Efficiency versus wavelength of the holographic grating of Fig. 2.29. [From Hunter (1980). © North-Holland Physics Publishing, Amsterdam, 1980.]

efficiency," which is independent of the coating, and the location of the blaze wavelength, if there is one, should be easily found.

Efficiency measurements of plane gratings seldom show any change in efficiency across the grating surface. There is no reason to expect such a change unless the diamond wears severely during ruling.

Because change of blaze across a grating surface seldom occurs with plane gratings, they are extremely useful as test gratings to investigate the effect of different groove profiles. Hunter *et al.* (1977) have compared the efficiencies of both laminar and blazed profiles from about 300 Å to wavelengths slightly longer than 600 Å at normal incidence. Each grating had 1200 g/mm and a gold coating and was made by using a holographic technique. The laminar grating had a sharply peaked efficiency in the strong first order of 3.75% at about 550 Å, which dropped to both long and short wavelengths. Actually, each first order had the same efficiency to within a few percent. At 300 Å the efficiency in the strong first order was about 0.2%. The zeroth order was suppressed at 480 Å to about 0.2% because the depth of the grooves was about half that value, but to both longer and shorter wavelengths it increased.

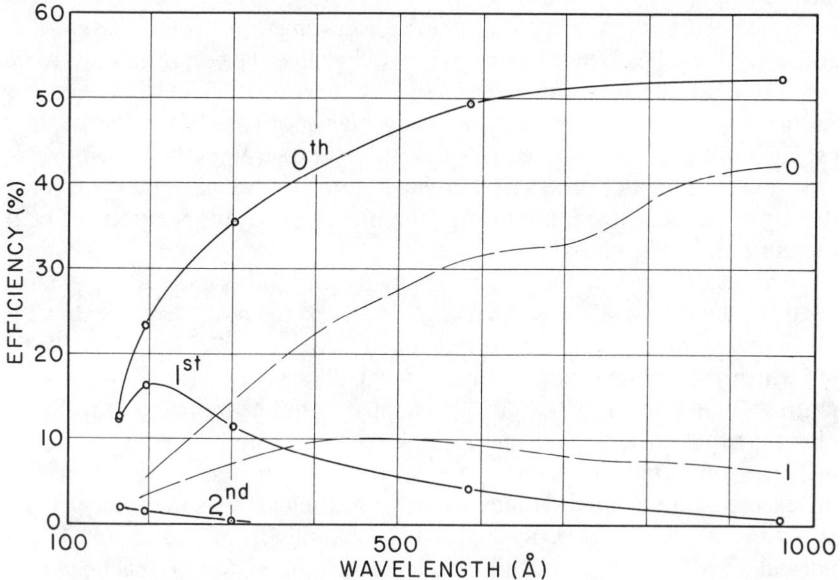

FIG. 2.31. Efficiency versus wavelength of the conventional grating of Fig. 2.29 (solid lines) compared with the efficiency versus wavelength of the holographic grating of Fig. 2.30 (dashed lines). [From Hunter (1980). © North-Holland Physics Publishing, Amsterdam, 1980.]

The blazed grating was one that had been made by the Sheridon technique. The strong first-order efficiency reached a peak at 550 Å of about 5.5%, and at 300 Å was 1.2%. Generally the weak first order was about three to four times less efficient than the strong first order. The zeroth-order efficiency was quite small at the short wavelengths (<400 Å) but rose rapidly to equal that of the strong first order at 570 Å. From the measurements on these two gratings it was obvious that the blazed grating was the most useful.

Haelbich *et al.* (1978) have made a similar comparison in the wavelength range from 55 to 560 Å. Their laminar grating was generated holographically but their blazed grating was a conventionally ruled grating. They chose different wavelengths lying in the range mentioned and measured the zeroth and strong first orders as functions of glancing angle, the angle between the grating surface and the incident beam. They found that the efficiency values for both gratings were about equal, despite the theoretical predictions that the blazed grating should have larger efficiency values. They suggest that the ruled gratings may have considerable deviations from the ideal sawtooth profile.

Neviere *et al.* (1982) have done a theoretical study of laminar gratings for use in soft x-ray constant-deviation monochromators. Their calculations included optimizing the ratio of groove width to groove spacing. They compare the results with calculations made for gratings with sinusoidal profiles and blazed profiles. Their results indicate that the blazed profiles are more efficient than the other two profiles, and that both blazed and laminar profiles are more efficient at suppressing higher orders. When the laminar profile is optimized for a given wavelength, it is better than the blazed profile at suppressing higher orders of that wavelength. At wavelengths other than the optimized wavelength, however, the higher-order suppression is about the same as for the blazed profile.

There are times when a grating is not used at either normal or grazing incidence but at some intervening angle. Perhaps the best known example is the Seya–Namioka scanning monochromator (Seya, 1952; Namioka, 1959b), for which the nominal angle of incidence is 35°. One might assume that a grating illuminated at 35° angle of incidence would be more efficient than if illuminated at normal incidence because the reflectance of a coating usually increases with angle of incidence for most coating materials. However, this increase is seldom rapid. Hunter *et al.* (1971a) have measured the specular reflectance of Al + MgF_2 and Al + LiF coatings from 300 to 1600 Å at normal incidence, 35°, and grazing incidence. They found practically no increase in reflectance from normal incidence to 35°. Figure 2.32 shows their results for Al + MgF_2, where the dielectric thickness is 250 Å. Thus an uncorrected grating used in a Seya–Namioka monochromator results in less throughput than the same grating used at normal incidence because of losses caused by astigmatism. Even if the grating is corrected, there is no significant gain in throughput. The attraction of the Seya–Namioka monochromator is its mechanical simplicity rather than its efficiency.

If larger efficiency values are required at angles such as those used with the Seya–Namioka mounting, it might be possible to apply an interference coating to the grating that is designed for that particular angle of incidence. Unfortunately, such coatings usually have large reflectance values over a small wavelength range only; hence the instrument would be restricted to that range.

Naviere *et al.* (1978) have measured the efficiencies of plane gratings used in both classical and conical diffraction. They found that, for a given wavelength, as the grating is rotated about the facet normal N_f (see Subsection 2.2.B.1 and Fig. 2.6), its efficiency is increased. Figure 2.33 shows this result. Curve 1 corresponds to the MCD mount, and curve 4 corresponds to the classical blaze mount. The two positions are 90° apart. The other two curves correspond to rotations about N_f of 30° from the MCD position (2) and 60° from the MCD position (3). The angle φ shown in the scale at the bottom is

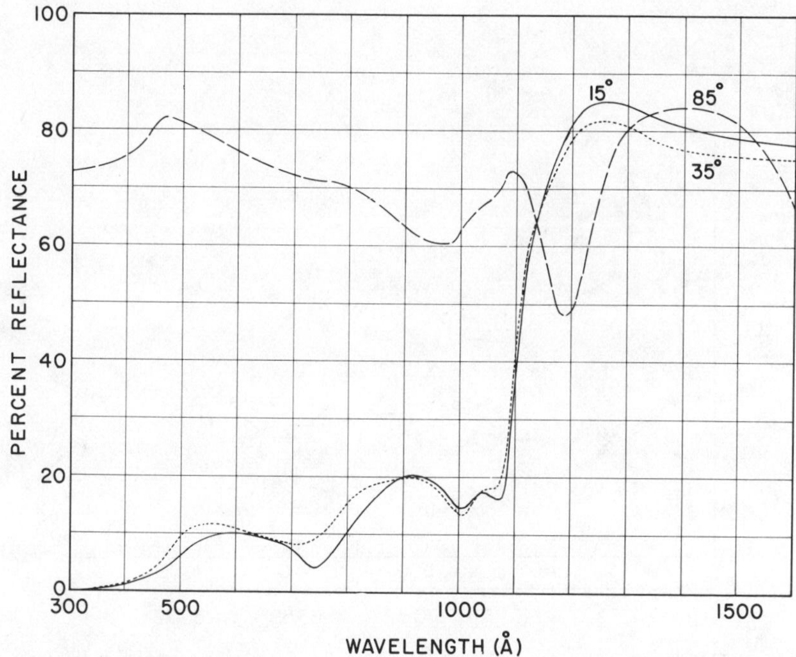

FIG. 2.32. Measured reflectance of a mirror coated with Al + MgF_2 at three angles of incidence: near-normal (solid line), 35° (dotted line), and 85° (dashed line). [From Hunter *et al.* (1971a).]

the angle the incident wave vector and the blazed, diffracted wavelength make with N_f. It is important to remember that for any given wavelength the grating is at blaze regardless of the amount of rotation about N_f.

They also point out that for the classical mount the angle of incidence α is equal to φ plus the blaze angle θ_B. Because α must be less than 90° it is impossible to have α larger than the complement of the blaze angle. Therefore there is a short-wavelength limit imposed when the grating is used classically. This type of limit does not exist for the MCD mounting.

During the last decade, considerable advances have been made in calculating grating efficiencies. At present the calculations are restricted to plane gratings. There are no restrictions, however, on the form of the groove profile or the coating material. Rather than list all the references to this work, we will mention a recently published book, "Electromagnetic Theory of Gratings" (Petit, 1980), that provides details of the calculations as well as an exhaustive, as of 1980, list of references. Although the theory cannot be applied to concave gratings, Neviere and Hunter (1980) found that efficiency maps of concave gratings can be calculated with a reasonable approximation by averaging the calculated efficiencies of plane gratings over the range of

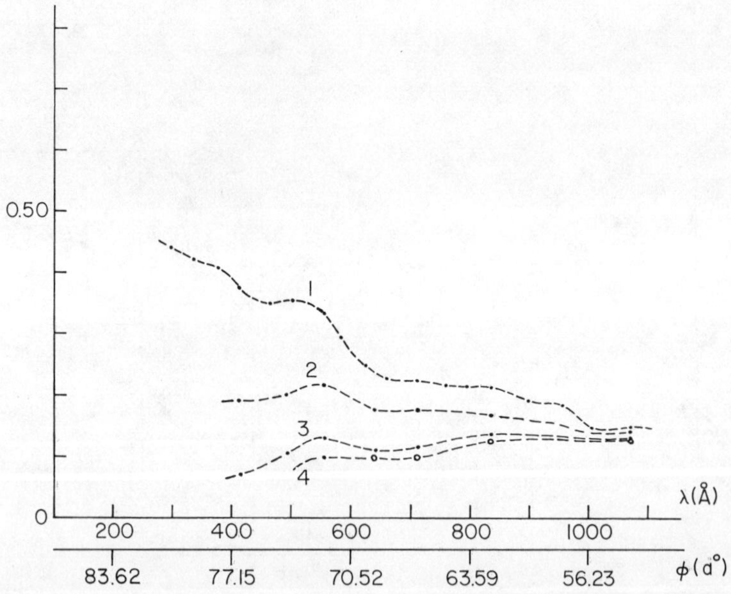

FIG. 2.33. Efficiency versus wavelength characteristic of a plane grating with 1800 g/mm, a gold coating, and a blaze angle of 9°18′. Curves 1 and 4 show the efficiency on conical and classical mountings, respectively. Curves 2 and 3 show the efficiencies after rotating the grating 30° and 60°, respectively, from the conical position. [From Neviere *et al.* (1978).]

incidence angles encompassed within the aperture of the concave grating. The validity of this approximation is based on the assertion that a finite grating has the same calculated efficiency as an infinite grating provided the number of grooves used in the calculation is 10 or more (Petit, 1980). As an example, for a grating with 600 g/mm, 10 grooves occupy a space about 17 μm wide. If the radius is 1 m, the change in blaze due to the curvature over this distance is negligible; therefore, it appears to be valid to consider a concave grating as made of many plane gratings with the same blaze angle but with angles of incidence varying as they would over the concave grating aperture.

Figure 2.34 (Neviere and Hunter, 1980) shows measured efficiency maps at 2530 Å for different angles of incidence and for a grating coating of $Al + MgF_2$. Note that the second-order efficiencies are multiplied by 10. Figure 2.35 shows the calculated efficiency maps. The computations were made for transverse electric (TE) polarization only because the λ/d ratio is 0.15, thus the grating behaves in a scalar manner, i.e., free of polarization effects, and the efficiency for TE polarization is the same as for nonpolarized radiation. Comparison of the two sets of curves shows that the main features of the experimental curves are predicted by theory. Neviere and Hunter also found that this approximate method is valid at grazing incidence and for both holographic and conventional gratings. The differences between the experimental and calculated efficiency maps are attributed to the facts that (1) the exact groove profile of the experimental grating is not known (the profile used for the calculation was assumed to be the same as that of the grating), and (2) the optical constants used in the calculation, especially those of MgF_2, may not be the same as those of the coatings.

A particularly simple method for calculating the efficiency of a plane grating used at blaze in the inside first order for classical diffraction has been given by Maystre and Petit (1976). Using rigorous electromagnetic theory, they have shown that the formula

$$E_1 = R(\theta)\min[(\cos\beta/\cos\alpha), (\cos\alpha/\cos\beta')]$$

predicts the efficiency to within a few percent if the ratio $\lambda/d < 0.3$. Here, E_1 is the efficiency at blaze in the inside first order, $R(\theta)$ the reflectance of the coating material at angle of incidence θ (where $\theta = (\alpha + \beta)/2$), and the term min means that the reflectance is to be multiplied by whichever of the two fractions is the smaller. Neviere *et al.* (1978) were able to show that this formula applies to conical diffraction as well.

Accurate measurement of a grating groove profile is difficult. For coarse gratings an interference microscope can be quite useful. Hutley (1982) shows an interference micrograph (p. 158) of a coarse grating from which one might obtain quantitative data on the blaze angle. If the grating spacing is less than

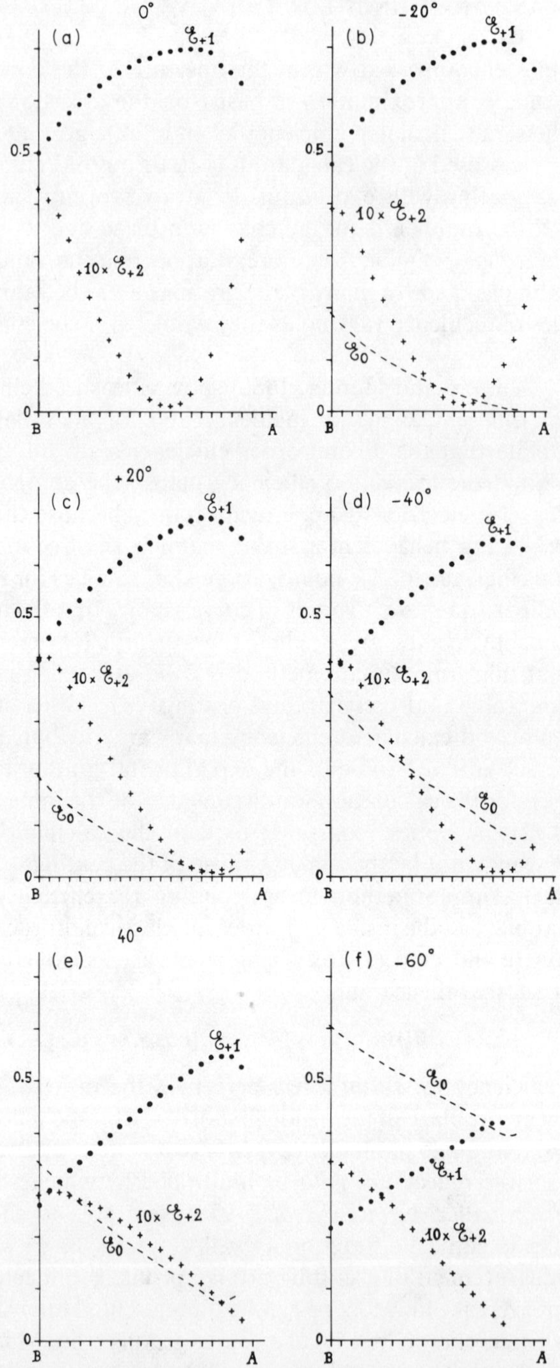

FIG. 2.34. Measured efficiency maps of a spherical, concave, monopartite, conventional grating at 2530 Å: (a) 0°, (b) −20°, (c) 20°, (d) −40°, (e) 40°, and (f) −60°. The coating is aluminum, the radius of curvature is 1 m, the blaze angle is 4.75°, and the groove density is 600 g/mm. [From Neviere and Hunter (1980).]

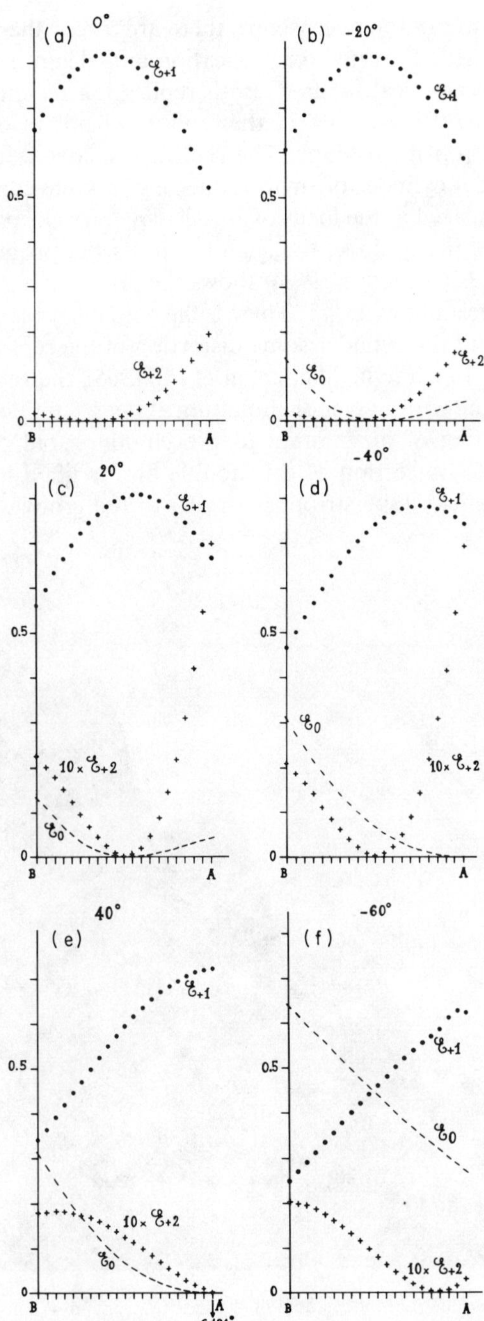

FIG. 2.35. Calculated efficiency maps based on a model of the grating of Fig. 2.34. (a) 0°, (b) −20°, (c) 20°, (d) −40°, (e) 40°, and (f) −60°. [From Neviere and Hunter (1980).]

the resolving power of the microscope, there are three other techniques that are commonly used. Two involve replication and electron microscopy and the third is a mechanical method. Both replication techniques differ. For the first technique (Bennett, 1971), the replica is made as one would make replicas for electron microscopy. The replica is coated with a metal, then wrapped around a cylinder of small radius, e.g., a knife edge. The wrapped cylinder is then placed at the focus of an electron microscope and its shadow is observed. If properly done, the shadow shows the profile of the grating grooves. Figure 2.36 (Loewen, 1984) shows the profile of a grating with 1200 g/mm and a blaze angle of 25°45′. There is the possibility that when wrapping the replica around the cylinder some distortion of the replica may occur.

For the second technique (Anderson *et al.*, 1965), the replica is made by coating the grating with a layer of aluminum about 1 μm thick, and then with a very thin coating of magnesium to prevent the rapid oxidation of the aluminum surface. A section of this double film is lifted from the grating with a piece of sticky tape stripped parallel to the grooves. Then asbestos

FIG. 2.36. Electron micrograph shadow of the groove profile of a conventional grating of 1200 g/mm and a blaze angle of 25°45′. [From Loewen (1984).]

fibers are sprinkled on the exposed aluminum surface, and the surface is coated with platinum at an angle to the surface and the centerline of the vapor stream parallel to the grooves. Finally, the surface is coated with carbon at normal incidence. The thick aluminum film is dissolved away with HCl, leaving only the platinum–carbon film. When the completed replica is examined by means of an electron microscope at normal incidence, the transmittance of the replica is less in the areas coated with heavy metal. One sees the grating grooves, the asbestos fibers, and a shadow of the fibers on the grooves. An example is shown in Fig. 2.37 (Loewen, 1984) for a blazed holographic grating with 1200 g/mm and a blaze angle of 8.6°. Knowing the angle of incidence of the Pt vapor stream with respect to the plane of the replica, the blaze angle can be calculated.

The mechanical technique (Verrill, 1973, 1975) uses a special measuring instrument called a Talystep machine, which was originally designed to measure small step heights. A fine diamond point, with a radius of 0.1 μm or more, is placed in contact with the grating surface. The grating is then moved in a direction perpendicular to the grooves. The point is driven up and down as the grooves pass under it and, through sensing coils and appropriate electronics, recordings of the groove profiles are obtained. This technique is limited in that the diamond point radius should be small compared to the groove spacing.

None of these techniques is very accurate for small or large blaze angles.

Some work has been done on the problem of calculating the groove profile from a knowledge of the grating efficiency by Roger and Breidne (1980).

Judging from the foregoing, it appears that the only certain knowledge of grating efficiencies is obtained through measurement. The complexities associated with efficiency calculations and their approximate applicability to concave gratings would seem to preclude simple criteria. Loewen and Neviere (1978), however, have shown that if gratings for VUV applications have small angles of incidence and shallow groove depths, there are some simple rules that allow prediction of grating efficiency. Such gratings can be treated by scalar theory, which is usually applicable if $\lambda/d < 0.2$. This value of λ/d is not a rigorous boundary because if the grooves are very shallow, accurate calculations can be obtained for λ/d up to about 0.4. Loewen and Neviere calculated efficiencies for a number of values of λ/d, or h/d for holographic gratings, where h is the groove, or modulation, depth and d is the grating spacing. They concluded that grating efficiencies can be approximated by the product of the coating reflectance and universal efficiency curves. They present two such curves in their paper, one for blazed gratings with a 90° groove apex angle and one for a sinusoidal groove form. Such simple rules do not apply to large angles of incidence if polarization effects invalidate the scalar theory.

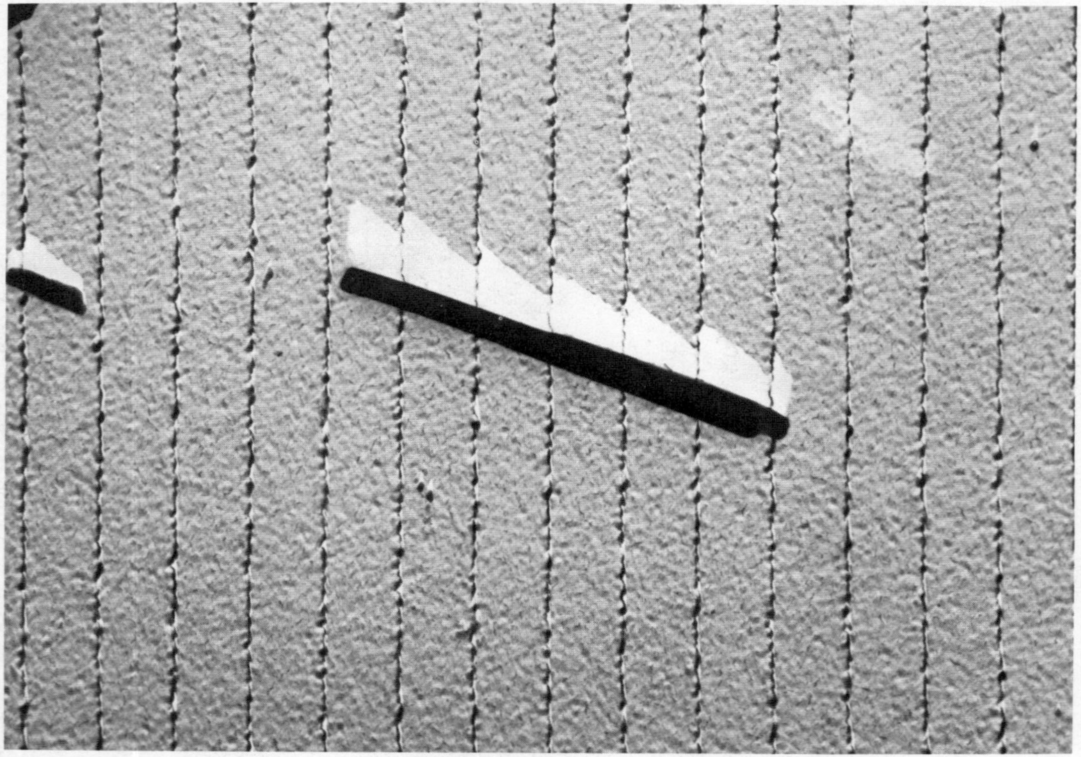

FIG. 2.37. Groove profile of a blazed holographic grating with 1200 g/mm and a blaze angle of 8°38′. [From Loewen (1984).]

2. *Stray Light*

Stray light, unwanted light in a spectrum, can arise from a number of sources. The two main sources are scattering of light by the interior of the spectrograph and scattering by the grating. Elimination of the first type of stray light is not always easy and requires some ingenuity on the part of the experimenter. First the scattering sources must be located, which sometimes can be done by taking a pinhole photograph of the interior of the instrument. Figure 2.38 (Hunter *et al.*, 1973) shows an example of such a photograph. Once the scattering sources have been located, it is not too difficult to mask them.

Stray light from the grating surface is much more difficult to eliminate. Perhaps the first step is to gain an understanding of how stray light originates. Generally errors in ruling cause light to appear in the spectrum where there should be none. If the properties of the stray light can be related to faults in the ruling process, the manufacturer may be able to correct these faults and improve the performance of future gratings. A few authors have written on the theory of imperfect gratings (Lord Rayleigh, 1902; Sparrow,

FIG. 2.38. Pinhole photograph in white light showing the interior of a spectrograph and the light scattered from the structural members. [From Hunter *et al.* (1973).]

1919; Fano, 1948; Meyer, 1949). One of these authors, Meyer, has discussed some of the errors that can occur during ruling and their consequences. They are listed below.

Curvature and nonparallelism of the grooves: A slight curvature of the grooves introduces a small amount of astigmatism, which, according to Meyer, is not harmful. Nonparallelism of the grooves, however, is more serious and leads to a loss in resolution. Note, however, that *corrected* holographic and conventional gratings have deliberate curvature and nonparallelism of the grooves.

Periodic errors of spacing: This error produces so-called ghosts, i.e., images of the parent line. Rowland ghosts lie close to the parent line and are caused by periodic errors in the precision screw driving the ruling carriage. Generally the intensity of these ghosts is a small fraction of that of the parent line, although this fraction increases as the order increases. Lyman ghosts usually lie far from the parent line and are caused by periodic changes in the driving mechanism of the ruling engine (not the screw).

Error of run: This is a nonperiodic, or extremely long period, change in the grating constant as the ruling progresses. If modern, interferometrically controlled ruling engines are used, the defects listed above are generally of little importance.

Accidental error of position of the grooves is, unfortunately, not as easily corrected by interferometric control of the ruling engine, and gives rise to scattered light that lies between the spectral lines and resembles a continuum background spectrum. The intensity of this background is zero in the vicinity of the central image (zero order) and increases with the square of the spectral order.

Accidental variation of groove form also produces scattered light resembling a continuum; however, the intensity of this pseudocontinuum is independent of spectral order and there will be light in the vicinity of the central image.

All of the errors listed above give rise to stray light localized in the plane of dispersion. We shall refer to this as focused stray light (FSL) because it is focused, along with the desired spectrum, in the plane of dispersion by the focusing agency of the spectrometer. Thus it is distinguished from general stray light, scattered by the grating surface, or the interior of the instrument, into a 2π solid angle. An example of FSL is shown in Fig. 2.39 (Bartoe, 1974). The glow discharge spectrum of helium was photographed using two gratings, grating 1 having a large stray light level. The gratings were installed in a Wadsworth mounting to simulate the SO82 A XUV spectroheliograph (Tousey *et al.*, 1977) that was flown on SKYLAB. The sun was simulated by a resolution mask, which is imaged on the film in the various lines of the discharge. Each grating has 3600 g/mm, a gold coating, and a 4-m radius of curvature. A thin aluminum film filter was placed just in front of the photographic film to eliminate the near ultraviolet and visible light; therefore the pseudocontinuum obtained is actually focused stray VUV radiation. Grating 1 had an unacceptably high FSL level but grating 2 was suitable for use in the spectroheliograph although it was not completely free of FSL.

As another example of FSL, Fig. 2.40 (Hunter, 1980) shows two spectra obtained with a Xe laser tuned to about 1720 Å. A conventional grating was used that had 600 g/mm, a radius of curvature of 1 m, and a coating of Pt. The zero orders are the bright lines at the left. The remainder of each spectrum is FSL, sometimes referred to as "grass." It is interesting to note that the

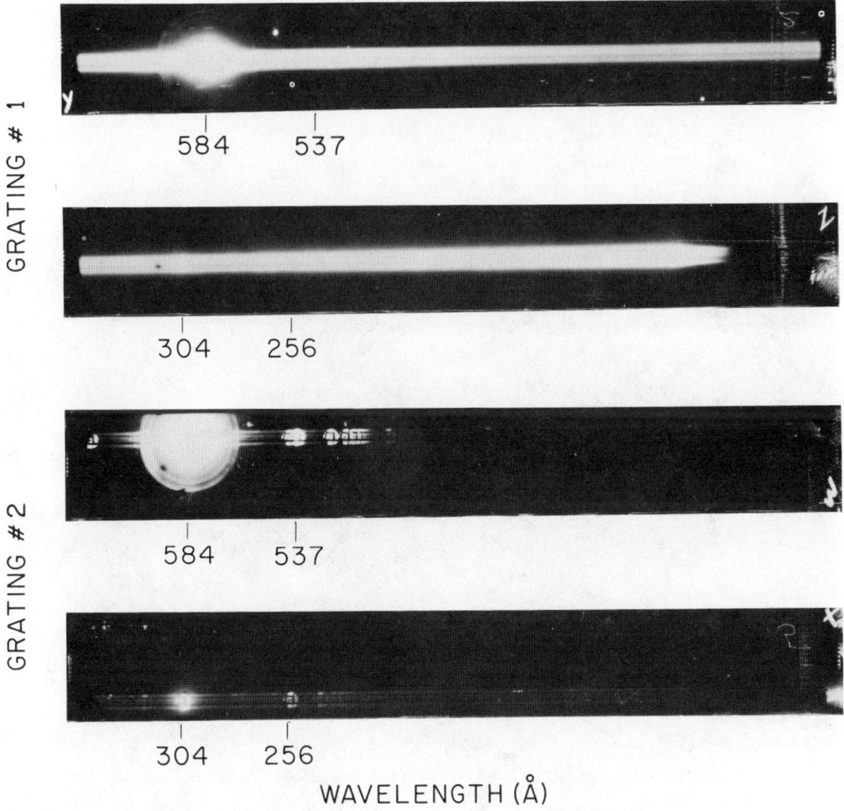

FIG. 2.39. An example of focused stray light from two gratings. Each grating has a radius of curvature of 4 m, 3600 g/mm, and a gold coating. The FSL of grating 1 was unacceptable; that of grating 2, while not zero, was acceptable. [From Hunter (1974).]

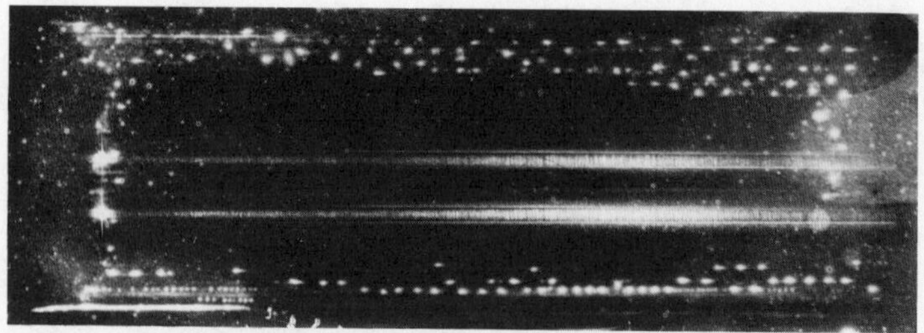

FIG. 2.40. Focused stray light from a conventional grating illuminated by a xenon laser tuned to about 1720 Å. [From Hunter (1980). © North-Holland Physics Publishing, Amsterdam, 1980.]

FSL peaks in the region of the blaze wavelength, about 900 Å, and that there is very little FSL in the region of the zeroth order. According to Meyer, this is to be expected if there is accidental error of position of the grooves.

In the two examples of FSL discussed above, the FSL appears to be confined to the plane of dispersion. One might argue that such a confinement could be caused by the design of the spectrograph and not necessarily be a

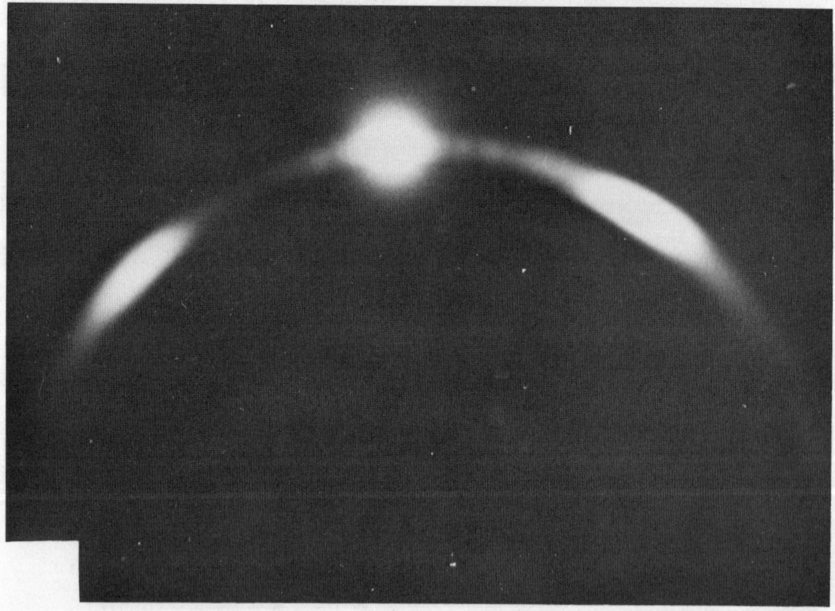

FIG. 2.41. Focused stray light (white light) for a grating in conical diffraction. The circular blob at the center is the zeroth order and the elongated blobs to the right and left are the first orders. They are connected by the FSL. [From Hunter (1980). © North-Holland Physics Publishing, Amsterdam, 1980.]

property of the grating. That this is not the case, and that FSL is a property of the grating. That this is not the case, and that FSL is a property of the grating, is demonstrated in Fig. 2.41 (Hunter, 1980), which shows FSL for a conical diffraction mounting. The figure shows the FSL in the form of an arc, as though it were part of a continuous spectrum recorded in conical diffraction. Since no instrument was involved in obtaining this photograph the spatial distribution of the FSL must be a characteristic of the grating only. The circular blob in the center is the zero order of a white light spectrum, and the first-order visible spectra appear as elongated, curved, patches on either side.

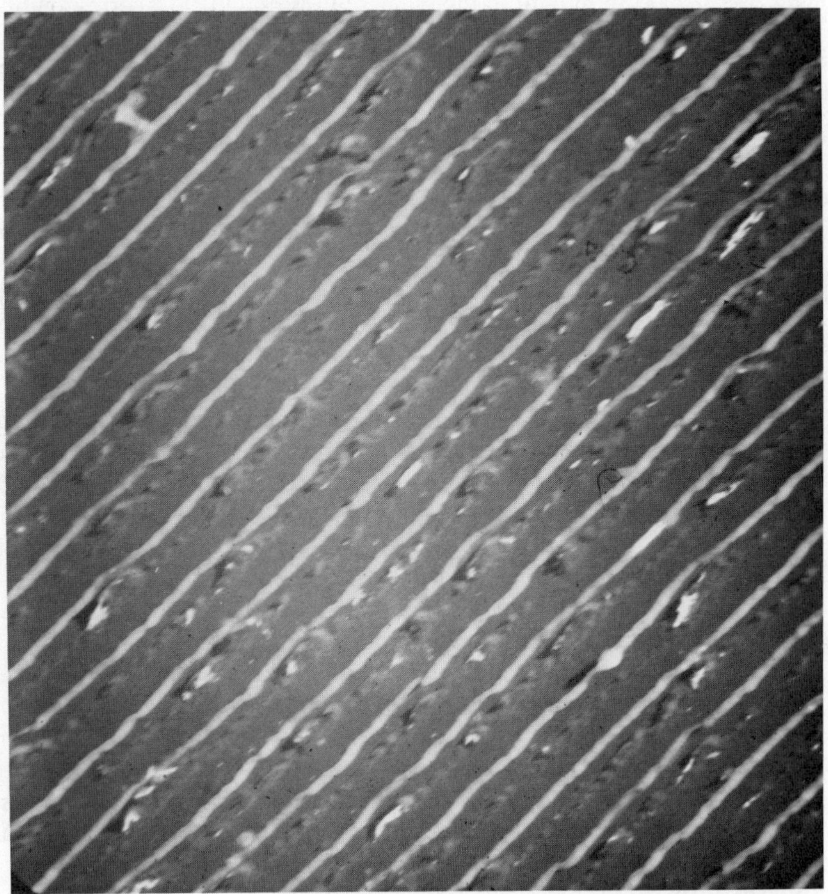

FIG. 2.42. Accidental error of position of grooves caused by too much weight on the ruling diamond.

There is, of course, the finite probability that the faults described above will combine to produce some effects not easily interpreted. Verrill (1970) has discussed scattered light and ghosts and shows an interesting example in the visible region of the combination of accidental error of position and periodic error associated with a ruling engine. The effect is localized areas of FSL rather than a continuous background. He calls them "scatter knots." Another source of FSL is caused by diamond chatter. The diamond point sometimes bounces when lowered onto the grating surface to begin a new groove, thus modulating the groove depth. Using an incoherent light source the FSL contribution due to chatter might not be discernible. If, however, the grating is illuminated by a coherent source, or a very small source, one finds a central strip of light in the plane of dispersion (FSL) corresponding to the prime focus of the spectrograph. In addition, there will be parallel strips on either side of the central strip arising from the coarse grating produced by the diamond chatter.

As mentioned, only the accidental errors of position and form are likely to be of much consequence when the grating is ruled on an interferometrically controlled ruling engine. However, sometimes accidental errors of position can occur that are not the fault of the positioning apparatus of the ruling engine. Figure 2.42 (Bach, 1983) is an electron micrograph of the ruled surface of a grating showing small areas where accidental error of position of the groove is caused by too much weight on the ruling diamond. The groove edges are not straight, thus the groove spacing is not precise. The roughness can be considered to be an accidental error of form.

The factors affecting the rulability of vacuum-deposited metal surface are not known, and the evaporation conditions required for producing good rulable films have been obtained empirically. Even so, the uncertainty is such that two coatings of the same metal, produced under apparently identical conditions, may not rule in exactly the same manner. Coatings with good optical properties may not rule well and coatings deposited by fast evaporations, usually required for good optical properties, may not be as useful as those deposited slowly. For example, fast evaporations of aluminum, with rates of 500 Å/s or more, result in coatings that have optimum optical properties and a specular appearance even though they are some micrometers thick. However, fast evaporations of aluminum have also been known to produce films containing voids, sometimes 1500 Å or more deep, that are exposed on ruling. Aluminum has been deposited at about 40 Å/s at a pressure of about 10^{-6} torr for some grating rulings (Bach, 1983). At this comparatively low deposition rate, films a few thousand angstroms thick have a specular appearance, but as the thickness increases to micrometers, light scattering due to surface roughness causes the surface to have a milky appearance.

Deposition rates for gold are usually kept below 100 Å/s when the source is a boat, and between 10 and 15 Å/s when filaments are used. Fast evaporations are more likely to eject small metal globules ("spit") from the melt with a velocity large enough to reach the substrate and adhere to the coating. These small globules can be smeared out by the diamond, as shown in Fig. 2.43 (Bach, 1983), and cause local errors in ruling. They can also lift the diamond so that small areas of the grating remain unruled, as shown in

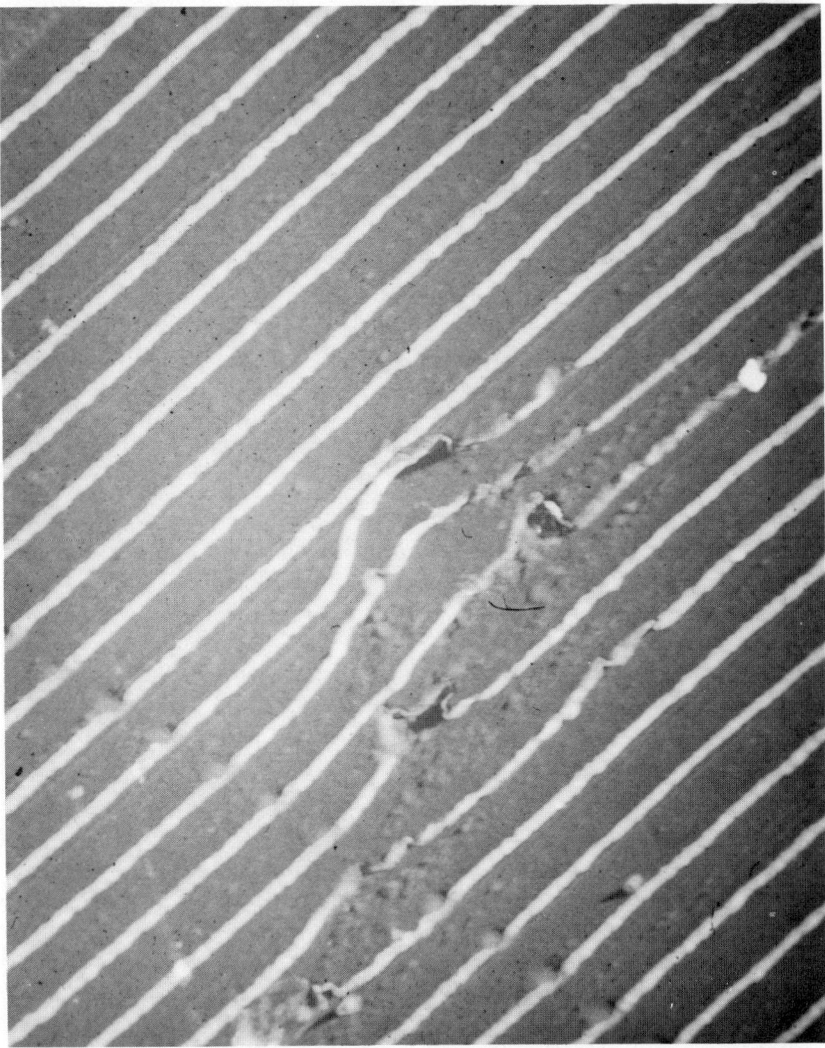

FIG. 2.43. A local error of position caused by the smearing of a globule of gold (spit) that had carried over to the grating blank when it was coated. [From Hunter and Hass (1980).]

Fig. 2.44 (Hunter, 1974). The effect of these imperfections on the stray light will depend on the spit density. Spit in gold films appears to have a higher density if the gold is evaporated from boats rather than filaments. It is also present in aluminum films but to a lesser degree.

Figure 2.45 (Hunter, 1974) shows what appear to be holes in a gold coating in which a grating has been ruled. It is probable that these holes are voids in the coating. These holes do not appear to interfere with the groove formation but may contribute to stray light.

Because of the necessity of using fairly thick coatings for grating ruling, the coating surface will be rough. This is not altogether a disadvantage because textured surfaces seem to have less tendency to stick to the diamond than very smooth surfaces and usually produce better rulings. Unfortunately, not all of the surface roughness is removed during ruling, as was shown in Fig. 2.5 in Subsection 2.2.B. Remnants of the surface roughness still exist on one side of the groove facet. One would expect that the random spacing of these protuberances would contribute more to general stray light than to FSL.

One would expect accidental error of position to be negligible for a holographic grating and usually this is the case. However, the etching process, which is neither linear nor always under tight control, may cause slight errors in both position and form of the grooves.

If the surface has just a few bad spots, that is, small areas that contribute most of the FSL, they can be masked, provided the loss in resolution is not

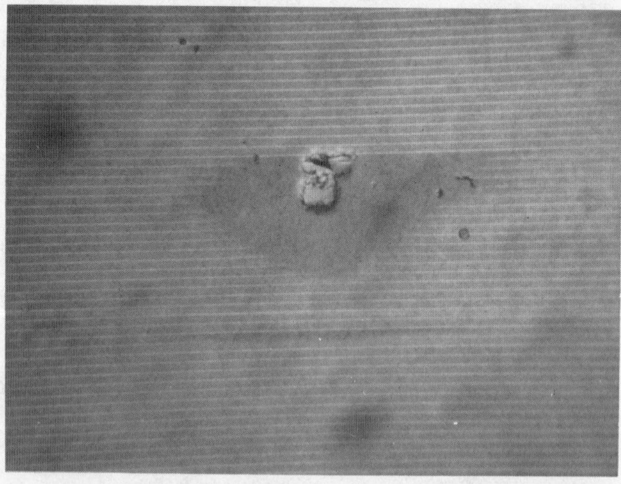

FIG. 2.44. A globule of gold ejected from the melt during evaporation that lifted the diamond during the course of a ruling. [From Hunter (1974).]

significant. Then the FSL contributed by these spots is eliminated from the spectrum. To find out whether such spots exist, one must look at the grating just off the zeroth order. In this way one sees the scattered light rather than the zeroth order itself. For example, if the grating is mounted in a monochromator, the wavelength should be set close to the zeroth order, the entrance slit illuminated with a strong white light, and a visual inspection made from the exit slit location. The wavelength setting can be adjusted for best illumination. Once the bad spots are located, baffles can be placed in the monochromator to shadow them. The baffles should not be visible from the exit slit because flat surfaces on the baffles may scatter light into the exit slit. In addition, diffracted light from the edges of the baffle may enter the exit slit. Placing baffles out of sight of the exit slit does not, of course, reduce scattering from them, but it prevents scattering directly into the exit slit.

Attempts have been made to measure the stray light of gratings; the better the grating, the more difficult the measurement. Figure 2.46 (Michels *et al.*, 1974) shows an example of such a measurement, the FSL found between orders of the same wavelength, 736 Å. The grating was mounted such that the exit slit of the monochromator supplying the radiation and the detector were approximately at the center of curvature of the grating. The grating was slowly rotated about a vertical axis through its apex and the signal level recorded. Because the FSL is a pseudocontinuum between the orders, the FSL intensity is also a function of the width of the detector aperture. For this reason the ordinate is given in terms of I/I_0 per angstrom

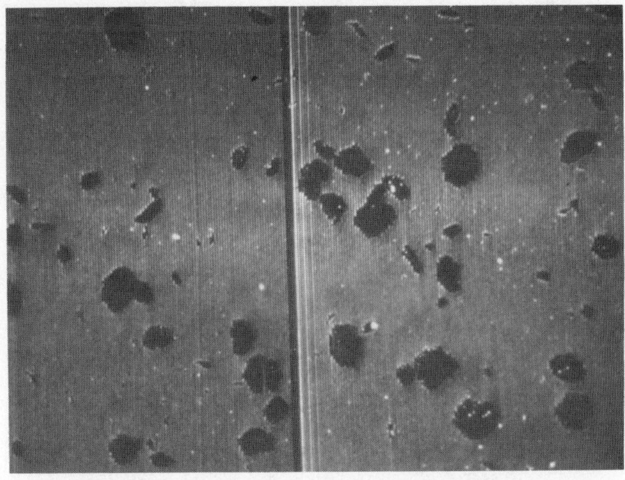

FIG. 2.45. Nonruled areas of a grating probably caused by voids in the coating. [From Hunter (1974).]

and applies only to the FSL and not to the different orders. The grating measured was the same as that used to obtain Fig. 2.22.

Verrill (1978) has discussed the specification and measurement of stray light from gratings. His work was done with a He–Ne laser and showed that, in general, holographic gratings can be expected to have less FSL than ruled gratings. Verrill's results should be indicative of what to expect when using gratings in the VUV.

Because of the difficulty in making quantitative measurements of stray light, it is often more informative and practical to compare the stray light levels of different gratings. In 1948, Johnson and Tousey (1948) evaluated the intensity of FSL from concave diffraction gratings by using a shielded carbon arc crater as a source. The gratings were set up in a spectrograph and the blackening of the film for wavelengths just shorter than the air cutoff at 1850 Å was compared with that just above the air cutoff. This was not an absolute test because an arbitrarily selected grating was used as a standard. They tested a series of 24 gratings and found useful-to-FSL ratios from as large as 40 to well below unity as compared to the arbitrary standard grating. This technique can be used at shorter wavelengths. For example, film blackening at 800 Å when using a glow discharge in hydrogen will give a rough idea of the FSL level throughout the hydrogen VUV spectrum

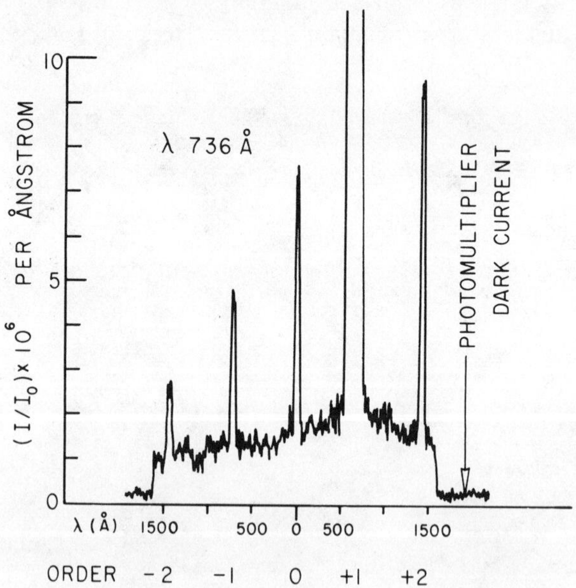

FIG. 2.46. Measurement of FSL between the orders of the grating of Fig. 2.22. [From Michels *et al.* (1974).]

since there is no emission from hydrogen at this wavelength. If, in addition, filters are used, such as LiF, CaF, or quartz, the film blackening at wavelengths just short of each filter cutoff can be used to obtain an approximate wavelength distribution of the FSL.

Namioka and Hunter (1973) have compared the FSL levels of a conventional and a holographic grating. Both gratings had a radius of curvature of 1 m, 1200 g/mm, and had been coated with gold during the same evaporation. Figure 2.47 shows a trace of the helium glow discharge spectrum from 600 Å to the zero order obtained with both gratings mounted successively in a McPherson 225 scanning monochromator. A slit width of 10 μm was used and the detector was a channel electron multiplier, used as a photon counter, so that only the focused stray VUV radiation was observed. Over almost the entire wavelength range both gratings have the same FSL level. However, in the vicinity of the zeroth order the conventional grating has less stray light than the holographic grating.

A similar comparison has been made by Caruso (1977) for gratings used in grazing incidence and is shown in Fig. 2.48. He found that the stray light component of the conventional grating was an average factor of 5.6 greater

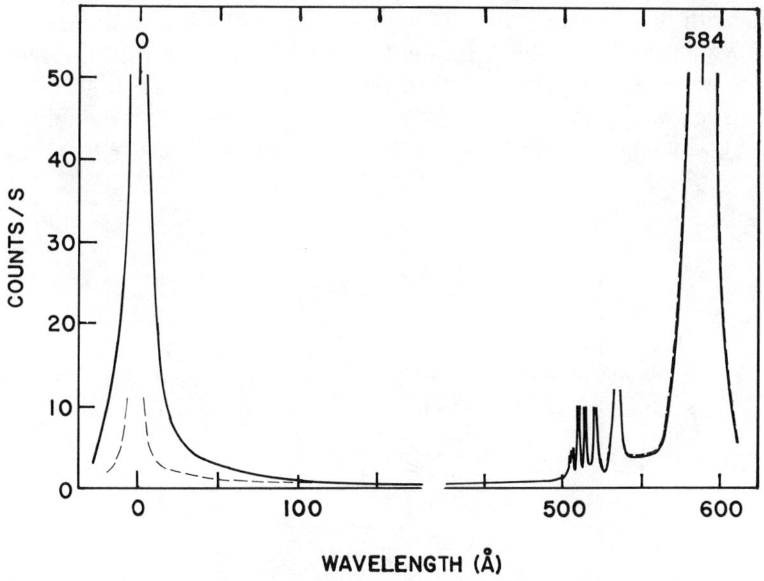

FIG. 2.47. Comparison of the FSL of a conventional, tripartite grating and a holographic grating with sinusoidal groove profiles in the VUV. Both gratings have a 1-m radius of curvature, a gold coating, and 1200 g/mm. (——, holographic grating; – – –, ruled grating.) [From Namioka and Hunter (1973). © North-Holland Physics Publishing, Amsterdam, 1973.]

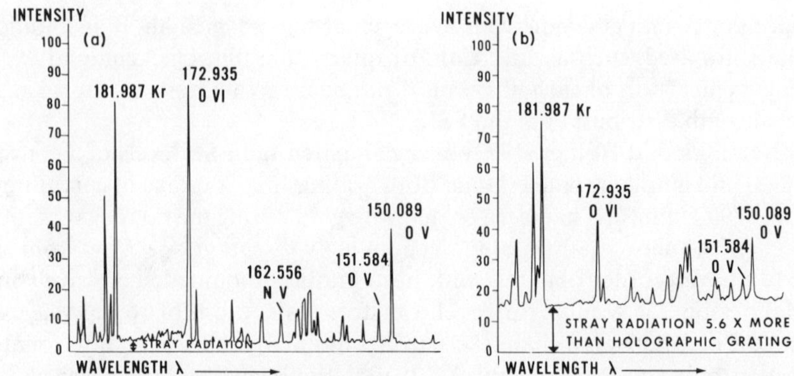

FIG. 2.48. Comparison of the FSL of (a) a holographic grating and (b) a conventional grating at grazing incidence in the extreme UV spectral region. [From Hunter (1974).]

than that of the holographic grating over the wavelength range from 400 to 80 Å.

Large stray light levels complicate the measurement of specular reflectances. Figure 2.49 compares some early (Hunter, 1958) normal-incidence reflectance measurements of an Al + LiF mirror. The measurements were made with two gratings; one had a large level of FSL and was coated with Al + MgF_2, and the other was a gold grating with a small FSL level. The source was a glow discharge in hydrogen. When the grating with the large FSL level was used, the uppermost curve was obtained (diamond data points), which gave a reflectance value close to 40% at 920 Å. When the gold

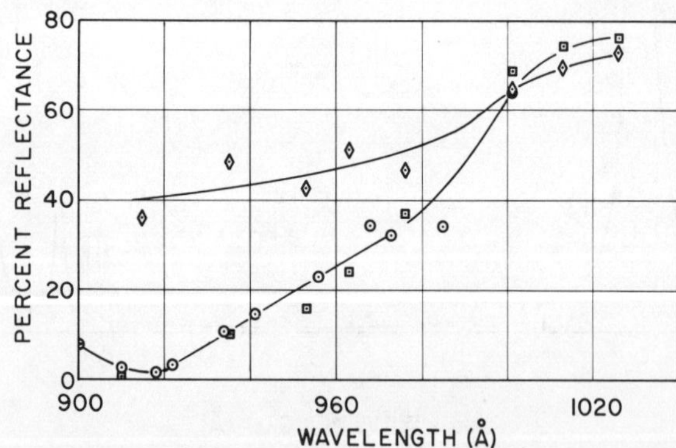

FIG. 2.49. Effect of FSL on the measurement of reflectance in the VUV. The diamonds show the reflectance values obtained before correcting for the FSL, and the circles and squares show the values obtained after correcting. [From Hunter (1974).]

grating was used the true reflectance values were obtained (circular data points), that at 920 Å being close to zero.

3. *Anomalies*

Grating anomalies were first observed by Wood (1902), who found narrow bands in what should have been a continuous spectrum that were either brighter or darker than the remainder of the spectrum. An explanation of these phenomena was first given by Lord Rayleigh (1907) in terms of a surface wave caused by an order with a diffraction angle of 90°, i.e., an order parallel to the grating surface. Subsequent work by Strong (1936) showed that some of the anomalies obeyed the explanation offered by Lord Rayleigh but others depended on the material with which the grating was coated. Furthermore, Hagglund and Sellberg (1966) found that the sum of the diffracted intensities measured with an integrating sphere did not equal the reflectance of the metal in the vicinity of an anomaly, nor did it remain constant. The results of Strong and of Hagglund and Sellberg, and theoretical results (Fano, 1941; Hessel and Oliner, 1965), indicated that agencies other than 90° diffraction were responsible for the anomalies observed. The other agency is the surface plasmon. Under certain conditions, the incoming photons couple with the surface plasmon and energy is absorbed at the grating surface. The coupling is much stronger for radiation polarized perpendicular to the grooves, sometimes referred to as s polarization by grating theorists, than for that polarized parallel to the grooves. Coupling for the latter case requires rather deep grooves, a requirement seldom called for in the VUV. The proper condition is the following:

$$k_{\mathrm{p}} \sin\theta + k_{\mathrm{g}} = k_{\mathrm{sp}}.$$

k_{p} is the wave vector of the incident photon, k_{g} that of the modulation of the grating surface, and k_{sp} that of the surface plasmon; θ is the angle of incidence. One can calculate the angle of incidence at which coupling takes place by using the formula (Hutley, 1982)

$$\sin\theta = \{E_1(\omega)/[1 + E_1(\omega)]\}^{1/2} - (n\lambda/d)\sin\varphi.$$

Here, φ is the angle at which the plasmon is traveling with respect to the groove direction, i.e., the effective grating spacing seen by the plasmon; E_1 is the real part of the dielectric function of the metal ($n^2 - k^2$, where n is the index of refraction and k the extinction coefficient); and n, λ, and d have their usual meanings. This formula does not take into account the shape of the groove profile, which can affect the angle at which coupling takes place.

It is also possible that photons will be reradiated by the surface plasmon. The wave vector k_{g} includes any roughness of the grating grooves as well as their period. Grime (1975) has obtained some dramatic photographs of patterns produced by surface plasmon scattering, using green light from an argon-ion laser.

Hutley (1982) has discussed the effect of dielectric overcoatings on the location of anomalies and points out that in the thicknesses usually used for coating gratings for the VUV, their location is only slightly shifted.

Because the surface plasmon anomalies are dependent on the grating coating, it might be possible to change their characteristics, or reduce their intensity, by putting different materials on different parts of the groove. Sugahara *et al.* (1974) have experimented along this line. They found that if aluminum was evaporated onto the steep groove facet of an aluminum replica, by evaporating at a steep angle between the angle of the large facet and the surface so that the vapor did not condense on the large facet, anomalies could be reduced and in one case eliminated. Unfortunately, such treatment also resulted in loss in efficiency and added scattering from the grating surface. Among other materials, they investigated an Al–Ag alloy, 1 part by weight of Al to 1.2 parts of Ag. This coating was helpful in reducing anomalies but did not have very large efficiency values. One promising trial involved evaporating aluminum on the large groove facet of the master grating and the Al–Ag alloy on the small groove facet and then replicating so that the Al and the alloy were still on the proper grooves of the replica but had the smoothness of the grooves of the master grating. This combination produced large efficiency values and reduced anomalies. They are of the opinion that the efficiency of the grating is controlled by the metal on the large facet and the anomalies by the metal on the small facet. This conclusion assumes that the large facets rather than the small facets are being used for diffraction.

Most of the discussion of anomalies above has dealt with the visible and near-UV regions of the spectrum. The theory, if correct, should apply equally well in the VUV; however, the optical constants of the coatings materials are somewhat different in the latter spectral region. Anomalies have not been observed in the VUV spectral region at the author's laboratory, or in rocket spectrograms obtained by his colleagues while he was working at the Naval Research Laboratory. The main reason for the lack of observations in the laboratory was the use of nonpolarized light sources. Also, there is the possibility that the gratings used in the laboratory experiments did not have anomalies large enough to be observed. The solar spectrometers were not designed to discriminate between different states of polarization. Furthermore, they used photographic films as detectors, which are notorious for their nonuniform response from one batch of film to the next and even within a given batch. In addition, the VUV solar spectrum is an inhomogeneous collection of emission lines and, at longer wavelengths, absorption lines overlying an emission continuum. Therefore, the subtleties of anomalies may be lost in the differences of sensitivity of the films and the varieties of expression of the solar spectrum.

Cowan and Arakawa (1970) have studied anomalies of conventional gratings coated with aluminum, gold, and silver in the vacuum ultraviolet and excited by polarized radiation. They did this by measuring the polarization ratio I_p/I_s from about 500 Å to longer wavelengths. A polarization maximum was found at about 1500 Å for freshly evaporated aluminum. This maximum deteriorated over a period of time due to the formation of an oxide layer. The property of changing the characteristics of the anomaly by use of a dielectric coating has led Cowan (1972) to propose using measurements of anomalies as an indication of contamination in the VUV.

4. *Contamination, Cleaning, Coating, and Coating Removal*

One of the truisms of VUV spectroscopy is that grating efficiencies do not remain constant when the grating is in use. Usually there is a slow decrease in efficiency that is wavelength-dependent and is caused by optical contamination of the grating surface. In an oil-pumped system, for example, oil vapor can condense on the grating surface, where it may be polymerized. If a polymerized layer develops, it consists largely of the element on which the oil is based, i.e., carbon or silicon. Such polymerized layers generally have a smaller reflectance value than the coating, thereby reducing the grating efficiency. Although these layers may be difficult, sometimes impossible, to remove, the grating efficiency may sometimes be recovered by recoating.

One usually expects contamination in oil-pumped systems because of the impossibility of perfect trapping of oil vapor. Even in UHV systems, however, carbon contamination occurs. Boller *et al.* (1983) have studied carbon contamination of mirror surfaces exposed to synchrotron radiation. They conducted their experiments at pressures rather higher than one expects in UHV systems; however, the systems were beam lines on the DORIS storage ring at Hamburg and were presumably clean, i.e., ion pumps rather than oil pumps. They have concluded that the breakdown of the carbon compounds leading to contamination is caused by photoelectrons rather than photons. It is probably safe to conclude that the same mechanism applies to contamination by oil vapor. The origin of the carbon in a supposedly carbon-free environment is not certain. One possibility is the outgassing of CO from stainless steel walls that migrates to the optical surfaces and is there dissociated.

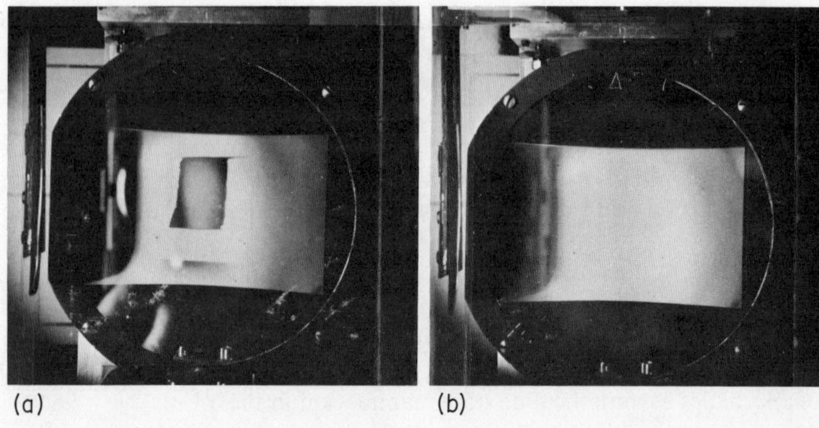

FIG. 2.50. Photograph in white light of a contaminated grating (a) and the same grating after cleaning (b). (Courtesy of D. J. Michels.)

Figure 2.50 is a photograph of a contaminated grating that was removed from a carbon oil-pumped grazing-incidence monochromator. The contamination is an irregularly shaped patch approximately centered on the grating. The grating had been in the monochromator for 4 to 5 years. Both a spark discharge (Hunter, 1963) and a dc glow discharge were used as light sources. Washing the grating with detergent and water removed the patch and increased the grating efficiency. Because efficiency measurements were not being made at the time, however, no quantitative efficiency data are available.

Thorough systematic studies of grating contamination have not, appar-

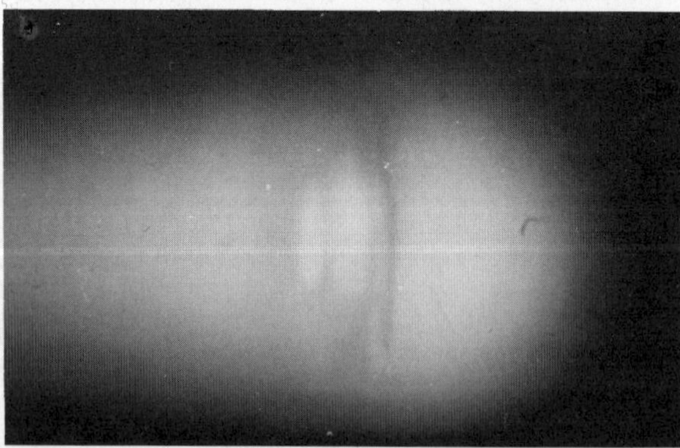

FIG. 2.51. Photograph in white light showing the contamination on the surface of a grating. [From Hunter and Angel (1979).]

ently, been made. One can attribute this lack of measurements to (1) lack of suitable equipment for the measurements and (2) general discouragement at the deterioration of an expensive component and a disinclination to pursue a distasteful subject.

Hunter and Angel (1979) published some measurements showing the effect of carbon oil contamination on the efficiency of a monopartite concave grating with a 1-m radius of curvature. The grating had been used in a McPherson 225 normal-incidence scanning monochromator for 8 years with a dc glow discharge light source. Figure 2.51 shows a picture of the grating surface in white light. The small, peculiarly shaped area at its center is the area exposed to the light source through the entrance slit. The exposed area is small because an adjustable aperture, located about $\frac{1}{3}$ m from the entrance slit, was used to limit the grating surface exposed to the VUV radiation to an area of approximately 1 cm parallel to the grooves by 5 mm perpendicular to the grooves. A sister grating from the same master, and with the same coating, was also measured as a control. Figures 2.52 and 2.53

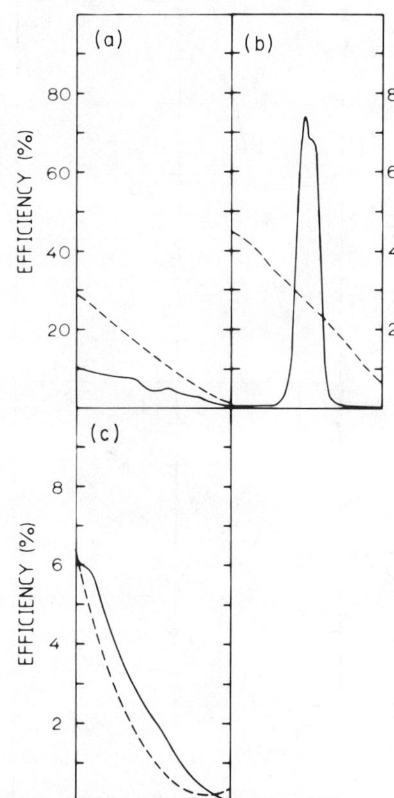

FIG. 2.52. Measured efficiency maps of the grating of Fig. 2.51 at (a) 1434, (b) 1580, and (c) 1216 Å (——) compared with measured efficiency maps of a grating from the same master that is unused (– – –). In (b) the efficiency scale to the right applies to the solid line curve. [From Hunter and Angel (1979).]

show efficiency maps of the contaminated grating (solid lines) and the control grating (dashed lines) surfaces for different wavelengths from 1216 to 4000 Å. At the extreme wavelengths, the two gratings have almost the same efficiency maps. At other wavelengths, however, the contamination causes large losses in efficiency. The authors concluded that the contaminating layer is absorbing because of the consistent loss in efficiency, but that it is thin enough to permit some interference effects.

Cleaning the grating by vapor degreasing using trichlorotrifluoroethane (TF) changed the efficiency map at 1580 Å from that shown in Fig. 2.52 to that shown in Fig. 2.54. The efficiency in the portion of the grating surface not exposed to VUV recovered from essentially zero to about one-third of the value of the control grating. Hence not all the oil collected on the grating had been polymerized.

After the efficiency measurements, both gratings were coated with gold

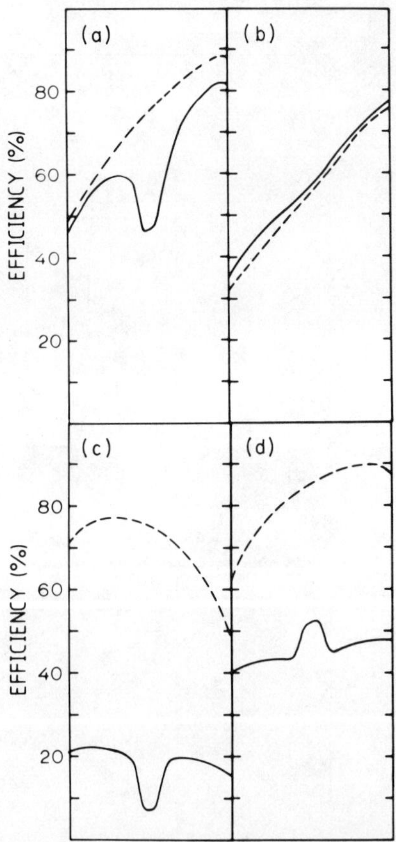

FIG. 2.53. Same as Fig. 2.52 but at (a) 3000; (b) 4000, (c) 2000, and (d) 2500 Å. [From Hunter and Angel (1979).]

and remeasured. Within the limits of error of the measurements no differences were found.

Because of the delicate nature of most grating surfaces, cleaning techniques must be chosen with care. There are no general rules for cleaning gratings—each case must be considered separately. It is the purpose of this section to provide some guidelines and to describe some cleaning techniques that have been used successfully (Hunter and Hass, 1980). These techniques are useful both for removing contamination and as preparation for coating.

Before cleaning one must consider the nature of the grating. Gratings formed on fused silica or SiC surfaces by etching the grooves into the surface are difficult to damage. In principle, these etched gratings can withstand any treatment the substrate can withstand and can be washed with soap and water and a washrag (if one can bring oneself to do it). Original gratings ruled in metal coatings that have been vacuum-deposited on fused silica or glass blanks are somewhat more vulnerable. There is always the possibility that the coating adherence is poor. If so, liquid cleaners can work their way between the substrate and coating and may release part, or all, of the ruled coating. Quite often the ruled layer is a double layer with two different metals. If so, immersion in an electrolyte may cause galvanic action and damage the grating surface.

If a suitable solvent is available, the grating can be rinsed or, even better, vapor degreased. The process of vapor degreasing is well known and consists

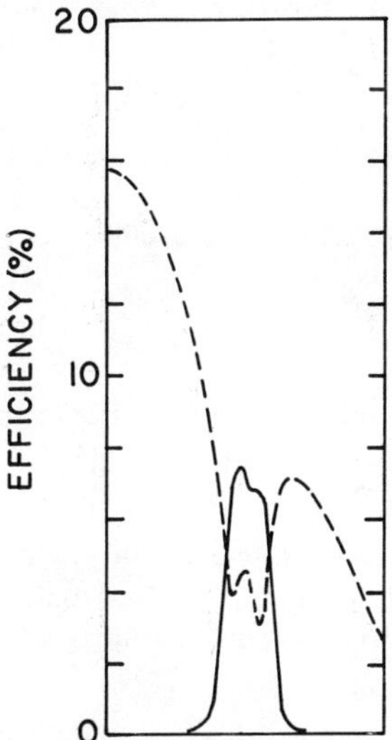

FIG. 2.54. Efficiency maps of the grating of Fig. 2.50 at 1580 Å before (——) and after (– – –) cleaning by vapor degreasing. [From Hunter and Angel (1979).]

of immersing the dirty object (grating) in the heated solvent vapor. The vapor condenses on the grating and drains off back into the solvent reservoir, taking with it the contamination. If the contaminant has a lower boiling point than the solvent, this method is not useful. Eventually the grating temperature approaches that of the vapor and condensation will slow and may stop. Usually the grating is clean long before the equilibrium temperature is reached.

The author uses a small vapor degreaser made from a stainless steel beaker with a few turns of copper tubing soft-soldered around the opening. Cool water is fed through the tubing to condense the vapor so that it is not lost into the laboratory. An electric hotplate is used as a heat source. After cleaning, the remaining solvent is poured into a glass-stoppered bottle reserved specifically for that purpose. This solvent can be used for subsequent degreasing operations provided it does not acquire too many volatile oils during degreasing.

Vapor degreasing is preferable to rinsing with room-temperature solvent because evaporation of the solvent may lower the temperature of the grating below the dew point so that water condenses on it. When the grating is removed from the vapor after degreasing, its temperature is well above room temperature and water condensation cannot occur. If rinsing must be used, the solvent should be heated somewhat above room temperature.

Trichlorotrifluoroethane in the so-called precision grade (high purity) is a very useful solvent for both rinsing and vapor degreasing. It is neither toxic nor flammable. Trichlorotrifluoroethane for rinsing should not be kept in plastic containers or used from plastic squeeze bottles because a residue may be left on the grating surface. This rule applies to any other solvent used in rinsing gratings.

Although alcohol and acetone can, in principle, be used as the solvent in vapor degreasing, they are not recommended because of the danger of fire or explosion.

Gross contamination, such as a fingerprint, is not easily removed by vapor degreasing. The author has removed fresh fingerprints by immersing the grating in a mild, warm, detergent and water solution and gently agitating the solution in the vicinity of the fingerprint with a bit of absorbent cotton that is loosely wadded. The cotton is not actually rubbed across the grating surface but passed back and forth just above the surface. After cleaning in the detergent, the grating should be rinsed with clean water or a solvent. Since fingerprints will eventually etch the grating surface, they should be removed as soon as possible.

Replica and holographic gratings can generally be cleaned in the same manner as original gratings; however, two additional precautions must be observed. The epoxy or photoresist layers may be damaged if their temperature exceeds about 50°, and these layers are attacked by some solvents.

If the grating has had a coating applied to it to change its spectral characteristics, for example, Pt, Os, Al + MgF_2, the types of cleaning may be restricted because of the adherence of the coating. Good adherence usually requires a very clean surface and additionally, for Pt metals, high substrate temperatures. With the exception of the etched gratings, grating surfaces can never be cleaned as thoroughly as a glass or fused silica surface; furthermore, it is inadvisable to heat gratings to the 300–400°C required for best adherence of the Pt metals. Consequently, such coatings may not have good adherence and, unless treated gently during cleaning, may be detached from the grating surface. The author uses only rinsing or vapor degreasing for such gratings.

Gillette *et al.* (1970; Gillette and Kenyon, 1971) have found that the optical properties of an optical surface contaminated by carbon-based oil or compounds can be restored by exposing them to an rf-excited discharge of oxygen. Oxygen of at least 99.5% purity was introduced into the vacuum system containing the mirror to be cleaned through a quartz tube of about 4-mm bore. The electrodes were metallic strips painted along the length of the tube and diametrically opposite. The rf power consumption at the input tube was about 20 W, for a frequency of 13.56 MHz, when the oxygen flow was adjusted to have a pressure in the tube of about 1 torr, and in the vacuum system of about 5×10^{-4} torr.

Removal of particulate matter (dust, etc.) from a grating surface can be done, in part, by using a jet of gas. Very small particles, however, are difficult to dislodge with a jet. If the conditions are favorable—good adherence of coatings, replica layers, etc.—one can use a technique devised by Purcell (1953) for cleaning mirrors with collodion. He has also used this technique for cleaning gratings. Collodion is poured onto the grating surface while it is horizontal; then the grating is turned on edge and the excess collodion allowed to drain off. After the collodion has dried, it can usually be peeled off. If some islands of dried collodion are left, the treatment is repeated until none are left. After each stripping the grating surface should be examined with care to see that it has not been pulled loose by the collodion. If looseness is suspected, further strippings should not be attempted.

For best results with collodion cleaning, the grating should be heated to about body temperature (37°C) or slightly higher so that cooling due to evaporation of the ether in the collodion will not depress the temperature of the grating surface below the dew point. An electric hair-dryer is sometimes useful for blowing warm air across the grating surface while the collodion is drying.

The final step in the cleaning procedure, preparatory to coating, is a dc glow discharge (Hunter and Hass, 1980). Because glow discharges cause heating of the object being cleaned, they must be used with caution with replica or holographic gratings. Standard coating procedures are usually adequate for coating gratings (Hunter and Hass, 1980). Some of the restrictions that apply to cleaning also apply to coating, i.e., replica and holographic gratings must not be overheated during the coating process. If the vapor source is resistively heated (filaments, boats) there is not too much danger of overheating unless the evaporation is very long. More care must be used if an electron gun is used to vaporize the metal for the coating. Osmium, for example, requires quite a high temperature for reasonable deposition rates (50 Å/s). If the deposition takes too long the epoxy, or photoresist, layer may be damaged.

Because replica or holographic gratings cannot be heated during deposition, their efficiency values, when coating with Pt or Ir or any metal that requires a high substrate temperature (300–400°C) for maximum reflectance, will not be as large as might be expected. Osmium, rhenium, and ruthenium do not require high substrate temperatures for highest reflectance values, hence they are quite useful for coating replica or holographic gratings. Such coatings, however, may not have good adherence because good adherence and high substrate temperatures go together for the Pt metals.

Coating of gratings should be carefully planned so as to avoid intermetallic diffusion. For example, if aluminum is evaporated onto gold, the two metals interdiffuse and change the optical characteristics of both the gold and aluminum drastically. Conversely, if gold is evaporated onto *aged* aluminum, that is, aluminum with the normal 30–40 Å of oxide on its surface, there is no interdiffusion, even at temperatures as high as 150°C. The natural oxide acts as a barrier layer and prevents interdiffusion.

The interdiffusion of gold and aluminum has been a well-known phenomenon in the electronics industry since the early 1960s. The end products are a number of intermetallic compounds, the most important of which are Au_2Al and $AuAl_2$. In appearance, the compounds exhibit a slightly purplish cast; hence the phenomenon was dubbed the purple plague. The effect of this interdiffusion on the optical properties of aluminum and gold was not discovered until the early 1970s and was reported by Hunter *et al.* (1971b, 1972). Figure 2.55 shows how the efficiency of a gold replica grating that had been overcoated with Al + MgF_2 decreased from March 1970 to June 1971 because of intermetallic diffusion. The figure is an efficiency map of the grating surface at 1216 Å and in the second order, the order in which the grating was to have been used. If the grating had been replicated in aluminum, the natural oxide would have acted as a barrier layer to prevent the loss in efficiency. If aluminum must be evaporated onto gold, a barrier layer must be evaporated first. A layer of SiO, about 50 Å thick, forms a barrier layer, but it should not be placed directly on the gold because it adheres very poorly to gold. A layer of Cr, about 50 Å thick, should be put down first to provide good adherence between the SiO and the gold. Finally, the aluminum layer can be put down.

Very few systematic studies of the interdiffusion of metallic layers have been carried out. The author found that aluminum and platinum have a negligible interdiffusion rate at room temperature but at temperatures of about 100°C the rate becomes appreciable and destructive interdiffusion takes place in about 1 h. In the usual laboratory work, optical components are seldom subjected to such temperatures. However, mirrors exposed to synchrotron radiation from high-energy storage rings can be expected to reach temperatures of several hundred degrees centigrade. In such an environment the barrier layers discussed above may not be sufficient to prevent interdiffusion.

Occasionally the grating coating becomes so severely contaminated that it must be removed and the grating recoated. Coating removal can be a difficult task if the coating adheres well. Etched gratings may have their coatings removed by the same procedures used for stripping mirrors. Aluminum coatings are removed with an NaOH solution; Au that has been bonded to the substrate with Cr may require aqua regia. Platinum and the Pt metals may also require aqua regia for removal. Fused silica and glass are etched by strong bases and acids so many strippings or long exposure to these corrosive liquids will eventually roughen the surface. Silicon carbide is reputed to be immune to acids and bases.

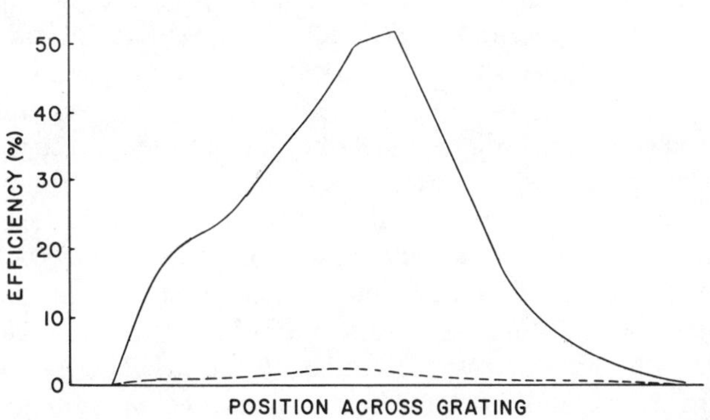

FIG. 2.55. Efficiency maps showing the change in efficiency caused by intermetallic diffusion. (——, measured March 1970; ---, measured June 1971.) [From Hunter *et al.* (1972).]

If the environment is such that frequent stripping, rather than cleaning, will be required, there is a definite advantage to coatings with poor adherence. Unfortunately, no studies, systematic or otherwise, have been made of conditions required for poor adherence. One might reduce the vigor of the cleaning procedure although this can lead to unfortunate consequences, such as the coating becoming loose in small areas, perhaps forming bubblelike protuberances.

Finally, if the adherence is poor, the coating may be removed with scotch tape (Purcell, 1952). A short length of tape is hand-held, sticky side out, and touched lightly to the grating surface, very much like daubing paint on a surface. This procedure is kept up until the grating appears to be free of the coating.

2.3. Grating Mountings

Many years of development have gone into VUV spectrometers for use in the laboratory. Their present state of development appears to have reached a plateau. Most of the nonspecialized instruments are much as they were described by Samson (1967). Changes since then have consisted mostly of refinements rather than radical changes in operation or construction. The aberrations of concave grating instruments have been reduced by the use of corrected gratings or gratings on toroidal surfaces or a combination of these two. Such corrections increase the instrumental transmission and resolution. Pouey (1974, 1978, 1980, 1982, 1983a–c) has studied the reduction of aberrations by using corrected gratings and by balancing compensating aberrations.

The number of photons per second available from the usual laboratory light sources causes laboratory instruments to be energy-limited. Thus the number of optical surfaces they can employ is restricted by the efficiencies of reflecting coatings. More flexibility is available when designing instruments for synchrotron radiation (SR) because the source supplies many more photons per second per bandwidth than most laboratory sources. Thus reflecting coating efficiencies are less of a restriction and more optical surfaces can be utilized before energy limitation makes itself felt.

Synchrotron radiation is not without disadvantages, however, and perhaps the most serious is the damage to optical elements by the large flux of hard x rays emitted by high-energy–high-intensity sources. There are other features of synchrotron radiation, the high degree of collimation and the continuum nature of the radiation, that require special design considerations.

Many instruments have been designed specifically, or adapted, for SR. Johnson (1983) has published a review article on synchrotron radiation that covers the field of instruments, as of 1981, quite thoroughly.

There remains the use of VUV instruments in space research. The instruments for this field can be divided into two classes; solar and stellar instruments. One would not expect solar spectrographs to be energy-limited because of the high solar intensity; however, this is not true in the VUV, where the spatially integrated flux at 1 astronomical unit (AU) is equivalent to, or sometimes less than, that of laboratory sources. In addition, the emphasis in solar spectroscopy is now on both greater spatial, spectral, and temporal resolution to solve the problem of solar flare morphology and other small active regions of interest. Thus the flux is further reduced by the restrictive designs of the instruments. An ever-present problem encountered in solar spectrographs is the control of visible and UV stray light because the intensity of the integrated visible and UV solar spectrum is about six orders of magnitude greater than that of the VUV. Some of the steps taken to alleviate the problem, such as the use of thin metal film filters, also reduce the VUV intensity.

Stellar spectrographs require a large light-gathering ability because the sources are faint. Wavelengths longer than about 1100 Å are fairly easy to record because of the highly reflecting Al + MgF_2 coatings for that region. Toward shorter wavelengths the radiation is more strongly absorbed by interstellar matter, particularly atomic hydrogen. As yet no observations have been made at wavelengths between about 1100 and 300 Å. To wavelengths shorter than 300 Å the absorption of hydrogen lessens and observations become easier.

There appears to be no general review of VUV stellar instruments in existence. There are scattered review papers, however, one being concerned with the International Ultraviolet Explorer (IUE). An account of the IUE instruments and their performance can be found in *Nature* (Boggess, 1978a,b). Another paper describes the instruments to be used on the Space Telescope. A description of the high-resolution spectrograph for that satellite can be found in volume 279 of the Proceedings of the Society of Photo-Optical Instrumentation Engineers (Brandt, 1981).

A description of the solar instruments carried in the Apollo Telescope Mount of SKYLAB will be found in the April 1977 issue of *Applied Optics* (Tousey *et al.*, 1977; Reeves *et al.*, 1977; Bartoe *et al.*, 1977; Garrett and Tousey, 1977). More recently, Brueckner (1980) has described solar instruments developed since the ATM. Neupert *et al.* (1981) have described a solar extreme ultraviolet telescope and spectrograph to be flown in the Shuttle/Spacelab.

Because there are many instrumental reviews, the scope of this portion of the chapter will be restricted to new and untried, but possibly useful, grating mountings.

A. Plane Grating Mountings

A well-known mounting for a plane grating is the "student spectrograph." A collimator is used to illuminate the grating with a parallel beam of light, and a telescope is used to observe the spectrum visually. Such an instrument is useless in the VUV because the collimator and telescope lenses would absorb the radiation. The student spectrograph can be modified to use reflecting optics, however, and a number of variations, intended for the VUV, are in use.

1. *The Plane Grating in Parallel Radiation*

Ebert–Fastie (Ebert, 1889; Fastie, 1952a,b) and Czerny–Turner (Czerny and Turner, 1930) mountings are the most common reflecting analogs of the student spectrograph. They are intended for use at near-normal incidence, hence are restricted to wavelengths longer than about 1100 Å. The essential characteristic of these two designs is the use of spherical mirrors: a collimating mirror to provide parallel radiation to the grating, and an objective mirror to provide an image of the entrance slit. In the Ebert–Fastie instrument a large concave mirror serves both purposes, and separate mirrors are used in the Czerny–Turner instrument. Miyake *et al.* (1969) introduced a version of the instrument, using only one mirror reflection, intended specifically for use with SR. The SR was considered to be sufficiently collimated so that no collimator mirror was necessary, only a focusing mirror. Actually this instrument is perhaps more closely related to the Monk–Gillieson mounting (Monk, 1928; Gillieson, 1949), in which the grating is illuminated by nonparallel radiation because SR does have a small divergence. West *et al.* (1974) modified the Miyake instrument by adding an extra mirror at a different angle of incidence that permitted better reduction of high-order contamination. Howells (1980) modified the instrument even further by adding a collimating mirror, thus producing a grazing incidence version of the Ebert–Fastie monochromator.

2. *Plane Grating On-Blaze Mountings*

Much has been said about blaze and its advantages. Experience has shown that a blazed grating is superior, in efficiency, to a grating with no blaze. Unfortunately, most monochromators are constructed such that during the scan over the monochromator's wavelength range the grating is at blaze for only one wavelength. It is of interest to inquire how the grating can be mounted to take better advantage of the blaze condition. Referring to Fig. 2.6, one sees that at blaze the incident beam and the diffracted blaze wavelength are inclined at equal angles to the facet normal. Therefore, to change wavelengths and remain on blaze, both the incident beam and the blaze wavelength must always make equal angles with respect to the facet normal. This implies that the angles of incidence and diffraction must increase or decrease simultaneously. Because most scanning monochromators have a constant deviation angle, the sum of these angles is fixed and the grating is at blaze at only one wavelength in the scan, if at all. If the monochromator is to be used constantly at blaze, however, the sum of the two angles cannot be constant. Thus on-blaze instruments using only one grating lose the advantage of constant deviation, which cannot be regained without the use of another optical element. A further limitation is imposed by the restricted wavelength range. For example, when $\alpha = \beta$, $nG\lambda = 2 \sin \alpha$, which determines the longest wavelength at which the grating can be used, the Littrow wavelength. Despite these shortcomings, the argument in favor of on-blaze operation, the large efficiency values of the grating over a comparatively wide wavelength range, is rather cogent and makes on-blaze operation worth investigating, which we will do in this section.

First, one may ask if it is possible to convert any of the conventional monochromators to on-blaze operation. In principle, some can be converted but at the cost of increased complexity (see Subsection 2.3.B.1). Consider, for example, the Ebert–Fastie mounting. As designed, the wavelength is changed by rotating the grating. On-blaze operation would eliminate the rotation but would require that the grating be translated to and from the mirrors along the centerline between the mirrors that is perpendicular to the line joining their centers. Since the mirrors are adjusted to illuminate the grating optimally when it is at a given distance from them, any change in this distance reduces the optimum grating illumination. It also changes the direction of the exit beam. One might argue that the mirrors could be rotated to maintain optimum illumination. However, this would introduce aberrations that would seriously impair the performance of the instrument unless a rather large f-number were to be used. It appears as though the Ebert–Fastie and the Czerny–Turner monochromators are not amenable to conversion to on-blaze operation.

The advantage of on-blaze monochromators was recognized as early as 1950 by Greig and Ferguson (1950). They used a blazed plane grating mounted in conical diffraction that rotated about an axis parallel to the large facets and perpendicular to the groove direction. Because they wanted constant deviation of the diffracted beam, they used a plane mirror that rotated and translated. A schematic diagram of the motions of their monochromator is shown in Fig. 2.56. One of the problems they encountered was the rotation of the slit image so that the exit slit had to be rotated as a function of wavelength. Greig and Ferguson designed their instrument for infrared work so they were not aware of the large increase in efficiency conferred by conical diffraction at the shorter wavelengths.

The scheme of Greig and Ferguson was rediscovered by Maystre and Petit (1972) some 22 years later and again by Werner (1977b). Werner and Visser (1981) implemented this scheme, in somewhat modified form, for use with synchrotron radiation. Figure 2.57 shows a schematic diagram of their monochromator. Radiation from an entrance slit illuminates a grazing-incidence paraboloidal mirror, which is the collimator. The principal ray is in the horizontal plane. The collimated radiation is reflected from a plane mirror to a plane grating used in conical diffraction, then diffracted to another plane mirror, and reflected from there to a grazing-incidence paraboloidal mirror identical to the first, which focuses the radiation onto the exit slit. The principal ray from the final paraboloidal mirror to the exit slit is also in the horizontal plane.

The plane grating is tilted so that the large facets are in the horizontal plane. A wavelength scan is accomplished by moving the grating vertical without changing the tilt, and the plane mirrors are rotated so that the radiation is directed to the grating. The authors calculated the resolving power in the wavelength interval 6 to 200 Å to range from 220 to 7500, using 20-μm-wide slits. If larger slits are used, say 100 μm, the resolving power ranges from 45 to 1500 over the same range.

Finkelstein (1951) produced an on-blaze plane grating monochromator that was quite similar to that of Greig and Ferguson except that the grating

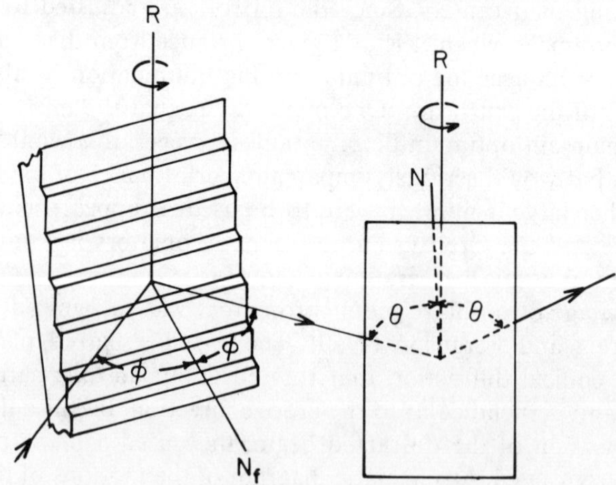

FIG. 2.56. A schematic diagram of the monochromator of Greig and Ferguson (1950).

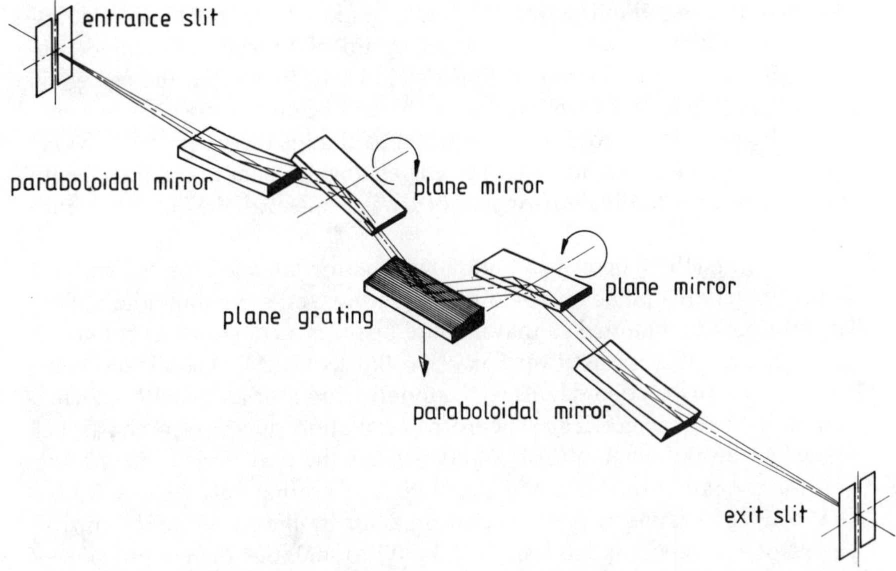

FIG. 2.57. A schematic diagram of the monochromator of Werner and Visser. [From Werner and Visser (1981).]

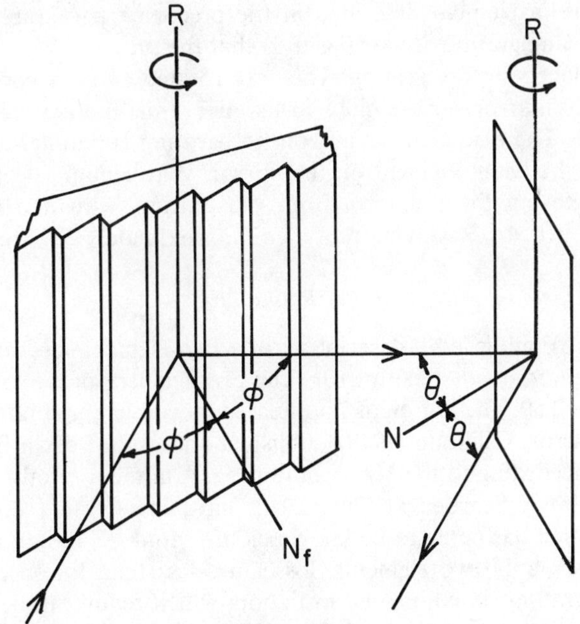

FIG. 2.58. A schematic diagram of the monochromator of Finkelstein (1951).

was used in classical diffraction. Thus no rotation of the exit slit was necessary. Figure 2.58 shows a schematic diagram of Finkelstein's monochromator. Kessler (1970) simplified Finkelstein's scheme so that the change in wavelength is achieved by mounting both mirror and grating on a common turntable; thus only a rotation is required to change the wavelength. Along with this simplification, however, there is an abridgement of the wavelength range because the folding mirror cannot always collect all the flux if it cannot be translated.

Kunz *et al.* (1968) described a monochromator intended for use with SR that consisted of a plane mirror, a plane grating, and a paraboloidal mirror. The grating was mounted so that it could be translated as well as rotated in such a manner that it was always on blaze. Subsequently, Dietrich and Kunz (1972) gave construction details of the monochromator along with information on its performance. The synchrotron radiation, assumed to be parallel, is incident on the plane mirror, which deflects the radiation to the grating. This mirror can both rotate and translate. The grating only rotates. Radiation from the grating is then focused on a slit by the paraboloidal mirror. The resolving power is modest, $\lambda/d\lambda = 300$ to 400, but the suppression of higher orders is good.

Jark *et al.* (1983) report a monochromator, intended for use with synchrotron radiation, for the energy range from 5 to 1000 eV that is a simpler version of the instrument described in the preceding paragraph. A plane mirror and plane grating are arranged so that the mirror surface is parallel to the large facets on the grating. They are rotated about a common axis that lies in the mirror surface close to its edge; thus the grating is always used at blaze. The emergent beam from the grating is parallel to, but displaced from, the beam incident on the mirror. Wavelength selection is obtained by focusing the radiation from the grating, with a paraboloidal mirror, to an exit slit. Resolving powers of approximately 300 are obtained.

3. *The Plane Grating in Nonparallel Radiation*

Monk (1928) published a description of a two-element spectrograph—a plane grating and a spherical mirror. The arrangement of elements is that shown in Fig. 2.59. The grating is illuminated by converging radiation from a concave mirror. Gillieson (1949) published an account of an instrument constructed according to the Monk mounting. A number of others (Smyth, 1935; Hall, 1966; Schroeder, 1966, 1970) have investigated this type of mounting, which has come to be known as the Monk–Gillieson mounting. Because it uses only two elements, losses are less than for spectrometers using plane gratings in collimated radiation, which require three elements. Thus the instrument could be useful for VUV applications. The main objection to this mounting is the excessive coma and higher order aberrations caused by the spherical mirror being used off-axis and the focusing action of the grating. Murty (1962) suggested correcting the coma by a number of ways. One is to vary the groove spacing on the grating such that the grooves form confocal hyperbolas. In effect, Murty suggested corrected gratings long before practical holographic gratings were made. He also suggested that the coma of paraboloidal, or ellipsoidal, mirrors could be used to correct the coma of the uncorrected plane grating. Seya *et al.* (1967) have analyzed the Monk–Gillieson mounting and found that coma can be eliminated at one wavelength of the designer's choice without the use of special optical elements. Usually some version of the Rowland circle mounting, or the Wadsworth mounting, can be employed in place of the Monk–Gillieson mounting; consequently the Monk–Gillieson mounting has been neglected.

Two variations of the Monk–Gillieson mounting have recently been reported. Hettrick and Bowyer (1983) use a plane grating in a converging VUV beam from the collector mirror of a Wolter telescope (Wolter, 1952a,b). The arrangement is shown in Fig. 2.60. The real image produced by the collector mirror is labeled *mirror focus.* It is imaged by the zeroth order of the grating at $m = 0$. The grating has nonuniform groove spacing that varies according to the equation

$$d(x) = m\lambda_0/[\cos\beta(x) - \cos\alpha(x)],$$

where λ_0 is the correction wavelength, and $\cos\beta$ and $\cos\alpha$ are the local glancing angles for the diffracted and incident rays, respectively. The focal surface has a radius L_0. The meridional rays (along AB) form a perfect image at λ_0, as do the rays that are diffracted from the line CD. Other regions of the grating contribute aberrations. The use of inside spectral

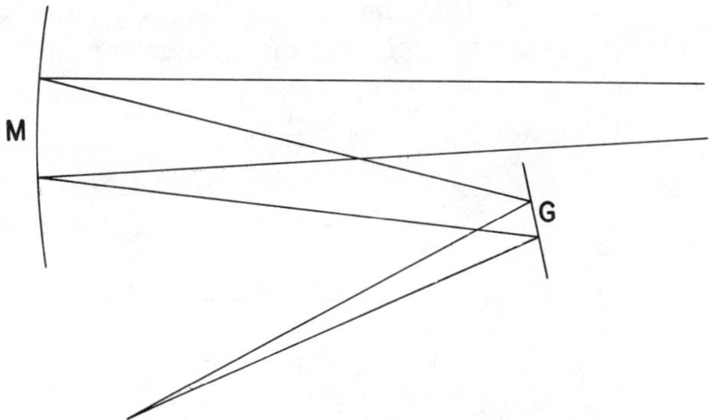

FIG. 2.59. A schematic diagram showing the Monk–Gillieson mounting. (Monk, 1928; Gillieson, 1949).

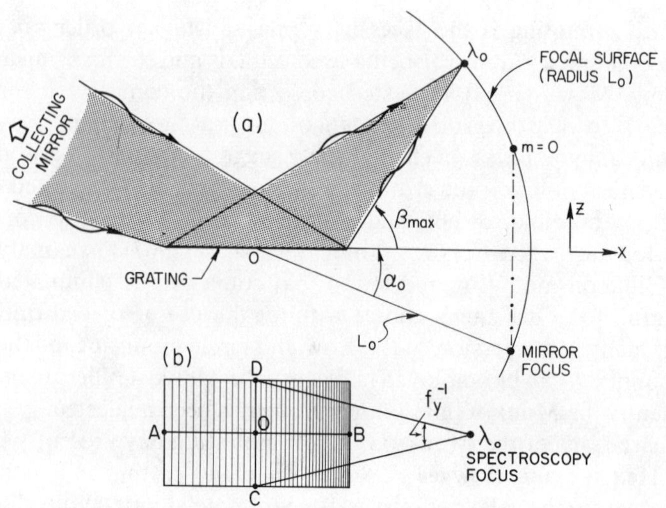

FIG. 2.60. A schematic diagram of the mounting devised by Hettrick and Bowyer; (a) looking parallel to the grating surface; (b) looking down on the grating surface. [From Hettrick and Bowyer (1983).]

orders, between $m = 0$ and λ_0, minimizes the aberrations and provide higher diffraction efficiency at a given resolution. Ray tracing with converging radiation of $f/5$ and including the aberrations of the converging mirror showed a resolving power of 700–1100 and a large wavelength range, from 100 to 1000 Å.

The use of a properly corrected grating can make the point λ_0 completely stigmatic. Such a grating could be recorded holographically by putting the recording sources at $m = 0$ and λ_0. The resulting grooves would be hyperbolas, as shown in Fig. 2.61. If the line joining the two recording sources is perpendicular to the plane of the grating, the grooves are concentric circles and the focal curve is the line joining those sources. For example, in Fig. 2.60, if the sources are at *mirror focus* and $m = 0$, the focal curve is a line

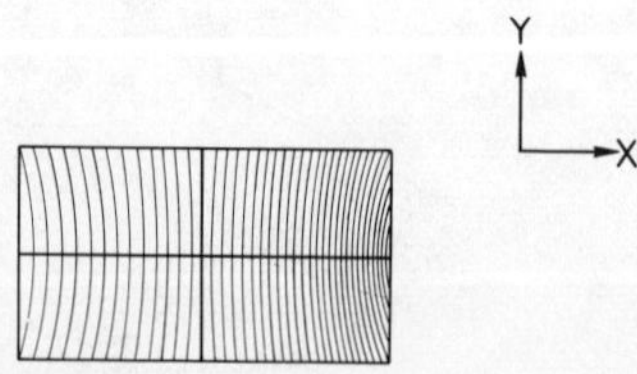

FIG. 2.61. The corrected grating proposed by Hettrick and Bowyer to correct astigmatism of the mounting of Fig. 2.60. [From Hettrick and Bowyer (1983).]

coinciding with the dot–dash line shown in the figure. There is a large increase in resolving power, about three orders of magnitude. It is, however, coupled with a drastic reduction in wavelength coverage.

Another approach is to place the recording sources at equal distances on either side of the plane of dispersion of Fig. 2.60, but not in the plane of the grating. The grooves are hyperbolas but oriented such that the central straight line is in the plane of dispersion. Rather than use the entire grating, Hettrick and Bowyer use that part of the grating between line AB and the line through D, and approximate the holographic recording with a ruled grating on which the grooves radiate from a hub like the spokes of a wheel, as shown in Fig. 2.62. Cash (1983) has independently had the same idea. The light converging onto this radial grating, which is in conical diffraction,

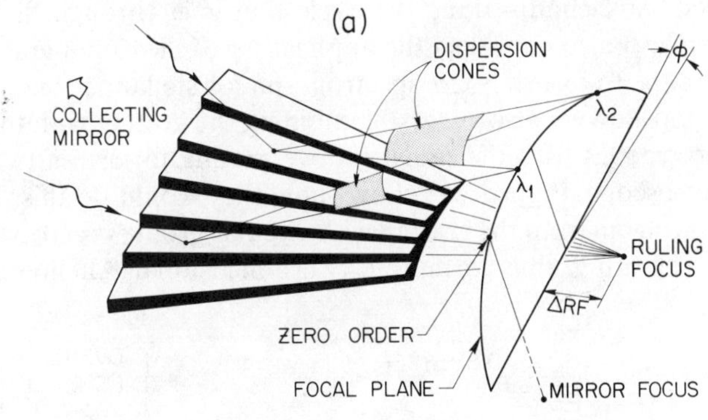

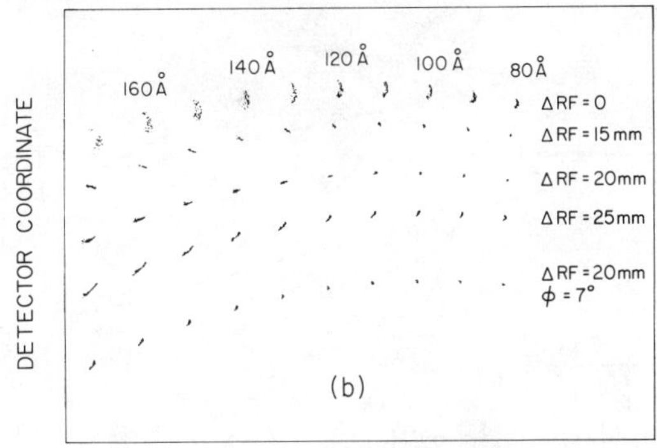

FIG. 2.62. (a) The radial grating approximation to the grating of Fig. 2.61 used by Hettrick and Bowyer, and (b) some ray tracings showing the expected quality of wavelength images. [From Hettrick and Bowyer (1983).]

comes to a focus on a circle, as shown in Fig. 2.62. The so-called ruling focus, or hub, where the radial grooves originate does not exactly coincide with the focal plane for best focus. Figure 2.62 contains some ray traces that show how the focus changes with ΔRF. Cash has also done some ray tracing and shown that the resolution is independent of wavelength but that the astigmatism increases with wavelength.

Cash suggests that a radial grating can be used with a grazing incidence ellipsoidal mirror to form an x-ray spectrograph. An entrance slit is used. The ellipsoidal mirror brings the radiation to a focus but a radial grating is interposed between the mirror and the focal plane. Such an instrument can also be made into a monochromator by placing an exit slit in the appropriate location and rotating the radial grating about its center groove. Such a rotation keeps the half-angle of the cone of diffraction constant but moves the dispersed wavelengths along the circle that goes through the center of the exit slit. Cash also considers the application of the radial grating to the Wolter telescope to form a VUV spectrograph for stellar astronomy.

Hettrick and Bowyer also suggest combining the grating with the concentric circular grooves with the radial groove grating to form a two-element echelle spectroscope. Figure 2.63 shows how they would do this. The high-resolution spectrum from the grating with circular grooves is cross-dispersed by the radial grating, thus forming a two-dimensional echellogram at the

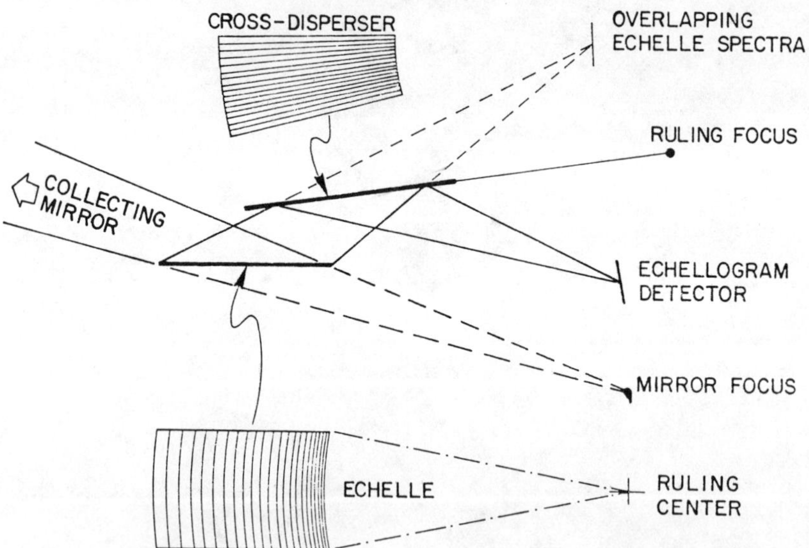

FIG. 2.63. A schematic diagram of the grazing incidence echelle proposed by Hettrick and Bowyer. [From Hettrick and Bowyer (1983).]

detector. Thus a large range of wavelengths at large spectral resolution can be recorded.

4. *Dual Grating Mountings*

The use of two gratings in tandem, the second to rediffract light from the first, can be divided into three cases; double, zero, or crossed dispersion. Crossed dispersion, which involves conical diffraction, is frequently used to separate high orders of diffraction and will be dealt with later. The usual condition for double or zero dispersion has both gratings mounted in classical diffraction. Double dispersion provides an instrumental resolution greater than would be obtained with a single grating. In zero dispersion, the dispersion of the first grating is nullified by that of the second grating to provide an undispersed band of wavelengths—a sort of bandpass filter. True double or zero dispersion occurs only if both gratings have the same groove densities and their surfaces are parallel. The terms are applied in a loose sense, however, to include both nonidentical gratings and nonparallel grating surfaces.

Figure 2.64 illustrates qualitatively both zero and double dispersion. Two identical gratings are set parallel and the first, G_1, illuminated by collimated radiation at normal incidence. Then, since $\alpha = 0$, the angle of diffraction is

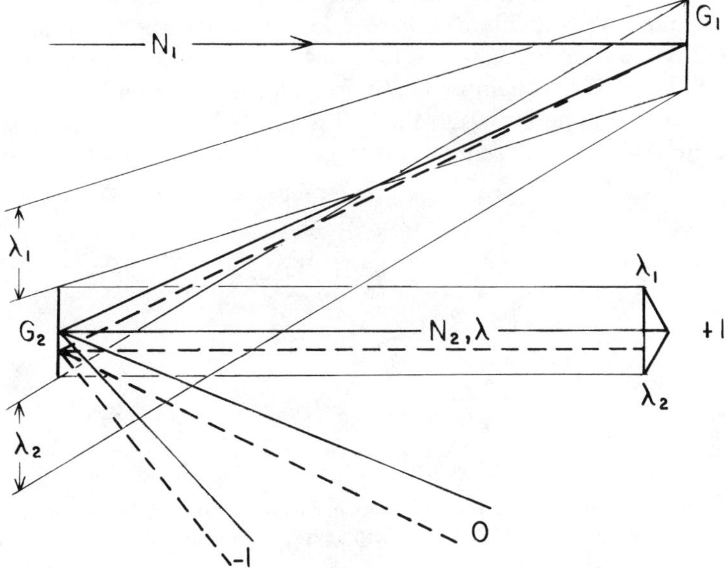

FIG. 2.64. An illustration of zero and double dispersion.

obtained from $-n_1, G_1, \lambda = -\sin \beta_1$. Because the two grating normals are parallel, $\beta_1 = \alpha_2$, where α_2 is the angle of incidence on the second grating G_2. Then, because the gratings are identical, $n_2 G_2 \lambda - \sin \alpha_2 = 0$ and the diffracted wave vector is parallel to the normal of G_2, N_2. The negative first order, making an angle β_2 with respect to N_2, is the doubly dispersed beam. The solid lines show the directions taken by the wave vectors for λ. If the wavelength is increased by $d\lambda$, the new directions of the wave vectors are shown by the dashed lines. Although α_2 increases in value because β_1 has increased, the positive 1st order is still parallel to the normals. Thus the different wavelengths in the positive first order are not dispersed in the usual sense (angularly) but are parallel to one another. The spectral distribution of wavelengths diffracted from G_2 parallel to one another will depend on the angular dispersion of G_1 and the angular subtense of G_2 as seen from G_1. The greater the angular dispersion of G_1 and the greater the distance between G_1 and G_2, the smaller the spectral bandwidth of the parallel beam.

The parallel beam obtained from G_2 does not have a uniform spatial distribution of wavelengths but has approximately a triangular distribution. The limiting wavelengths λ_1 and λ_2 are those wavelengths that just touch the grating edges. The same argument applies to the doubly dispersed beam. If the gratings are not parallel then strict zero and double dispersion do not occur.

Hunter *et al.* (1982) have designed and built a double-grating monochromator for use with SR wherein the gratings are used in double dispersion and always at blaze. Figure 2.65 is a schematic diagram of the monochromator. In the figure, S is the source, the electron beam in a storage ring; M_1 is an off-axis paraboloidal mirror, located 10 m from the source, that reflects the radiation up to the first grating G_1. The radiation is then diffracted to the second grating G_2, thence to a second paraboloidal mirror

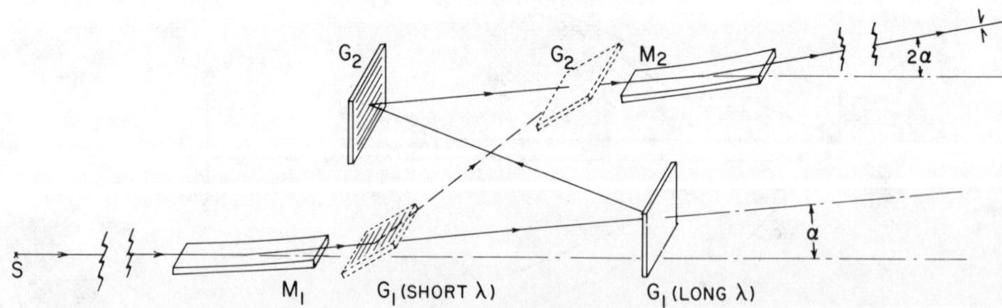

FIG. 2.65. A schematic of the double-grating monochromator of Hunter *et al.* [From Hunter *et al.* (1982). © North-Holland Physics Publishing, Amsterdam, 1982.]

M_2, which is identical to the first. Finally the radiation is reflected from M_2 through 10 m to an exit slit. Changes in wavelength are accomplished by translating G_1 and G_2 along the parallel paths shown, while rotating them about axes in their surfaces that are perpendicular to the translation paths. The positions of the gratings shown by the solid lines are the long-wavelength positions; those shown by the dashed lines are the short-wavelength positions. This physical arrangement enables one to have a fixed exit slit and fixed direction of the exit beam. The two gratings are also arranged so that the large facets are parallel and maintained that way during the wavelength scan. This satisfies the condition for on-blaze operation.

The authors estimate that the resolving power will be at least 1500 at the long-wavelength positions of the gratings, and will increase to double that at the short-wavelength positions.

Hunter (1982) has investigated the aberrations of this instrument and found that the second mirror M_2 can be inverted without significant loss in resolving power. He has also investigated the possibility of using paraboloidal mirrors with shorter, as well as different, focal distances, and the effect of larger horizontal acceptance angles, different glancing angles on the paraboloidal mirrors, and other parameters of the instrument. Focal distances of 10 m for both mirrors appear to be optimum, and acceptance angles up to about 16 mrad do not decrease the resolving power by very much.

Hunter and Rife (1984) have calculated the transmittance and higher order suppression for the double-grating monochromator, but using a mirror in place of the first grating. The reason for the substitution is that for certain grating positions, i.e., wavelengths, the untrapped zeroth order of the first grating is incident on the second. Although the first grating can be used in a higher order until the relative grating positions are such that the zeroth order of the first no longer illuminates the second, their simple calculation is suitable only for gratings used at blaze. Two types of gratings were used in the calculation; one with 2400 g/mm for wavelengths from 300 to about 15 Å, and the other with 600 g/mm for wavelengths from 1200 to about 100 Å.

Four different metals were considered for the coatings of the mirrors and the gratings; Al, Au, Ni, Os, Pt, and Si. The final choice was Ni coatings for the two paraboloidal mirrors, an Au coating for the short-wavelength grating, and Si for the long-wavelength grating. The two coating schemes were studied in some detail. Transmitted flux calculations were made for the first five orders, assuming the storage ring will be run at 2.5 GeV with 0.5-A ring current. The results of these calculations are shown in Fig. 2.66, where the wavelength ranges for the two gratings have been drawn separately to avoid confusion. Solid lines are used for the first-order curves; the higher order curves have the order designated by the number of short dashes. The wavelength scale factor fits only the 1st order; the nth-order spectral contamination is at a wavelength $1/n$ times that of the first order. In the short-wavelength range the orders do not overlap in magnitude. The second-order transmittance is less than the first by about an average of 1.5 orders of magnitude. At the very short wavelengths the separation is even greater.

In the long-wavelength range, the higher orders have overlapping magnitudes from 1200 to 300 Å and are somewhat difficult to identify. All of them, however, are two orders of magnitude, or more, less than the first order. At the shorter wavelengths, the first and second orders remain about equal to the shortest wavelength shown, 40 Å, but the higher orders are once again separated by at least an order of magnitude. If Al had been chosen rather

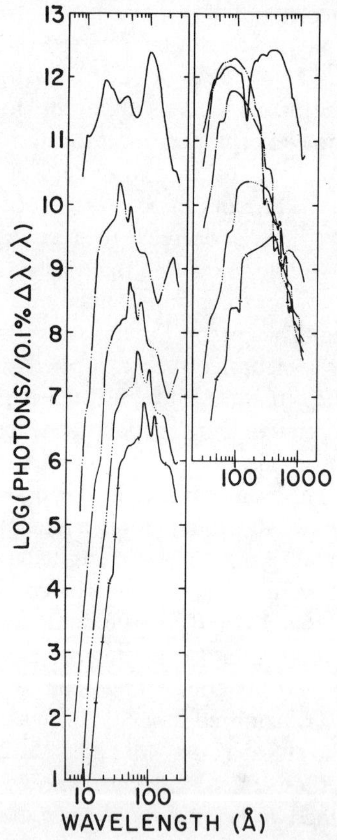

FIG. 2.66. A calculation of the flux through the monochromator of Fig. 2.65. Solid lines show first order. Higher orders are designated by the number of short dashes, except the fifth, which has a hash mark. [From Hunter and Rife (1984).]

than Si, the increase in second order would have started at a longer wavelength because the first x-ray absorption edges $L_{2,3}$ are at 170 Å for Al but at 125 Å for Si.

The first-order flux in the short-wavelength region ranges from 10^{10} to 10^{12} photons/s, and for the long-wavelength region, slightly more. The second-order flux in the short-wavelength region is approximately two orders of magnitude less than that of the first order, but it is still an impressive number of photons per second. It is, in fact, so large that extra attenuation of the higher orders will be necessary for experiments unable to discriminate against the higher order radiation.

5. *Crossed Dispersion*

If two gratings are used in tandem in such a way that their grooves are not parallel, the direction of dispersion from the second grating will be inclined to the usual direction of dispersion of both gratings. Figure 2.67 illustrates qualitatively crossed dispersion from two plane gratings. The two grating surfaces are perpendicular to a reference plane P_r, which goes through the grating centers. Rays and surfaces below this plane are shown with dashed lines, as are any hidden rays and surfaces. The first grating G_1 has its rulings perpendicular to P_r and its normal lies in P_r. It is used classically with the incident wave vector lying in P_r; therefore the direction of dispersion is parallel to P_r. The second grating, G_2, has its rulings parallel to P_r and its normal lies in P_r. The radiation it intercepts from G_1 will be separated into the zeroth orders of the different wavelengths, which will lie in P_r, and the

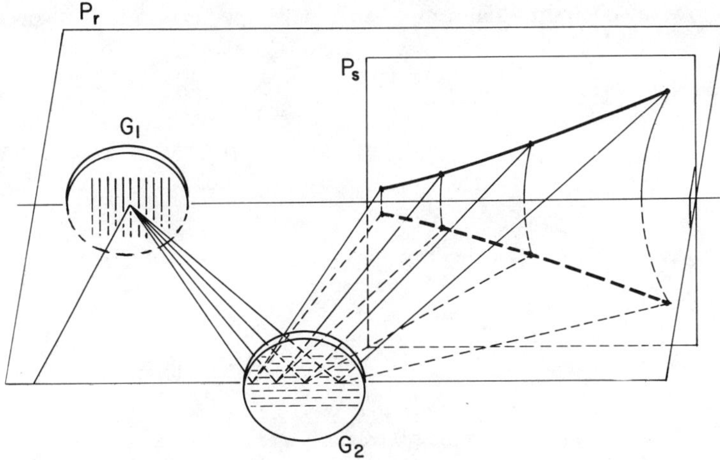

FIG. 2.67. A qualitative illustration of crossed dispersion.

higher orders that are dispersed at an angle with respect to P_r. The higher orders are shown intersecting a plane P_s that is perpendicular to P_r. The points of intersection with P_s are connected by the "spectral curve," which shows the direction of dispersion. Because the wavelengths from G_1 go into both positive and negative orders after diffraction from G_2, two spectral curves are shown, one above and one below P_r. If G_2 is blazed the relative intensities of these two sets of orders may differ considerably.

Because G_2 operates in conical difftraction, the different orders of the same wavelength will lie on a cone. Hence the positive and negative orders shown in the figure are connected by a curved line denoting the intersection of the cone and P_s.

Any wavelength λ from G_1 will also contain components of higher orders, such as $\lambda/2$. On diffraction from G_2, however, some of $\lambda/2$ forms a new spectrum, so there will be two other spectral curves lying between P_r and the two curves shown. This illustrates an important characteristic of crossed dispersion: that different orders of the same wavelength can be separated, although not completely. There will always be a component of $\lambda/2$ in λ.

The slope of the spectral curve is determined to a first approximation by the relative dispersions of the two gratings. If they have the same dispersion, the slope will be approximately unity. If that of G_1 exceeds that of G_2, the slope will be larger than unity, and vice versa.

One of the earliest crossed-dispersion devices was the echelle spectrograph (Harrison, 1949b). An echelle grating is used in very high orders (see Subsection 2.2.B.1) to produce a highly dispersed spectrum but with very small free spectral range. If the spectrum is crossed with a device of low or medium dispersion, the high orders of the echelle grating can be separated. Figure 2.68 shows a schematic diagram of an echelle spectrograph (Tousey *et al.*,

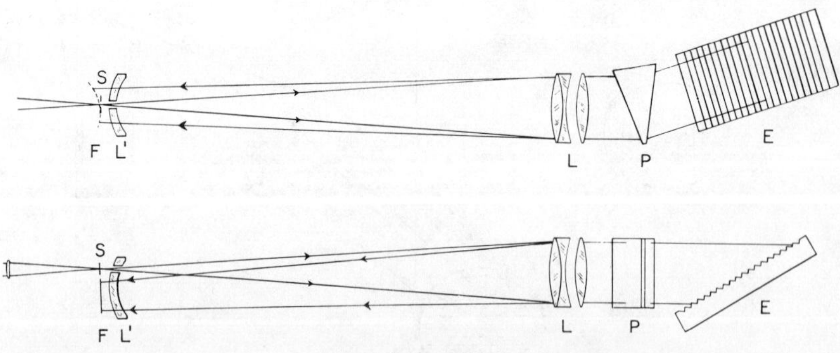

FIG. 2.68. A diagram of an echelle spectrograph used by Tousey *et al.* (1967). Crossed dispersion is achieved with a prism. A field flattening lens L′ is required because of the change in focal length with wavelength of the lens L. [From Tousey *et al.* (1967).]

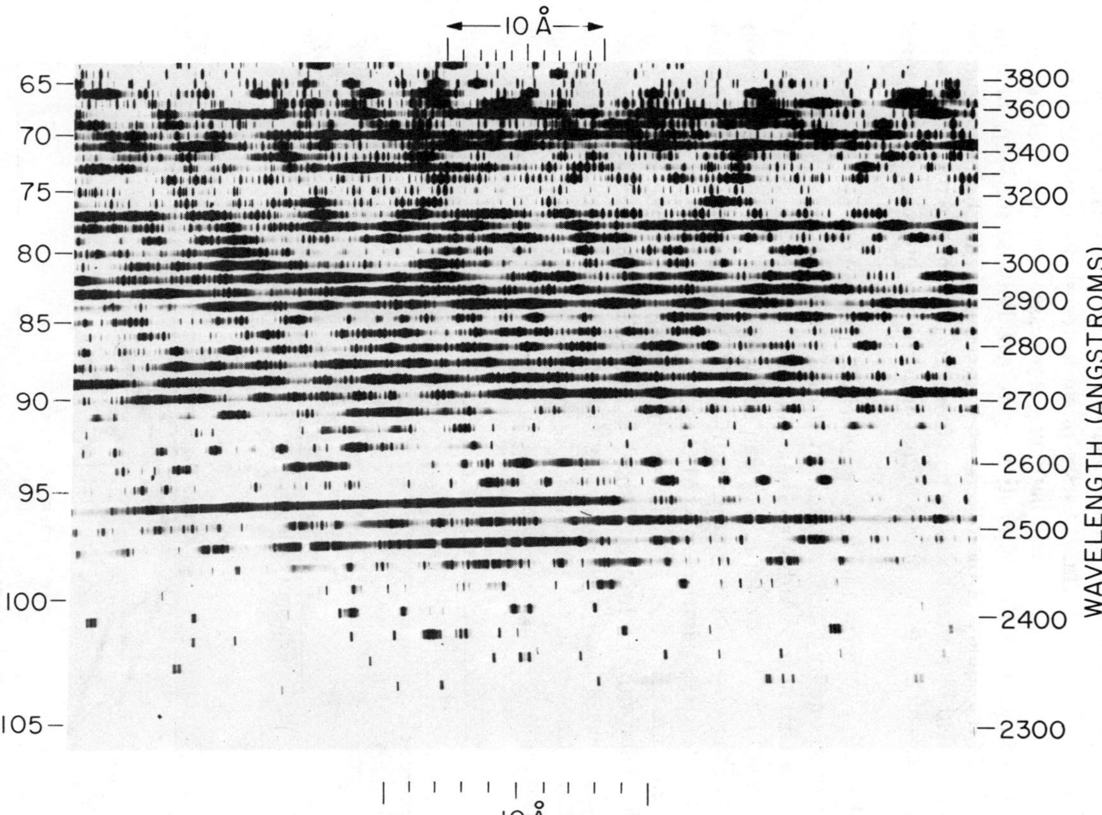

FIG. 2.69. A photograph of the iron arc spectrum obtained with the instrument of Fig. 2.68. [From Tousey *et al.* (1967).]

1967) and Fig. 2.69 shows an iron arc spectrum as recorded by that spectrograph. The entire spectrum covers an area 2.5 cm on a side, and the linear dispersion varies from 2.5 Å/mm in order 60 near 4000 Å to 1.25 Å/mm in order 120 near 2000 Å. The instrument itself was contained in a volume of 13.3 cm × 15 cm × 80 cm. It uses a prism for cross-dispersion and a field flattening lens of quartz. Field flattening is necessary because of the change in focal length L of the collimating achromat. Because the stray light increases as the square of the order (see Subsection 2.2.D.2), this instrument was preceded by a predispensing spectrometer to eliminate the visible solar spectrum, which is many orders of magnitude more intense that the desired spectrum.

The echelle spectrograph lends itself readily to use with imaging detectors such as secondary electron conduction (SEC) vidicons or charge-coupled device (CCD) arrays. Although these detectors are not responsive to VUV radiation in their usual form, they can be modified to detect radiation over most of the VUV (Tousey and Limansky, 1972; Loter *et al.*, 1981; Michels and Burstein, 1980; Burstein and Michels, 1980). As mentioned, echelle spectrometers are being used in stellar spectroscopy from satellites and could be quite useful with synchrotron radiation spectroscopy for electronic recording of extensive absorption spectra as a function of time. Although Harrison (1949b) used a prism for the crossed dispersion, as does the instrument described above, gratings can also be used.

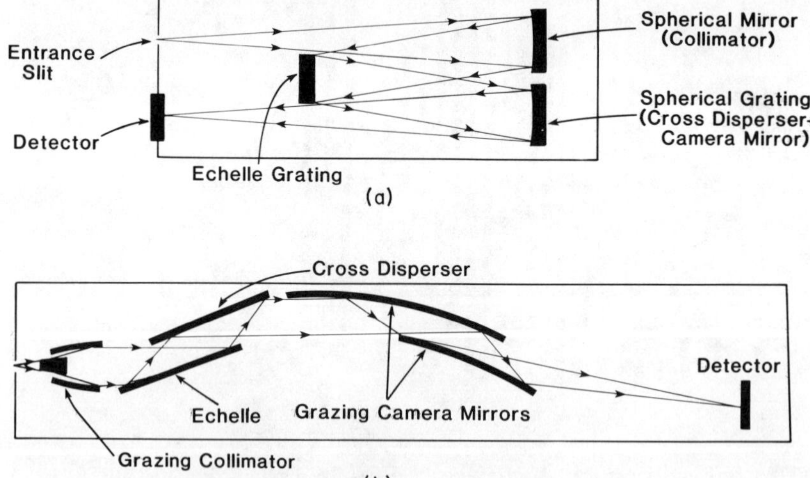

FIG. 2.70. A comparison of (a) a conventional reflecting echelle spectrograph and (b) one intended for use at grazing incidence. [From Cash (1983).]

Echelle gratings are usually used in the classical mounting, however, Cash (1983) has designed a grazing-incidence echelle spectrograph for short wavelengths that makes use of the large efficiency values obtained in conical diffraction. Figure 2.70 is a diagram of his echelle design compared with the more conventional design. This new instrument can cover large wavelength bands with high resolution and is used coupled with a two-dimensional imaging detector. The first optical component after the slit is a Wolter–Schwarzschild (WS) type II telescope set with its focus on the entrance slit, which acts as a collimator. The echelle grating is next followed by the cross-disperser (both gratings are flat) and finally by another WS telescope. Although the WS telescope is considerably more complex than a simple paraboloidal collimating mirror, it is necessary for this application because it has a small f-number with little distortion. Thus a fairly large slit can be used before the resolution is spoiled because of aberrations. The echelle grating is used in the conical diffraction mode but the cross-disperser can be used either classically or conically, depending on the application.

The use of the echelle grating in conical diffraction gives rise to slit distortion. The slit image rotates with wavelength (see Subsection 2.3.A.2) and also changes shape. Cash shows that slit distortion can be minimized by proper orientation of the entrance slit. In addition, the beam leaving the gratings no longer has an annular cross section but has been distorted into an ellipse. The second WS telescope, which Cash refers to as the camera mirror, must be carefully designed. The size of the mirror must be large enough to accept the beam, the focal length must not contribute to the blur circle and must match the detector resolution, and the field of view of the camera must be broad enough to accommodate the range of dispersion angles in the beam. Details of design fundamentals, along with two sample designs, one for the VUV and the other for the x-ray region, are given in the paper.

Crossed dispersion is also used with concave gratings, usually to reduce stray light.

6. *Plane Gratings as Beam Splitters*

The use of interferometry in the VUV, and in the infrared, has been hampered by the lack of transmitting beam splitters. Diffraction gratings are natural beam splitters and can be used in both the VUV and IR regions. A number of studies of interferometers employing grating beam splitters have been made (Barus, 1911; Weinberg and Wood, 1959; Connes, 1959; Strong and Vanasse, 1960; Yoshihara, 1963; Lohman and Bryngdahl, 1967; Munnerlyn, 1968). Despite the obvious application of these beam splitters in the VUV, there appears to be no actual use as yet; at least none has been

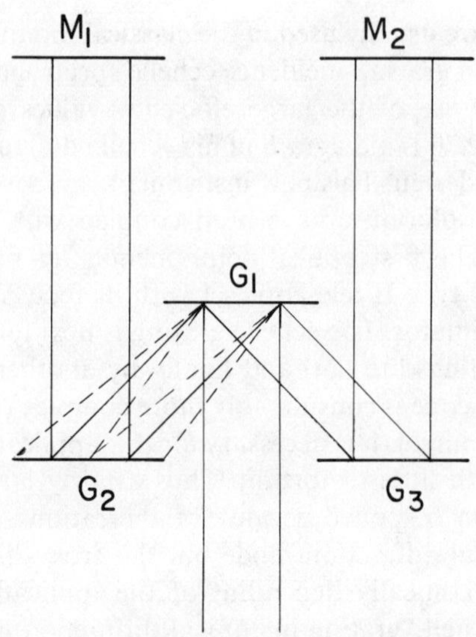

FIG. 2.71. An interferometer using a grating (G_1) as a beam splitter and two plane gratings (G_2 and G_3) as components.

reported. As an example we will consider the interferometer reported by Kruger *et al.* (1972). A schematic diagram is shown in Fig. 2.71. Parallel radiation illuminates grating G_1. This grating has symmetrical grooves so that approximately equally intense radiation is thrown into both positive and negative orders. The diffracted radiation is incident on two identical gratings, G_2 and G_3, which in turn diffract radiation to the two mirrors M_1 and M_2. The radiation is incident normally on these mirrors and is reflected back to G_2 and G_3, then diffracted back to G_1., where the two beams recombine, and finally diffracted by G_1 parallel to, but in the opposite direction to, the incoming radiation. One of the mirrors is movable along its normal. This movement is used to generate the interferogram.

The three gratings are parallel and have the same groove densities, thus they are used in zero dispersion. The bandwidth is determined by the dispersion of G_1 and the wavelength spread intercepted by G_2 and G_3.

Analyses of this instrument have been published by Kruger *et al.* (1972, 1973) and by Fonck *et al.* (1978). An instrument has been made for the 500–1000-μm spectral region and the results have been successful.

B. Concave Grating Mountings

Concavity in its general sense is not restricted to a spherical shape, but includes also toroidal, ellipsoidal, and cylindrical shapes, to mention a few possibilities. Diffraction gratings have been produced on all of the forms listed above. Perhaps the most familiar and most generally used mounting for concave spherical gratings is the Rowland circle mounting, with the Wadsworth mounting a close second. Toroidal grating mountings have also come into wide use for synchrotron radiation and are also used in soft x-ray spectrographs. A toroid is not an easy shape to make, nor is an ellipsoid, and for this reason these gratings are expensive. Replication is equally expensive, again because of the requirements placed on the figure of the blank. Cylindrical blanks are cheaper to make but have not been used to date, although some designs involving cylindrical gratings have been published and will be discussed below.

Another noticeable omission in the design of concave grating mountings has been the use of on-blaze mountings. Such a mounting is more difficult for spherical concave gratings than for plane gratings because of the focusing properties of the grating. On-blaze operation with cylindrical gratings is much simpler and may come into more widespread use in the future. In the paragraphs below, we shall discuss on-blaze operation of some concave grating mountings.

1. *Concave Grating On-Blaze Mountings*

Hulthen and Lind (1950) devised a spectrograph for photographing small portions of spectra with a blazed concave grating used always at blaze. Figure 2.72 is a schematic diagram of their arrangement. The source is placed on the grating normal at a distance of $r/(1 + \cos\beta)$, where r is the radius of the grating and β is the angle of diffraction. This point is the stigmatic point for a Wadsworth mounting. The different wavelengths are diffracted from the grating in parallel beams. A plane mirror is placed with its normal pointing toward the apex of the grating, and in a position such that the angle β is the diffraction angle corresponding to the blaze wavelength. In operation, a small band of wavelengths is diffracted to the mirror, reflected back to the grating, and brought to a focus in the vicinity of the source. Actually these wavelengths have been diffracted twice, so the resolving power is double what one would obtain with a single diffraction from the grating.

Such a mounting is quite restrictive in that for a given grating there is only one position for the mirror for which both on-blaze and stigmatic operation occur. At the expense of increasing astigmatism, the mirror can be mounted on an arm that rotates about the center of the grating. In fact, a simple mechanical arrangement can be made such that the mirror normal always points in the direction of the blaze wavelength vector.

Hunter (1982) has devised an on-blaze Rowland circle mounting, for grazing incidence, which is shown in Fig. 2.73. The upper part of the figure shows the locations of the entrance slit N, the exit slit X, and the grating. The slits are connected to the grating enclosure with extensible bellows B. The grating enclosure consists of two large flanges, F_1 and F_2, that are connected by a large diameter bellows, B. These two flanges are mechanically connected so as to pivot about an axis parallel to, and coincident with, the grating surface. Assuming the exit slit to be fixed, the wavelength is changed by moving the grating along the line perpendicular to the exit slit plane and at the same time moving the entrance slit along a curved path so as to keep all three components on the Rowland circle. There is no simple mechanical motion to maintain the proper relative positions of the three components, so a triangle, made up of three lead screws driven by computer-controlled stepping motors, must be used for this purpose. Two of the screws, each with its own stepping motor, are pivoted under the exit slit, and a third is located under the grating enclosure. The label M denotes a stepping motor and the letters in parentheses refer to distances. For example, M(N–X) is the motor that drives the screw that controls the distance between the entrance and exit slits, M(G–X) is the motor that drives the screw that controls the distance between the grating and exit slit. The letter N denotes nuts that are attached to the different optical components by swivels, if necessary, and the letters in parentheses have the same function as those associated with the stepping

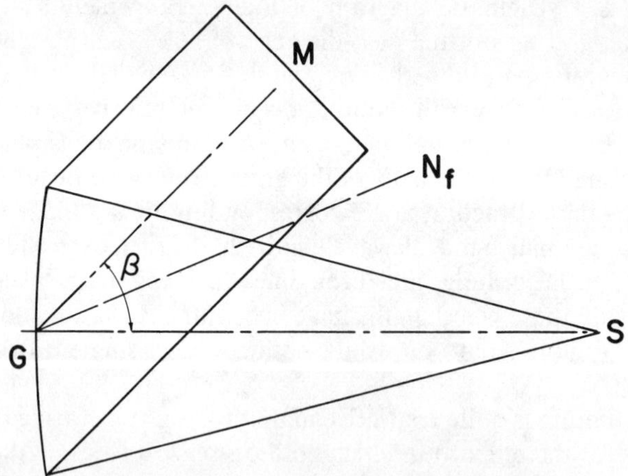

FIG. 2.72. An on-blaze spectrograph using a spherical concave grating devised by Hulthen and Lind (1950). S is the source, G the grating, M the plane mirror, N_f the facet normal, and β the diffraction angle.

motors. The swivel points are the three points of the triangle that lies on the Rowland circle.

The grating must be oriented so that the normal to the large facet N_f always divides the angle between the entrance and exit slits as seen from the grating. This is accomplished with an angle divider as shown in Fig. 2.74. Figures 2.74c and d show the angle divider and the pivot for the larger flanges, respectively; R_1 is a short rod fastened to ring R, which holds the grating mount; R_1 and N_f must be adjusted, initially, to be parallel. As F_1 and F_2 rotate about the pivot, shown in part d, a slider moves along R_1. The slider is connected to F_1 and F_2 by rods of equal length with pivots at each end; hence as F_1 and F_2 rotate, the slider moving along R_1 keeps R_1 pointing in the proper direction.

As with all on-blaze mountings, the wavelength range is limited; therefore more than one grating is required to provide a useful wavelength range. If

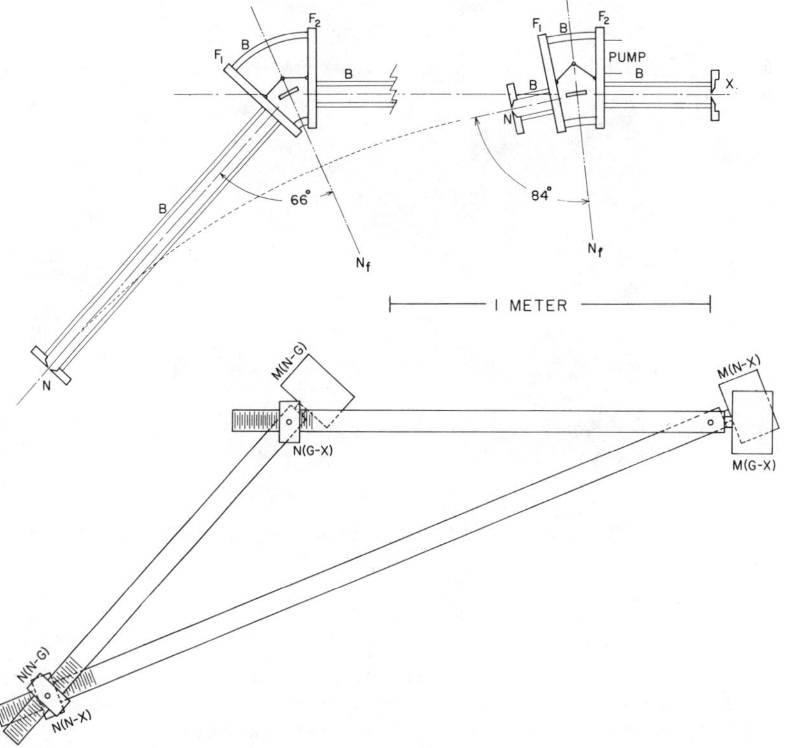

FIG. 2.73. An on-blaze Rowland-circle-mounting scanning monochromator devised by Hunter. [From Hunter (1982).]

the limiting angles are 66° and 84°, as shown in Fig. 2.73, the wavelengths from 946 to 27 Å can be covered by using the four gratings shown in Table 2.2. Sketches a and b of Fig. 2.74 show a carousel designed to carry these gratings with one in the operating position.

On-blaze Rowland circle mountings can also be made for normal incidence; however, the wavelength range is so restricted that many gratings would be required to cover a reasonable range.

Two papers have appeared suggesting the use of a cylindrical grating in a scanning monochromator. Aspnes (1982) has designed a mounting shown in Fig. 2.75. The source and exit slit are located on a line parallel to the *y* axis at S and I, respectively. The grating is located in the *x*–*y* plane with its axis

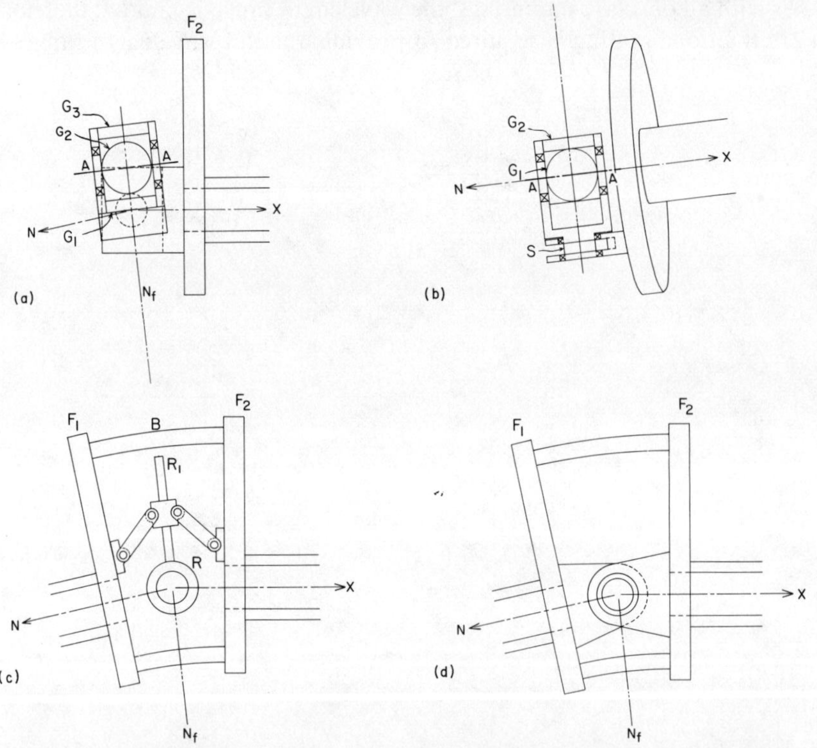

FIG. 2.74. Details of the grating mounting and the angle divider used in the monochromator of Fig. 2.73. (a), (b) Plan and elevation views of the grating carousel mounted on flange F_2. G_1 is in position for wavelength scanning while G_2 and G_3 are stored on the carousel. S is the shaft about which the rotation takes place for wavelength scanning. Rotation of the carousel about the axis AA will bring another grating into use. (c) Plan view of the angle divider that keeps the grating oriented. (d) Plan view showing how flanges F_1 and F_2 are pivoted. [From Hunter (1982).]

TABLE 2.2

WAVELENGTH LIMITS IN ANGSTROMS FOR A GRAZING INCIDENCE ON-BLAZE MONOCHROMATOR FOR GRATINGS WITH DIFFERENT GROOVE DENSITIES[a,b]

Grooves/mm	Short-wavelength limit $a = 86°$	Long-wavelength limit $a = 68°$
300	243	946
900	81	315
1167	62	243
2700	27	105

[a] From Hunter, 1982.
[b] Angles of incidence range from 68° to 86°.

of revolution on the line containing S and I. The radius of the cylinder is r_s. Angles α and β are the angles of incidence and diffraction, respectively, and do not change during a wavelength scan. Angle δ is the divergence of the incident beam. The grooves are the intersections of planes parallel to the x–z plane with the cylinder. They are not equally spaced; the spacing changes exponentially along the y axis in a predetermined manner. Changing the wavelength is accomplished by translating the grating parallel to its axis of revolution. The acceptance angles for a resolution of 0.001 are on the order of 100 mrad (6°), a value compatible with SR sources.

Aspnes has compared his design to the toroidal grating monochromator (straight, uniformly spaced grooves on the toroid) and concludes that the performance of the cylindrical grating monochromator can always be made

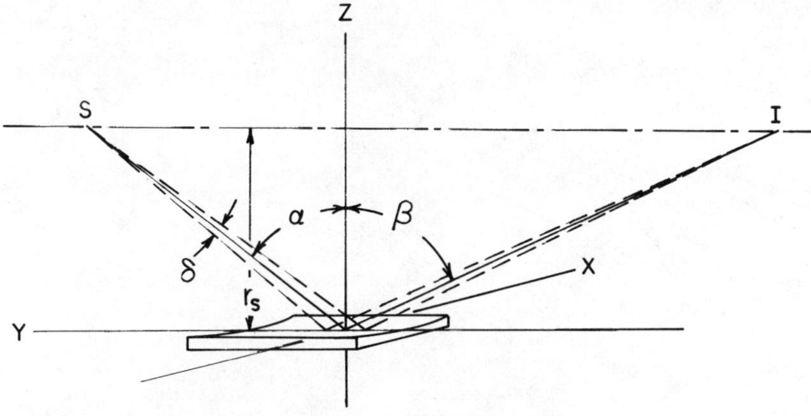

FIG. 2.75. An on-blaze monochromator using a cylindrical grating with nonuniformly spaced grooves devised by Aspnes (1982). [From Aspnes (1982).]

better than that of the toroidal grating monochromator for the same acceptance angle. Oshio *et al.* (1983) used the same scheme and also introduced curved grooves to improve the focusing.

2. *Dual Grating Mountings*

Bartoe and Brueckner (1975) have designed a spectrograph for solar spectroscopy that is essentially free of astigmatism and coma over a wide wavelength range. In this case, "essentially" means that the residual astigmatism and coma are very small. They use two conventional spherical concave gratings in tandem such that each is used in a Wadsworth mounting. A schematic diagram of their instrument, which they refer to as a symmetric tandem Wadsworth mount, is shown in Fig. 2.76. The entrance slit is placed on the normal of the first grating and at its focus. Therefore each wavelength diffracted from the first grating forms a parallel beam. A second grating, having the same radius of curvature and groove density as the first, is located on the circle defined by the radius of the first grating. Under these conditions, any wavelength impinging on the second grating from the first is diffracted along the local normal of the second grating. Thus the images formed in the focal plane are free of astigmatism and coma. The focal plane is curved and has a radius of curvature half that of the gratings. The wavelength range of the instrument is governed by the width of the second grating. They designed their instrument to cover the wavelengths between 1200 and 1700 Å, which required a grating width of 270 mm for the second grating. This large grating was made holographically because conventional ruling would have been extremely difficult, if possible.

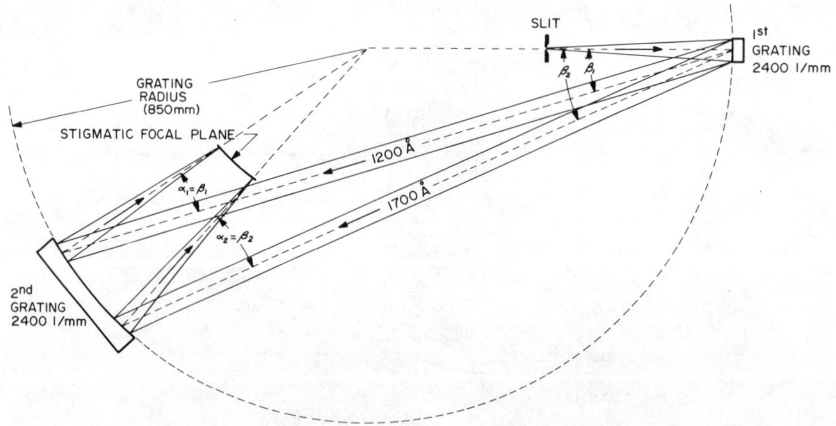

FIG. 2.76. The symmetric tandem Wadsworth mounting of Bartoe and Brueckner (1975). [From Bartoe and Brueckner (1978). Copyright 1978, Pergamon Press.]

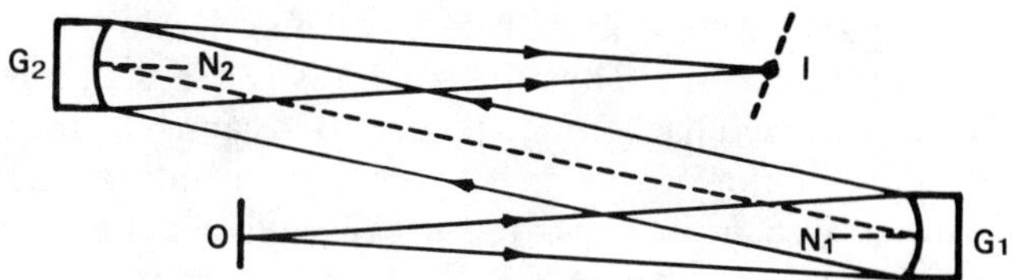

FIG. 2.77. A zero-dispersion broadband spectroheliograph used by Bartoe and Brueckner (1978). The bandwidth is given by the equation $\Delta\lambda = \omega(1 - \lambda^2 l^2)^{1/2}/lD$. [From Bartoe and Brueckner (1978). Copyright 1978, Pergamon Press.]

The authors discuss the general design considerations for the instrument and point out that there are five parameters that can be chosen at will: the groove densities and radii of curvature of the two gratings as well as the stigmatic wavelength. One possibility is to choose different radii of curvature so that magnification can be achieved if desired. As an extreme case, a plane grating can be used for the first grating. It is placed tangent to the circle defined by the radius of the second grating, i.e., substituted for the first grating in Fig. 2.76. With a plane grating, the instrument is completely free of astigmatism and can be used to obtain stigmatic spectra of objects at infinity.

The same authors have also designed a zero-dispersion broadband spectroheliograph for imaging the solar disk in a narrow band of VUV wavelengths (Bartoe and Brueckner, 1978). A diagram of the instrument is shown in Fig. 2.77. The source, S, is located on the normal of the first grating and at its focus. The second grating has its normal parallel to that of the first grating and the desired image is located on its normal and at its focus, at I. The bandwidth is determined by the size of the second grating, its distance from the first grating, and the dispersion of the first grating. According to the authors, the focal properties of this instrument are such that an extended source is imaged in a plane that is approximately perpendicular to the line joining the centers of the two gratings rather than a plane perpendicular to the second grating normal. Also, wavelengths shorter than that centered on

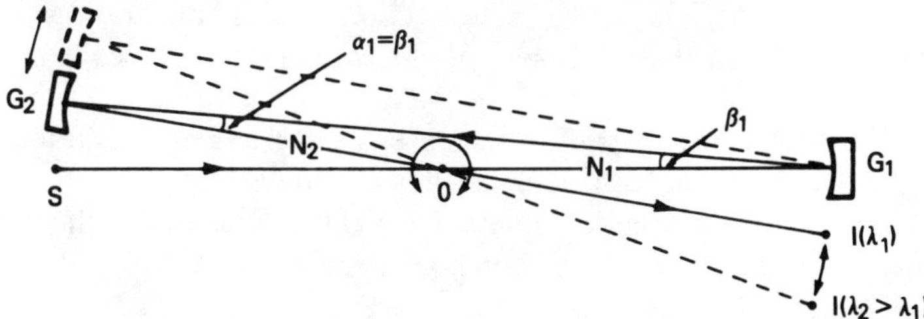

FIG. 2.78. A stigmatic, coma-free scanning spectrometer proposed by Bartoe and Brueckner (1978). [From Bartoe and Brueckner (1978). Copyright 1978, Pergamon Press.]

the second grating come to a focus before reaching I, while longer wavelengths are focused beyond I. Thus the bandpass is less than might be expected; however, there is a background illumination caused by the unfocused images. If a grid collimator is installed between the two gratings, the bandpass can be narrowed even further and the background illumination reduced considerably.

Bartoe and Brueckner (1978) have also suggested that a variation of the symmetric tandem Wadsworth mount can be used as a double-dispersion, coma-free scanning spectrometer. Their design is shown in Fig. 2.78. Two gratings, G_1 and G_2, have equal radii of curvature and equal groove densities. They are arranged so that OG_1 and OG_2 are equal. If a source S is placed at the focus of G_1 and on its normal, the diffracted beam will be parallel, and G_2 will image the source on its normal. Thus the image is essentially stigmatic and coma-free. If G_2 and the detector are mounted on a rod that pivots about O, the instrument becomes a scanning spectrometer. Because the focus of a grating in a Wadsworth mount is wavelength-dependent, $f = R/(1 + \cos\beta)$, where R is the grating radius and β is the angle of diffraction, G_1 and the detector must be made to follow a focus-correcting cam during rotation about O. This design can be made very compact because long focal lengths are not necessary to reduce aberrations.

C. Transmission Grating Mountings

Caldwell *et al.* (1981) have reported a VUV transmission grating monochromator, using a grating made by the method described by Arakawa and Caldwell (1980) (Subsection 2.2,B,7). The grating consisted of an aluminum support layer 1200 Å thick and silver strips 300 Å thick. Radiation from a condensed discharge in air at 10 torr was collected by a spherical mirror of 2-m focal length at an angle of incidence of 84°. The grating was placed in the reflected beam close to the mirror. The focal curve is approximately a $\cos^2$ curve. The authors arrived at this curve from elementary considerations of diffraction by calculating the intersection of the extreme rays, using the grating equation. As was shown in Subsection 2.2.C, plane gratings in nonparallel light have an aberration resembling coma that increases as the angle of incidence increases. For a plane transmission grating illuminated at normal incidence, the aberration increases as the angle of diffraction increases. Thus the exact focal lengths they calculated for the extreme rays were not consistent for large values of the diffraction angle, the angle of incidence, and the angle of convergence of the radiation from the mirror. Their approximate equation is

$$r = r_0 \cos^2(\theta + \varphi)/\cos^2 \varphi,$$

where r_0 is the distance from the grating to the zeroth-order focal point, φ is the angle of incidence, and θ is the diffraction angle. If the grating is rotated to increase the angle of incidence, the value of r_0 remains fixed and the curve remains a $\cos^2$ curve, but its amplitude is increased and it is symmetrical about the normal of the grating.

In testing the instrument, they were restricted to wavelengths between 170 and about 600 Å because of the transmission characteristics of the aluminum supporting layer, and they further restricted the long-wavelength values to less than 340 Å to avoid second-order lines. The detector–slit assembly was mounted on an arm that pivoted about a point not quite centered on the grating to try approximating the focal curve. The entrance and exit slits were 17 and 25 μm, respectively. The resolution they measured was about 0.8 Å at 283.5 Å, a value double the calculated value. They attribute the loss in resolution to both imprecise alignment of the components and image aberration due to the large angle of incidence on the mirror.

Caldwell *et al.* point out that wavelength scanning by rotating the grating is inadvisable. First, the wavelength changes very little as the grating is rotated, and second, because of the increase in amplitude of the focal curve, the detector would have to be translated to and from the grating as it rotates. An alternative method, for a fixed exit slit, is to choose the grating spacing and angle of incidence such that the wavelength region of interest is close to the normal of the grating, then rotate the source, focusing mirror, and grating. Because their system is small, only 90 cm from entrance to exit slit, they do not consider such a scheme impractical. A third method is to use a channel plate to record that portion of the spectrum in the neighborhood of the grating normal. Thus, for different parts of the spectrum, the grating could be rotated and the channel plate repositioned to best focus.

References

Anderson, W. A., Griffin, G. L., Mooney, C. F., and Wiley, R. S. (1965). *Appl. Opt.* **4,** 999.

Aoyagi, Y., and Namba, S. (1976). *Opt. Acta* **23,** 701.

Arakawa, E. T., and Caldwell, P. J. (1980). *Nucl. Instrum. Methods* **172,** 293.

Aspnes, D. E. (1982). *J. Opt. Soc. Am.* **72,** 1056.

Austin, S., and Stone, F. T. (1976) *Appl. Opt.* **15,** 1071.

Bach, B. W. (1983). Hyperfine, Inc., private communication.

Bartoe, J.-D. F. (1974). Naval Research Laboratory, Washington, D.C., private communication.

Bartoe, J.-D. F., and Brueckner, G. E. (1975). *J. Opt. Soc. Am.* **65,** 13.

Bartoe, J.-D. F., and Brueckner, G. E. (1978). *In* "New Instrumentation for Space Astronomy," *Proc. Plenary Meeting COSPAR, 20th* (K. A. Van Der Hucht and G. Vaiana, eds.), p. 81. Pergamon, Oxford.

Bartoe, J.-D. F., Brueckner, G. E., Purcell, J. D., and Tousey, R. (1977). *Appl. Opt.* **16,** 879.

Barus, C. (1911). "The Interferometry of Reversed and Non-Reversed Spectra." Publ. 149, Part 1, Carnegie Institute of Washington, Washington, D.C.

Beesley, M. J., and Casteldyne, J. G. (1970). *Appl. Opt.* **9,** 2721.

Bennett, J. M. (1971). Ph.D. thesis, London Univ., London.

Beutler, H. G. (1945). *J. Opt. Soc. Am.* **35,** 311.

Boggess, A., Carr, F. A., Evans, D. C., Fischel, D., Freeman, H. R., Fuechsel, C. F., Klinglesmith, D. A., Krueger, V. L., Longanecker, G. W., Moore, J. V., Pyle, E. J., Rebar, F., Sizemore, K. O., Sparks, W., Underhill, A. B., Vitagliano, H. D., West, D. K., Macchetto, F., Fitton, B., Barker, P. J., Dunford, E., Gondhalekar, P. M., Hall, J. E., Harrison, V. A. W., Oliver, M. B., Sandford, M. C. W., Vaughan, P. A., Ward, A. K., Anderson, B. E., Boksenberg, A., Coleman, C. I., Snijders, M. A. J., and R. Wilson (1978a). *Nature* **275,** 2.

Boggess, A., Bohlin, R. C., Evans, D. C., Freeman, H. R., Gull, T. R., Heap, S. R., Klinglesmith, D. A., Longanecker, G. R., Sparks, W., West, D. K., Holm, A. V., Perry, P. M., Schiffer, F. H., Turnrose, B. E., Wu, C. C., Lane, A. L., Linsky, J. L., Savage, B. D., Benvenuti, P., Cassatella, A., Clavel, J., Heck, A., Macchetto, F., Penston, M. V., Selvelli, P. L., Dunford, E., Gondhalekar, P., Oliver, M. B., Sandford, M. V. W., Stickland, D., Boksenberg, A., Coleman, C. I., Snijders, M. A. J., and Wilson, R. (1978b). *Nature* **275,** 7.

Boller, K., Haelbich, R.-P., Hogrefe, H., Jark, W., and Kunz, C. (1983). *Nucl. Instrum. Methods* **208,** 273.

Brandes, R. G., and Curran, R. K. (1971). *Appl. Opt.* **10,** 2101.

Brandt, J. C., and members of the HRS Investigation Definition and Experiment Engineering Teams (1981). *Proc. Soc. Photo-Opt. Instrum. Eng.* **279,** 183–194.

Brown, B. J., and Wilson, I. J. (1977). *Opt. Commun.* **20,** 418.

Brueckner, G. E. (1980). *Appl. Opt.* **19,** 3994.

Bryngdahl, O. (1970). *J. Opt. Soc. Am.* **60,** 140.

Burch, J. M. (1960). *Research* **13,** 2.

Burch, J. M. and Palmer, D. A. (1961). *Opt. Acta* **8,** 73.

Burstein, P., and Michels, D. J. (1980). *Appl. Opt.* **19,** 1563.

Caldwell, P. J., Arakawa, E. T., and Callcott, T. A. (1981). *Appl. Opt.* **20,** 3047.

Caruso, A. J. (1977). Goddard Space Flight Center, Greenbelt, Maryland, private communication.

Caruso, A. J., Mount, G. H., and Woodgate, B. E. (1981). *Appl. Opt.* **20,** 1764.

Cash, W. C., Jr. (1982). *Appl. Opt.* **21,** 710.

Cash, W. C., Jr. (1983). *Appl. Opt.* **22,** 3971.

Clark, K. G. (1971). *Solid State Technol.* June, p. 52; Sep., p. 48.

Connes, P. (1959). *Rev. Opt.* **38,** 198.

Cowan, J. J. (1972). *Proc. Symp. Summer School Phys. Ionized Gases, 6th* (M. V. Kurepa, ed.), p. 785. Institute of Physics, Belgrade, Yugoslavia.

Cowan, J. J., and Arakawa, E. T. (1970). *Z. Phys.* **235,** 97.

Czerny, M., and Turner, A. F. (1930). *Z. Phys.* **61,** 792.

Delvaille, J. P., Schnopper, H. W., Kallne, E., Lindau, I., Tatchyn, R., Gutchek, R. A., Bachrach, R. Z., and Dijkstra, J. H. (1980). *Nucl. Instrum. Methods* **172,** 281.

Dietrich, H., and Kunz, C. (1972). *Rev. Sci. Instrum.* **43,** 434.

Dijkstra, J. H., and Lantward, L. J. (1975). *Opt. Commun.* **15,** 300.

Dill, F. H., Tuttle, J. A., and Neureuther, A. R. (1974). *Proc. Kodak Microelectron. Seminar, San Diego, California.*

Dill, F. H., Neureuther, A. R., Tuttle, J. A., and Walker, E. J. (1975). *IEEE Trans. Electron Devices* **22,** 456.

Ebert, H. (1889). *Wied. Ann.* **38,** 489.

Fano, U. (1941). *J. Opt. Soc. Am.* **31,** 213.

Fano, U. (1948). *J. Opt. Soc. Am.* **38,** 921.
Fastie, W. G. (1952a). *J. Opt. Soc. Am.* **42,** 641.
Fastie, W. G. (1952b). *J. Opt. Soc. Am.* **42,** 647.
Finkelstein, N. A. (1951). *J. Opt. Soc. Am.* **41,** 179.
Fonck, R. J., Huppler, D. A., Roesler, F. L., Tracy, D. H., and Daehler, M. (1978). *Appl. Opt.* **17,** 1739.
Fonck, R. J., Ramsey, A. T., and Yelle, R. V. (1982). *Appl. Opt.* **21,** 2115.
Fujita, T., Nishihara, H., and Koyama, J. (1982). *Opt. Lett.* **7,** 578.
Garrett, D. L., and Tousey, R. (1977). *Appl. Opt.* **16,** 898.
Gillette, R. B., and Kenyon, B. A. (1971). *Appl. Opt.* **10,** 545.
Gillette, R. B., Hollahan, J. R., and Carlson, J. (1970). *J. Vac. Sci. Technol.* **7,** 534.
Gillieson, A. H. C. P. (1949). *J. Sci. Instrum.* **26,** 335.
Greig, J. H., and Ferguson, W. F. C. (1950). *J. Opt. Soc. Am.* **40,** 504.
Grime, G. W. (1975) Ph.D. thesis, Oxford Univ., Oxford.
Haber, H. (1950). *J. Opt. Soc. Am.* **40,** 153.
Haelbich, R.-P., Kunz, C., Rudolph, D., and Schmahl, G. (1978). *Nucl. Instrum. Methods* **152,** 127.
Hagglund, J., and Sellberg, F. (1966). *J. Opt. Soc. Am.* **56,** 1031.
Hall, J. T. (1966). *Appl. Opt.* **5,** 1051.
Hanson, W. R., and Arakawa, E. T. (1966). *J. Opt. Soc. Am.* **56,** 124.
Harada, T., and Kita, T. (1980). *Appl. Opt.* **19,** 3987.
Harada, T., Moriyama, S., and Kita, T. (1975). *Jpn. J. Appl. Phys.* **14,** Suppl. 1, 175.
Harrison, G. H. (1949a). *J. Opt. Soc. Am.* **39,** 413.
Harrison, G. H. (1949b). *J. Opt. Soc. Am.* **39,** 522.
Hessel, A., and Oliner, A. A. (1965). *Appl. Opt.* **4,** 1275.
Hettrick, M. C., and Bowyer, S. (1983). *Appl. Opt.* **22,** 3921.
Howells, M. R. (1980). *Nucl. Instrum. Methods* **177,** 127.
Huber, M. C. E., Jannitti, E., Lemaitre, G., and Tondello, G. (1981). *Appl. Opt.* **20,** 2139.
Hulthen, E., and Lind, E. (1950). *Arkiv Fyzik* **2,** 253.
Hunter, W. R. (1958). *Unpublished data.*
Hunter, W. R. (1963). *Proc. Colloq. Spectroscopicum Internationale, 10th* (E. R. Lippincott and M. Margoshes, eds.), p. 247. Spartan Books, Washington, D.C.
Hunter, W. R. (1974). "Vacuum Ultraviolet Radiation Physics," *Proc. Int. Conf. VUV Radiation Phys., 4th, Hamburg* (E-E. Koch, R. Haensel, and C. Kunz, eds.), p. 683. Pergamon-Vieweg, Braunschweig.
Hunter, W. R. (1980). *Nucl. Instrum. Methods* **172,** 259.
Hunter, W. R. (1982). *Proc. Soc. Photo-Opt. Instrum. Eng.* **315,** 19.
Hunter, W. R. (1982). *Appl. Opt.* **21,** 1634.
Hunter, W. R., and Angel, D. W. (1979). *Appl. Opt.* **18,** 3506.
Hunter, W. R., and G. Hass, (1980). *Phys. Thin Films* **11,** 1.
Hunter, W. R., and Prinz, D. K. (1977). *Appl. Opt.* **16,** 3171.
Hunter, W. R., and Rife, J. C. (1984). *Appl. Opt.* **23,** 293.
Hunter, W. R., Osantowski, J. F., and Hass, G. (1971a). *Appl. Opt.* **10,** 540.
Hunter, W. R., Mikes, T. L., Anstead, R. J., and Osantowski, J. F. (1971b). *Appl. Opt.* **10,** 2199.
Hunter, W. R., Purcell, J. D., and Steele, G. N. (1973). *Appl. Opt.* **12,** 1874.
Hunter, W. R., Mikes, T. L., and Hass, G. (1972). *Appl. Opt.* **11,** 1594.
Hunter, W. R., Williams, R. T., Rife, J. C., Kirkland, J. D., and Kabler, M. N. (1982). *Nucl. Instrum. Methods* **195,** 141.
Hunter, W. R., Hutley, M. C., Stuart, P. R., Rudolph, D., and Schmahl, G. (1977). *Int. Conf. VUV Rad. Phys., 5th, Extended Abstr.* **3**(5), 5–9.

Hutley, M. C. (1982). "Diffraction Gratings." Academic Press, New York.
Hutley, M. C., and Hunter, W. R. (1981). *Appl. Opt.* **20,** 245.
Ishiguro, E., Iwanaga, R., and Oshio, T. (1979). *J. Opt. Soc. Am.* **69,** 1530.
Jark, W., Haelbich, R.-P., Hogrefe, H., and Kunz, C. (1983). *Nucl. Instrum. Methods* **208,** 315.
Johnson, F. S., and Tousey, R. (1948). *J. Opt. Soc. Am.* **38,** 1103 (abstract).
Johnson, R. L. (1983). *In* "Handbook on Synchrotron Radiation" (E-E. Koch, ed., D. E. Eastman and Y. Farge, general eds.), Vol. 1A, p. 173. North-Holland Publ., Amsterdam.
Kallne, E. (1982). *Nucl. Instrum. Methods* **195,** 105.
Kallne, E., Schnopper, H. W., Delvaille, J. P., Van Speybroek, L. P., and Bachrach, R. Z. (1978). *Nucl. Instrumen. Meth.* **152,** 103.
Kessler, F. R. (1970). *Optik* (Stuttgartt) **32,** 254.
Kita, T., Harada, T., Nakano, N., and Kuroda, H. (1983). *Appl. Opt.* **22,** 512.
Kruger, R. A., Anderson, L. W., and Roesler, F. L. (1972). *J. Opt. Soc. Am.* **62,** 938.
Kruger, R. A., Anderson, L. W., and Roesler, F. L. (1973). *Appl. Opt.* **12,** 533.
Kunz, C., Haensel, R., and Sonntag, B. (1968). *J. Opt. Soc. Am.* **58,** 1415.
Labeyrie, A., and Flamand, J. (1969). *Opt. Commun.* **1,** 5.
Loewen, E. G. (1984). Bausch & Lomb, Inc., Rochester, New York, private communication.
Loewen, E. G., and Neviere, M. (1978). *Appl. Opt.* **17,** 1078.
Lohman, A., and Bryngdahl, O. (1967). *Appl. Opt.* **6,** 1934.
Loter, N. G., Burstein, P., Krieger, A., Ross, D., Harrison, D., and Michels, D. J. (1981). *Proc. Soc. Photo-Opt. Instrum. Eng.* **290,** 58.
Mack, J. E., Stehn, F. R., and Edlén, B. (1932). *J. Opt. Soc. Am.* **22,** 245.
McPhedran, R. C., Wilson, I. J., and Waterworth, M. D. (1973). *Optics Laser Technol.* **5,** 166.
Maystre, D., and Petit, R. (1972). *Opt. Commun.* **5,** 35.
Maystre, D., and Petit, R. (1976). *Nouv. Rev. Opt.* **7,** 165.
Meyer, C. F. (1949). "The Diffraction of Light, X-Rays, and Material Particles," p. 130. J. W. Edwards, Ann Arbor, Michigan.
Michels, D. J. (1974). *J. Opt. Soc. Am.* **64,** 662.
Michels, D. J., and Burstein, P. (1980). *Int. Conf. VUV Rad. Phys., 6th, Extended Abstr.* **3,** paper 66.
Michels, D. J., Mikes, T. L., and Hunter, W. R. (1974). *Appl. Opt.* **13,** 1223.
Michelson, A. A. (1927). "Studies in Optics," p. 103. Univ. of Chicago Press, Chicago.
Miyake, K. P., Kato, R., and Yamashita, H. (1969). *Sci. Light* **18,** 39.
Monk, G. S. (1928). *J. Opt. Soc. Am.* **17,** 359.
Muller, J., Nietz, R., and Unrau, U. (1979). *Proc. Soc. Photo-Opt. Instrum. Eng.* **192,** 244.
Munnerlyn, C. R. (1968). *Appl. Opt.* **8,** 827.
Murty, M. V. R. K. (1962). *J. Opt. Soc. Am.* **52,** 768.
Namioka, T. (1959). *J. Opt. Soc. Am.* **49,** 446.
Namioka, T. (1961). *J. Opt. Soc. Am.* **51,** 4.
Namioka, T., and Hunter, W. R. (1973). *Opt. Commun.* **8,** 229.
Nature (1978). Volume **275.**
Neupert, W. M., Epstein, G. L., and Thomas, R. J. (1981). *Space Sci. Rev.* **29,** 425.
Neureuther, A. R., and Dill, F. H. (1974). *Symp. Opt. Acoust. Microeletron.* Polytechnique Institute of New York, MRI Symposie Series, Vol. 23.
Neureuther, A. R., and Hagouel, P. I. (1974). *Electron Ion Beam Sci. Technol., 6th Int. Conf., San Francisco, California.*
Neviere, M., and Hunter, W. R. (1980). *Appl. Opt.* **19,** 2059.
Naviere, M., Maystre, D., and Hunter, W. R. (1978). *J. Opt. Soc. Am.* **68,** 1106.
Neviere, M., Flamand, J., and Lerner, J. M. (1982). *Nucl. Instrum. Methods* **195,** 183.
Noda, H., Namioka, T., and Seya, M. (1974a). *J. Opt. Soc. Am.* **64,** 1031.

Noda, H., Namioka, T., and Seya, M. (1974b). *J. Opt. Soc. Am.* **64,** 1037.
Noda, H., Namioka, T., and Seya, M. (1974c). *J. Opt. Soc. Am.* **64,** 1043.
Oshio, T., Ishiguro, E., and Iwanaga, R. (1983). *Nucl. Instrum. Methods* **208,** 297.
Palmer, E. W., Hutley, M. C., Franks, A., Verrill, J. F., and Gale, B. (1975). *Rep. Prog. Phys.* **38,** 975.
Petit, R., ed. (1980). "Electromagnetic Theory of Gratings." Springer-Verlag, Heidelberg.
Pouey, M. (1974). *J. Spectrosc. Soc. Jpn.* **23** (Suppl. 1), 67.
Pouey, M. (1978). *J. Phys. Colloq. (Orsay, Fr.)* **C4,** 189.
Pouey, M. (1980). *Nucl. Instrum. Methods* **172,** 177.
Pouey, M. (1982). *Nucl. Instrum. Methods* **195,** 407.
Pouey, M. (1983a). *C. R. Acad. Sci.* **296,** 225.
Pouey, M. (1983b). *Nucl. Instrum. Methods* **208,** 835.
Pouey, M. (1983c). *J. Opt.* **14,** 235.
Purcell, J. D. (1952). Naval Research Laboratory, Washington, D.C., private communication.
Purcell, J. D. (1953). *J. Opt. Soc. Am.* **43,** 1166.
Quincke, G. (1872). *Pogg. Ann.* **146,** 1.
Lord Rayleigh (1899a). "Scientific Papers," Vol. 1, p. 157. Cambridge Univ. Press, London and New York.
Lord Rayleigh (1899b). "Scientific Papers," Vol. 1, p. 160. Cambridge Univ. Press, London and New York.
Lord Rayleigh (1899c). "Scientific Papers," Vol. 1, p. 199. Cambridge Univ. Press, London and New York.
Lord Rayleigh (1899d). "Scientific Papers," Vol. 1, p. 504. Cambridge Univ. Press, London and New York.
Lord Rayleigh (1902). "Scientific Papers," Vol. 3, p. 112. Cambridge Univ. Press, London and New York.
Lord Rayleigh (1903). "Scientific Papers," Vol. 4, p. 226. Cambridge Univ. Press, London and New York.
Lord Rayleigh (1907). *Philos. Mag.* **14,** 60.
Reeves, E. M., Huber, M. C. E., and Timothy, J. G. (1977). *Appl. Opt.* **16,** 837.
Roger, A., and Breidne, M. (1980). *Opt. Commun.* **35,** 299.
Roszhart, T. (1984). Perkin–Elmer Corp., Norwalk, Conn., private communication.
Rowland, H. A. (1883a). *Philos. Mag.* **16,** 197.
Rowland, H. A. (1883b). *Philos. Mag.* **16,** 210.
Rudolph, D., and Schmahl, G. (1967a). *Umsch. Wiss. Tech.* **67,** 225.
Rudolph, D., and Schmahl, G. (1967b). *Mitt. Astron. Ges.* **23,** 46.
Sai, T., Seya, M., and Namioka, T. (1968). *Sci. Light* **17,** 11.
Samson, J. A. R. (1967). "Techniques of Vacuum Ultraviolet Spectroscopy." Wiley, New York.
Sawyer, R. A. (1963). "Experimental Spectroscopy," 3rd ed. Dover, New York.
Sayce, L. A., and Franks, A. (1964). *Proc. R. Soc. (London)* **A282,** 353.
Schmahl, G. (1974). "Vacuum Ultraviolet Radiation Physics," *Proc. Int. Conf. VUV Rad. Phys., 4th, Hamburg* (E-E. Koch, R. Haensel, and C. Kunz, eds.), p. 667. Pergamon-Vieweg, Braunschweig.
Schroeder, D. J. (1966). *Appl. Opt.* **5,** 545.
Schroeder, D. J. (1970). *J. Opt. Soc. Am.* **60,** 1022.
Seya, M. (1952). *Sci. Light* **2,** 8.
Seya, M., Namioka, T., and Sai, T. (1967). *Sci. Light* **16,** 138.
Shams, M. K., Botez, D., and Wang, S. (1979). *Opt. Lett.* **4,** 96.
Sheridon, N. K. (1968). *Appl. Phys. Lett.* **12,** 316.
Singh, M., and Majumder, K. (1969). *Sci. Light* **18,** 57.

Smyth, H. T. (1935). *J. Opt. Soc. Am.* **45,** 312.

Sparrow, C. M. (1919). *Astrophys. J.* **49,** 65.

Speer, R. J., Turner, D., Johnson, R. L., Rudolph, D., and Schmahl, G. (1974). *Appl. Opt.* **13,** 1258.

Speer, R. J., Chrisp, M., Turner, D., Mrowka, S., and Tregidgo, K. (1979). *Appl. Opt.* **18,** 2003.

Spencer, G. H., and Murty, M. V. R. K. (1962). *J. Opt. Soc. Am.* **52,** 672.

Stroke, G. W. (1967). *In* "Handbuch der Physik" (S. Flugge, ed.), Vol. 19, p. 426. Springer-Verlag, Berlin.

Strong, J. (1936). *Phys. Rev.* **48,** 480.

Strong, J., and Vanasse, G. (1960). *J. Opt. Soc. Am.* **50,** 113.

Sugahara, K., Kita, T., and Shimotakahara, T. (1974). *J. Spectrosc. Soc. Jpn.* **23** (Suppl. 1), 21.

Tousey, R., and Limansky, I. (1972). *Appl. Opt.* **11,** 1025.

Tousey, R., Purcell, J. D., Austin, W. E., Garrett, D. L., and Widing, K. G. (1964). *Space Res.* **4,** 703.

Tousey, R., Purcell, J. D., and Garrett, D. L. (1967). *Appl. Opt.* **6,** 365.

Tousey, R., Bartoe, J.-D. F., Brueckner, G. E., and Purcell, J. D. (1977). *Appl. Opt.* **16,** 870.

Verrill, J. F. (1970). *Opt. Acta* **17,** 747.

Verrill, J. F. (1973). *J. Phys. E.* **6,** 1199.

Verrill, J. F. (1975). *J. Phys. E.* **8,** 522.

Verrill, J. F. (1978). *Opt. Acta* **25,** 531.

Weast, R. C., ed. (1968). "Handbook of Chemistry and Physics," 49th ed., p. F-18. Chemical Rubber Company, Cleveland, Ohio.

Weinberg, F. J., and Wood, N. B. (1959). *J. Sci. Instrum.* **36,** 227.

Werner, W. (1967). *Appl. Opt.* **6,** 1691.

Werner, W. (1970). Imaging properties of diffraction gratings. Thesis, Delft Univ., Delft.

Werner, W. (1977a). *Appl. Opt.* **16,** 2078.

Werner, W. (1977b). Institute of Applied Physics, Delft, The Netherlands, private communication.

Werner, W., and Visser, H. (1981). *Appl. Opt.* **20,** 487.

West, J. B., Codling, K., and Marr, G. V. (1974). *J. Phys. E.* **7,** 137.

Wilson, I. J., and Brown, B. (1976). "Diffraction Grating Groove Profiles," Report DGRG 76/2, Dept. of Physics, Univ. of Tasmania, Hobart, Tasmania, Australia.

Wilson, M. E. (1982). *Appl. Opt.* **21,** 537.

Wolter, H. (1952a). *Ann. Phys.* (*Leipzig*) **10,** 94.

Wolter, H. (1952b). *Ann. Phys.* (*Leipzig*) **10,** 286.

Wood, R. W. (1902). *Philos. Mag.* **4,** 396.

Wood, R. W. (1910). *Philos. Mag.* **20,** 770.

Yoshihara, K. (1963). *Jpn. J. Appl. Phys.* **2,** 818.

Chapter **3**

Mass Spectrometric Techniques

EDMOND MURAD

AIR FORCE GEOPHYSICS LABORATORY
HANSCOM AIR FORCE BASE
BEDFORD, MASSACHUSETTS

	List of Abbreviations	182
3.1.	Introduction	182
3.2.	Ion Sources	183
	A. Electron Impact	184
	B. Surface Ionization	186
	C. Chemical Ionization	187
	D. Photon Impact	189
	E. Field Ionization	190
	F. Radioactive Sources	191
	G. Discharges	193
	H. Spark Sources	195
	I. Laser Desorption	195
	J. Sources of Negative Ions	196
3.3.	Major Types of Mass Spectrometers	197
	A. Magnetic Analyzers	197
	B. Double-Focusing Mass Spectrometers	199
	C. Quadrupole, Monopole, and 3-D Quad Mass Filters	200
	D. Time-of-Flight Mass Analyzers	204
	E. Ion Cyclotron Resonance	206
3.4.	Detectors	209
	A. Photographic Plates	209
	B. Single Collector	210
	C. Electron Multipliers	211
	D. RF Absorption in ICR	216
3.5.	Uses of Mass Spectrometry	216
	A. Isotope Analysis, Geochemistry, and Isotope Separation	216
	B. Analytical Chemistry	218
	C. Analysis of Solids	221
	D. Composition Measurements in the Atmosphere	223
	E. High-Temperature Mass Spectrometry and Thermochemistry	226
	F. Ion–Molecule Reactions	230

SPECTROMETRIC TECHNIQUES, VOL. IV

ISBN 0-12-710404-6

G. Ionization Potentials and Ion Thermochemistry 236
H. Miscellaneous Comments 240
References 240

List of Abbreviations

CCEM	continuous-channel electron multiplier
CI	chemical ionization
EI	electron impact
FAB	fast atom bombardment
FD	field desorption
FI	field ionization
FT-ICR	Fourier transform ion cyclotron resonance
GC/MS	gas chromatograph coupled to mass spectrometer
ICR	ion cyclotron resonance
LC/MS	liquid chromatograph coupled to mass spectrometer
MPI	multiphoton ionization
MS	mass spectrometry
MS/MS	mass spectrometer coupled to another mass spectrometer
PES	photoelectron spectroscopy
PI	photoionization
Quad	quadrupole mass filter
Quistor	quadrupole ion storage
SI	surface ionization
SIMS	secondary ion mass spectrometry
SIFT	selected ion flow tube
TOF	time-of-flight

3.1. Introduction

Since J. J. Thomson's (1897) first measurement of m/e for a beam of negatively charged particles (called *cathode rays* and consisting mainly of electrons) and Wien's (1898) determination of m/e for a beam of positively charged particles (called *kanalstrahlen*), mass spectrometry has evolved from an esoteric academic research subject into a rather commonplace and varied research technique. This transition was aided by two outstanding experimentalists who realized quite early its potential for isotope determination and for chemical analysis: Dempster (1916, 1918) and Aston (1919, 1920). It is not the purpose of this review to provide a historical description of the subject; an excellent summary of the earliest work is given by Thomson and Thomson (1928), while the history of later developments is available in books by Duckworth (1958), Beynon (1960), and Kiser (1965) and a brief historical review by Beynon and Morgan (1978).

Two urgent needs contributed to the early conversion of mass spectrometry into a common analytical technique: (1) the need to analyze accurately the contents of crude oil, and (2) the potential use of mass spectrometry for isotope separation. The first need was largely spurred by research done by or sponsored by oil companies [see, for example, Hood and O'Neal (1959) and Carlson *et al.* (1963)], while the latter was largely spurred by research done during World War II under the auspices of the Manhattan Project.

The purpose of this review is to summarize briefly the current state of the subject. Naturally, the references are very selective, since in the current year thousands of papers dealing with mass spectrometry will be published. It is hoped, however, that the reader will become familiar enough with the subject to be able to use a variety of bewildering acronyms with ease. Where possible, reference will be made to other publications that treat a given topic more fully.

Briefly, a mass spectrometer has three parts: (1) an ion source, (2) an analyzer to separate the ions according to their mass, and (3) a detector to measure the abundance of a given ion. These parts will be discussed in that order separately before proceeding to a discussion of some of the uses of mass spectrometry. Before proceeding, however, it would be worthwhile to define two terms. *Fragmentation:* When a molecule (e.g., AB) is excited by an energy above its ionization potential, it may, if the energy is sufficiently high, dissociatively ionize (e.g., into $A^+ + B$, $B^+ + A$, or both). *Mass spectrum:* In a given method of ionization (e.g., electron impact) and at a given energy (e.g., 70 eV), the molecule may fragment into many different ionized species. The pattern of abundance of each ion is characteristic of a particular molecule and is called the mass spectrum. The early uses of maxs spectrometry for analysis of oil centered on compiling the mass spectra of many thousands of compounds, and much of this work was coordinated by the American Petroleum Institute.

3.2. Ion Sources

Because of the limited scope of this review, only those ion sources which have received the most attention in terms of usage will be described. An ion source converts neutral molecules into ions; the ions are then extracted from their point of formation by an electrostatic lens, which focuses them and injects them into a mass analyzer. A typical electrostatic lens is shown in Fig. 3.1. In this review the lens will not be considered further and the discussion will concentrate on the different ways of generating ions. Inghram

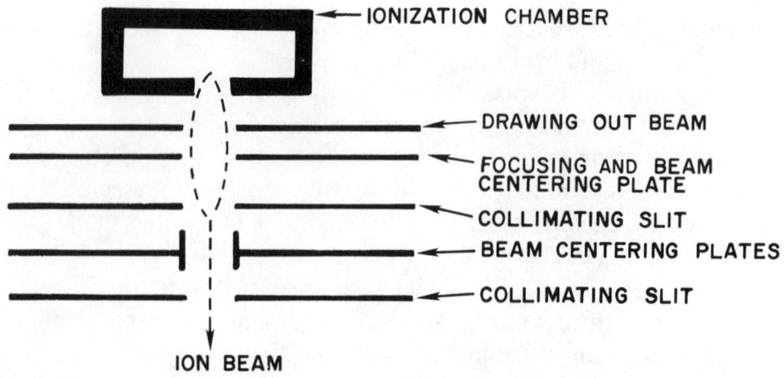

FIG. 3.1. Typical ion lens.

(1948), Barnard (1953), and Kerwin (1956) have excellent discussions of electrostatic lenses and their use in mass spectrometry. In addition, Klemperer and Barnett (1971), Grivet (1972), and El-Kareh and El-Kareh (1970) have written monographs devoted solely to this subject.

A. Electron Impact

In this method, ionization takes place when electrons with large kinetic energies collide with neutral gas molecules, causing ionization:

$$A + e \rightarrow A^+ + e. \tag{3.1}$$

The most common source of electrons for this type of work is a filament (generally a ribbon having a cross section 0.001 in. thick × 0.030 in. wide) heated to 2000–3000 K, at which temperature most metals emit electrons. The electron current density that is obtainable from a filament depends on the work function of the filament material and on the temperature. The relationship of these quantities is given by the Richardson equation [see Kaminsky (1965)], which has the form

$$i_e \propto T^2 \exp(-\beta\phi/T), \tag{3.2}$$

where i_e is the electron current density, T the filament temperature, ϕ the work function, and β a proportionality constant. The emitted electrons are accelerated to some potential and enter a field-free region (the ion box), where they collide with the gas: a sketch of a typical ion source is shown in Fig. 3.2. The electrons that are neither scattered nor deflected in the ionization process exit the ion box and are collected by the trap. The filament current is controlled in one of two ways: (1) the trap current is constant, or (2) the

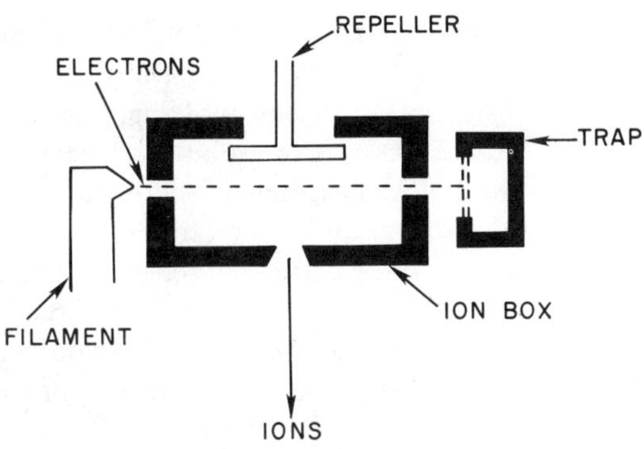

FIG. 3.2. Ion source.

total electron emission current is constant. The ions that are formed in the ion box are gently pushed out by a repeller field (low voltages of the order of 1 to 3 V are used so as not to affect the electron energy). The number of ions that are eventually detected is given by the expression

$$[A^+] = S \cdot [A] \cdot \sigma_i \cdot l \cdot [e], \tag{3.3}$$

where brackets denote number densities, S the sensitivity of the mass spectrometer (including such factors as collection efficiency of the ion optics, transmission of the analyzer, and efficiency of the detector), σ_i the ionization cross section at a given electron energy, l the effective path length, and e the electron current. While the ion current I^+ and the ion count rate $[A^+]$ are directly proportional to the pressure, [A], the electron current, and l, there are practical limits to how much these quantities can be increased. At pressures greater than 10^{-4} torr, ion–molecule reactions and scattering out of the repeller field begin to affect (adversely) the sensitivity and the mass spectrum. In addition, at high ion source pressures, enough gas may begin to reach the hot filament that it may burn out (especially if the gas is an oxidizing gas). Space charge effects limit the electron current (the limit on the electron density is different for each ion source and will depend on the electron energy, the ion source geometry, and the field lines). Indeed, the effect of space charges has been purposely incorporated into the design of some ion sources [e.g., Plumlee (1957)]. Moreover, since increasing the electron current entails increasing the filament temperature, the energy distribution of the electrons is altered by increasing the high-energy tail of the Maxwellian curve, causing (sometimes) a change in the fragmentation pattern. In analytical applications, the electron energy is maintained at a high value ($\sim$70 eV) so that the energy spread, which is of the order of

$\sim$0.5 eV (Franzen and Porter, 1975), is not a serious handicap for most applications. There are also practical limits to the path length, since scattering of ions by background gas and scattering by fringe fields become important loss mechanisms. Nonetheless, there are many specially designed electron impact sources for special applications which try to circumvent one or more of these limitations. For example, in an attempt to reduce the thermal heating from a hot filament, a cold electron source utilizing electrons ejected from photocathodes by optical radiation has been designed (Testerman *et al.*, 1965); the electron energy distribution for such a source is higher than for the hot filament source. Likewise, efficient electron impact ion sources for measuring the electron impact cross sections (Crawford, 1968), for measuring weakly bound molecular beams (Parks *et al.*, 1971), and for low-pressure work (Koontz and Denton, 1981) have been described.

A major disadvantage of electron impact is the often complex fragmentation pattern that is generated. This complexity is compounded when isotopic (contributions can be resolved (as in high-resolution mass spectrometry of organic compounds), a fact that has led to the development of libraries of mass spectra (American Petroleum Institute Mass Spectral Library). In some applications this complexity has served to provide unambiguous identification of compounds and their mixtures, as, for example, in the fingerprinting of oil spills. A further complication arises when a molecule does not have a stable parent ion and ionizes only by fragmentation. The great advantage of electron impact is that it is a universal method of ionization.

B. Surface Ionization

This source of ions, utilized by Dempster (1918) in his pioneering work, was first used by Gehrcke and Reichenheim (1906) to study *kanalstrahlen.* It has been used for numerous measurements of isotopic structure of metallic species [cf. Inghram and Hayden (1954)] and for analysis of elemental composition of solids. Briefly, this phenomenon refers to the desorption of ions from a hot metal surface when the latter is exposed to neutral atoms. For this to happen, the atom that is being ionized must transfer an electron to the hot filament surface. The ease with which the atom loses an electron (i.e., its ionization potential) and the ease with which the filament will accept an electron (i.e., its work function) determine the probability that the neutral atom will be ionized. The understanding of this phenomenon is associated with Langmuir, who, in a study of the desorption of Cs^+ from a hot tungsten filament (Langmuir and Kingdom, 1925), made use of the Saha equation (1920, 1921) to derive the fractional abundance of ions desorbed from the surface,

$$N^+/N^0 \propto \exp[W - I)A/T], \tag{3.4}$$

where N^+/N^0 is the ratio of ions to neutrals desorbed from the hot surface, W the work function of the metal (filament), I the ionization potential of the atom to be ionized, T the filament temperature, and A a constant ($A = e/k$, where e is the electronic charge and k is the Boltzmann constant. Equation (3.4) is referred to as the Langmuir–Saha equation. The ratio N^+/N^0 and the desorption energies of the ions and neutrals have been measured, and the results have been consistent with the terms of the Langmuir–Saha equation (Zazula, 1968). A fairly complete discussion of this topic is given by Kaminsky (1965).

The Langmuir–Saha equation shows that N^+/N^0 increases as $(W - I)$, which means that essentially the method is ideal for the ionization of metals having low ionization potentials. In practice, the metal that is to be ionized is deposited on the hot filament either as a vapor [e.g., Moon and Oliphant (1932) studied the surface ionization of potassium from hot tungsten by impinging the vapor on the surface] or by the deposition of a salt containing the metal in question on the filament before heating (Dempster, 1918; Blewett and Jones, 1936). Other, more complex, arrangements, such as the use of multiple filaments, have been described (Inghram and Chupka, 1953), and filaments that are coated with other materials (e.g., thoriated tungsten or tungsten–rhenium), which increases their yield, have been used (Husmann, 1966; Persky *et al.*, 1968). In any case, the most common metals for surface ionization are Pt, W, Rh, and Re since they have the largest work functions, 5.65, 4.55, 4.98, and ~5 eV, respectively (Weast, 1981). As mentioned above, special alloys can sometimes raise the value of W enough to increase the ionization to an acceptable value.

The disadvantages of surface ionization are: (a) it is limited to low-ionization-potential atoms; (b) contamination is a serious problem, since the ionic abundance depends on the ionization potential; for example, a sample of Al_2O_3 containing 0.1% impurity of K or Na may show $K^+/Al^+ \sim 1$ (Murad, 1980, unpublished data); (c) sample depletion necessitates frequent opening of the mass spectrometer; and (d) excited states of ions are sometimes populated (Murad, 1982). The chief advantage of this method is that it yields a relatively pure beam of the ions.

C. Chemical Ionization

This relatively new method of ionization (Munson and Field, 1966) has quickly assumed a position of predominance for organic and biomedical applications [cf. Munson (1971), Field (1972a,b) and Levsen (1980)]. The method is essentially a proton transfer process. When a mixture of gases A and B is admitted to the ion source of a mass spectrometer and ionized by electron impact (or some other method), the ratio $A^+/B^+ \sim A/B$ (provided the electron impact ionization cross sections are approximately equal). When A ≫ B, most of the ions are A^+. When the pressure of A is very high (e.g., 1 torr), A^+ reacts with A to form ionic products, which may be more reactive with B. This is best illustrated by the case that Munson and Field (1966) initially used, namely, chemi-ionization using CH_4 as the reactant ion. When the pressure of CH_4 is raised to ~1 torr, the following reactions take place:

$$CH_4 + e \rightarrow CH_4^+ + 2e, \tag{3.5}$$

$$CH_4^+ + CH_4 \rightarrow CH_5^+ + CH_3. \tag{3.6}$$

The proton affinity of CH_4 is 5.51 ± 0.05 eV [see Hartman *et al.* (1979)] and reaction (3.6) has a rate constant of 1.5×10^{-9} cm^3 $molecule^{-1}$ s^{-1} (Albritton, 1978). If a second component, B, is present, proton transfer may take place:

$$CH_5^+ + B \rightarrow BH^+ + CH_4. \tag{3.7}$$

Reactions such as (3.7) are fast because many molecules seem to form stable ionic adducts. Dissociative proton transfer can also result, leading to the formation of fragment ions, but the resulting mass spectrum, which is characteristic of B, is much simpler than that obtained by electron impact. Table 3.1 shows an example of the difference in the fragmentation pattern obtained

TABLE 3.1

MAJOR FRAGMENT IONS FORMED BY CHEMI-IONIZATION AND BY ELECTRON IMPACT OF TRI-*n*-BUTYLAMINE (m/e = 185)[a]

	Ion intensity	
m/e	Chemi-ionization	Electron impact
29		10.4%
41		6.3%
57		4.0%
100		7.8%
142	19.9%	29.6%
170	3.5%	
184[b]	23.1%	
185[c]	10.8%	
186[d]	21.1%	

[a] Data taken from Munson and Field (1966).
[b] Loss of H atom from parent ion.
[c] Parent ion, formed by charge transfer.
[d] Proton transfer product.

by the chemical ionization and by the electron impact of tri-*n*-butylamine. Generally, the reactant gas (in this case CH_4) is much more abundant than the target gas (i.e., B), a ratio of ~1000 being reasonable. Of course, ions other than CH_5^+ can be used for chemical ionization, since ions other than H^+ can also attach to molecules with a seeming stabilization. Of particular interest in this connection have been the alkali ions, which have been used to analyze, for example, sugars (Röllgen *et al.*, 1977).

Negative ions have also been used to generate chemical ionization spectra. For example, Burke *et al.* (1982) used OH^- as chemical ionization agents, viz.,

$$OH^- + MH \rightarrow M^- + H_2O, \tag{3.8}$$

where MH is a hydrocarbon. Indeed, this method has been used to fingerprint oils. Similarly, Cl^- has been used for analysis (Morgan *et al.*, 1983).

A disadvantage of this method is that the high pressures used can pose serious problems for the filament, high voltages, and the associated vacuum system. Some of the requirements of the apparatus have been discussed by Mather and Todd (1979). Exotic filaments that operate at very low temperatures ($\leq 100°C$) have been designed in order to reduce fragmentation of weakly bound molecules [see, for example, Kelner *et al.* (1983)].

D. Photon Impact

A historical survey of photoionization in general is given by Marr (1967), while a review of this method of ionization for mass spectrometry has been given by Reid (1971). Briefly, however, it appears that the first attempt to use photoionization as a source of ions for mass spectrometric studies was made by Lossing and Tanaka (1956), who used a krypton resonance lamp ($\lambda = 1236$ and 1165 Å) separated from the ion source by a lithium fluoride window. In these experiments 1,3-butadiene and propane were studied, and the results indicated that photoionization gave much simpler mass spectra than electron impact, as Table 3.2 shows. Soon after these experiments, Hurzeller *et al.* (1957, 1958) described an elegant experiment in which they used the continuum radiation from a hydrogen lamp, dispersed through a 1-m monochromator, as a source of ionization. This and subsequent work (Schönheit, 1957; Steiner *et al.*, 1961; Berkowitz and Chupka, 1964; Murad and Inghram, 1964; Dibeler *et al.*, 1965) developed photoionization into a powerful tool of mass spectrometry, particularly after the development of differentially pumped helium light sources, which extended the energy range to 584 Å (Brion, 1965; Villarejo *et al.*, 1966; Beynon *et al.*, 1967). The method has given superb results on energy thresholds and ionization potentials. Attempts to adapt it to analytical work (Poschenrieder and Warneck, 1966) because of the great simplicity of the mass spectra have not succeeded so

TABLE 3.2

MAJOR IONS FORMED BY PHOTON AND ELECTRON IMPACT OF 1,3-BUTADIENE (C_4H_6)[a]

	Ion intensity	
m/e	Photon impact	Electron impact (70 eV)
26		6.6%
27		17.6%
28		12.5%
37		1.1%
38		1.5%
39	1.5%	22%
49		1.5%
50		5.1%
51		4.8%
52		2.6%
53	1.6%	9.5%
54	93.7%	15.2%

[a] Data taken from Lossing and Tanaka (1956).

far because of the very cumbersome apparatus and the low sensitivity. This situation may change in the near future because advances in laser techniques have resulted in the development of multiphoton ionization (MPI) sources that promise to eliminate both disadvantages [see, for example, Lubman *et al.* (1980) and references contained therein, Hunt (1982), Stuke (1982), and Bernstein (1982)].

E. FIELD IONIZATION

The idea for this type of ion source arose from the early experiments on the field emission microscope (Müller, 1951), and its first use to obtain mass spectra seems to have been by Inghram and Gomer (1954). Reviews of the subject have been given by Beckey (1978) and Robertson (1972). Much of the actual development of the technique and its adaptation to analytical mass spectrometry has been due to the determination of H. D. Beckey, who propounded the simplicity of the spectra obtained by this means (Beckey, 1962). To understand this phenomenon we may think of an atom as a positive core bound to an electron by some large potential. If the atom is adsorbed on a metal layer and an external electric field larger than the binding energy of the electron to the ion is applied, then there is a chance that the ion and electron will separate and that the ion will be pulled off the metal plate, while the electron tunnels into the metal. In practice, the experiment is

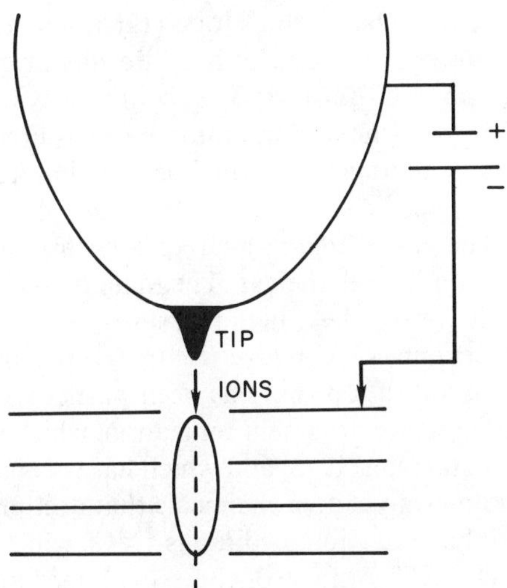

FIG. 3.3. Field ionization source.

performed on the apparatus sketched in Fig. 3.3. The tip from which the material to be ionized is desorbed is made of a very fine wire (generally, but not always, tungsten wire is used; the wire diameter is of the order of 0.01 mm [see Levsen and Beckey (1974)]). The molecule to be ionized is either introduced as a gas or coated on the tip as a solid. The field between the tip and the extracting plate may be of the order of 10^{10} V/m [e.g., Hanson (1975)]. The details of the process of ionization are complicated and fragmentation of the ion can take place in a number of ways (on the tip, just before desorption, or just before adsorption), leading to ions having different kinetic energy spectra (Jason, 1967). Mass spectra obtained in this way are again simpler than those obtained by electron impact, although this advantage is overshadowed by the complex instrumentation and by the care that has to be taken in preparing the ionizing surface, whether that be a tip or some other sharply defined surface (Beckey, 1969). Nonetheless, the method has had a number of specialized applications, such as the determination of Rydberg states of atoms (Vaille and Duong, 1979) and analysis of compounds for biochemical assay (Levsen, 1980). Other variations of this method have been described for special applications, such as fingerprinting oil spills (Aberth *et al.*, 1974).

F. Radioactive Sources

Natural radiation is known to cause ionization, but the utilization of radioactive sources for mass spectrometric work began with the need to work at high pressures. Kebarle and Hogg (1965) and Hogg and Kebarle (1965) described a source consisting of a ^{210}Po α-emitter, which operated at pressures between 5 and 200 torr. This source was used to study ion–molecule reactions in ethylene and in ammonia. A source that has become more universal is the β-emitter ^{63}Ni, which is used in atmospheric pressure ionization (API) mass spectrometry (Carroll *et al.*, 1973, 1981). Basically, ionization occurs when gas at high pressure passes through a cylinder made of ^{63}Ni. The β-radiation ionizes the gas. The main difficulty in API is posed by the need to sample ions at these high pressures, since ion–molecule reactions and cooling by expansion can give rise to extraneous masses.

A related source of ionization that has been particularly useful for high-mass analysis has been fission fragment ionization, which was first proposed by Macfarlane and Torgerson (1976) and which has become important in the analysis of solid, biologically active chemicals that decompose when vaporized. In this method the ionization medium is ^{252}Cf, which decays mostly by emission of α-particles (97%); most of the remainder (about 3%) proceeds by spontaneous fission (Metta *et al.*, 1965). The spontaneous fission fragments have typical double-humped mass distributions with peak intensities at masses 108 and 143 (Schmitt *et al.*, 1965). In every fission event two fragments traveling in opposite directions are produced. To use this method of ionization the sample of interest (molecular weight $= M$) is deposited on a nickel foil ($\sim 1\ \mu$m thick), which in turn is aligned with one of the fission products of ^{252}Cf. Since the charged fission fragments have energies varying between 60 and 120 MeV with peaks at ~ 80 and 110 MeV (Schmitt *et al.*, 1965), they penetrate the nickel foil and produce intense heating in a very short time ($\sim 19^{-12}$ s). This kind of energy deposition leads to desorption of substrate ions with masses of $(M + 1)^+$, $(M - 1)^+$ as well as other adducts such as $(M - \text{Li})^+$ and $(M + \text{Na})^+$. These ions then traverse a long flight path and are detected. The detector is gated by the fission fragments from ^{252}Cf, which went in the opposite direction. A sketch of the technique is

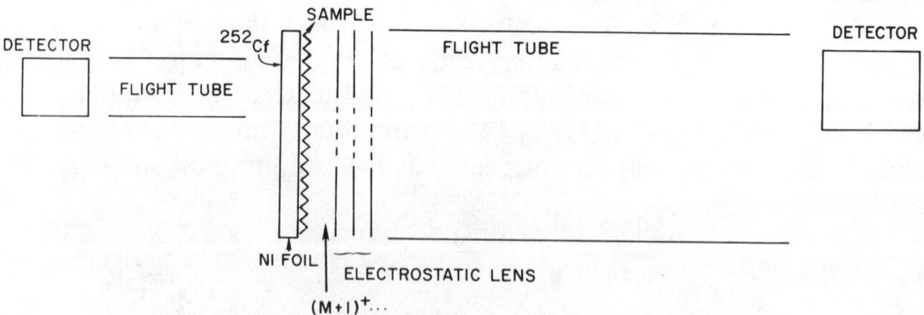

FIG. 3.4. ^{252}Cf fission ion source and mass spectrometer.

shown in Fig. 3.4. The flight times are then converted to mass units, since the flight length is known and the energy is set by the electrostatic potentials. This method can be used to produce both negative- and positive-ion spectra with mass resolutions of the order of 10^{-3} amu at $m/e \sim 500$ (Chait *et al.*, 1981). MacFarlane and Torgerson (1976) used this method for the analysis of high-molecular-weight compounds.

G. Discharges

The early experiments of Thomson (1897), Wien (1898), and Aston (1919), which began the field of mass spectrometry, used gas discharge ion sources. A sketch of such an ion source is shown in Fig. 3.5a. The operation of this source is simple in principle in that a large potential (10–60 kV) is maintained between anode and cathode; a gas at some pressure ($\sim 10^{-2}$ torr) is

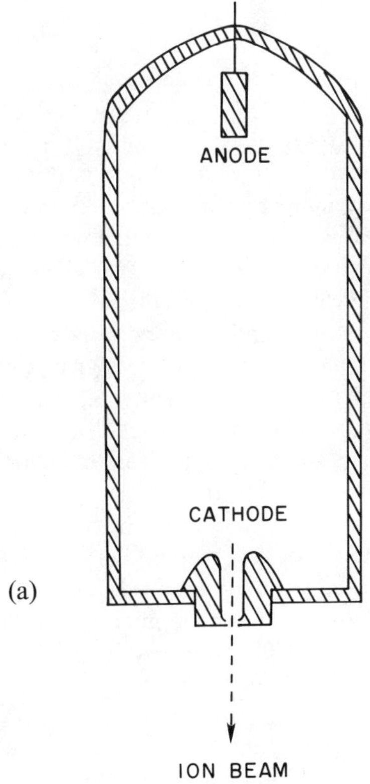

FIG. 3.5. (a) Discharge ion source and (b) discharge ion source used for flow tube work. (*Continued.*)

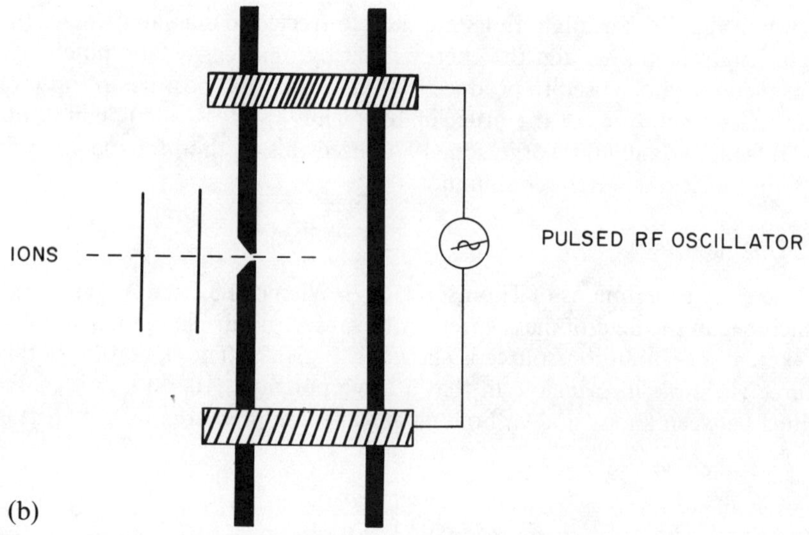

FIG. 3.5. (*Continued*).

introduced, causing a discharge. Because of the energy and the pressures used, complex spectra are obtained: singly charged and multiply charged ions and ions produced by ion–molecule reactions are observed. The large energies of the ions and the unsteadiness of the discharge have limited its use, even though the large ion intensities make it attractive. There are actually several types of discharges, among which are high-voltage dc discharges (mentioned above), low-voltage rf discharges, and the arc discharge source. An excellent discussion of discharge phenomena in general is given by von Engel (1965) and will not be attempted here. Suffice it to say that when a gas is discharged, current flows between anode and cathode; while the discharge is in progress, and while energy is supplied, the discharge is said to be active because of the presence of *energetic* particles. After the input of energy has stopped, an afterglow is observed (the name coming from the fact that many of the early studies wre concerned with the optical emission arising in this time interval), and now complex reactions between thermalized species take place. There are a few specialized descriptions of this phenomenon, and a good discussion is given by McDaniel *et al.* (1970). The uses of discharges as sources for analytical mass spectrometry are fairly limited [cf. Inghram and Hayden (1954)]; discharges are now used mostly to generate ions for studying reactions of ions in flow tuves, the discharge being excited by microwave or rf frequencies (Fite *et al.*, 1962; Studniarz and Franklin, 1968; Studniarz, 1972; Vasile and Smolinsky, 1973). A sketch of such a source is shown in Fig. 3.5b.

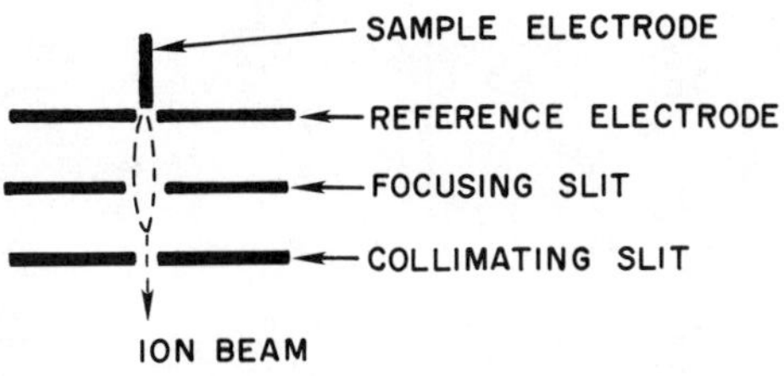

FIG. 3.6. Spark ion source.

H. Spark Sources

This type of source is actually a variation of the discharge source described above, and its development arose because of the need to obtain mass spectra of solids (Dempster, 1936a). Its initial uses were for the study of the isotope structure of the elements, but later studies (Hannay, 1954; Craig *et al.*, 1959) developed it as a source for measuring the impurities contained in solid materials. A comprehensive treatment of this ion source is given by Elliott (1963). Basically, as the name implies, the ions are generated by a spark between two electrodes in vacuum, one of the electrodes being made of the material to be analyzed. Voltages of the order of 50–100 kV are used in the spark, and, because of the tremendous energies, these voltages are usually applied in pulsed ac manner to reduce the heating effects on the electrodes. This method of ionization is not gentle and gives rise to many multiply charged ions as well as complex ions, thus confusing the mass spectrum. In addition, the pulses of ions tend to yield varying intensities and for that reason it is useful to have a detector with an integrating capacity, such as a photographic plate. A third disadvantage is that the ions that are generated in the spark tend to have a wide spread in kinetic energies, 1000 V being not uncommon. This energy spread often necessitates the use of a velocity selector, especially if high-resolution mass spectra are desired. An advantage of the technique is that it gives a mass spectrum that is representative of the sample, since the large spark energies tend to equalize the ionization probabilities. A sketch of such a source is shown in Fig. 3.6.

I. Laser Desorption

When a laser beam impinges on a surface, the heating may be enough to desorb not only atoms but ions as well. This technique was used initially to generate a beam of fast neutral atoms by evaporation of a solid (Friichtenicht, 1974; Utterback *et al.*, 1976) and has been successfully used to analyze solid materials for their elemental composition, since it is equally usable for conductive and nonconductive materials (Bingham and Saller, 1975). Later it

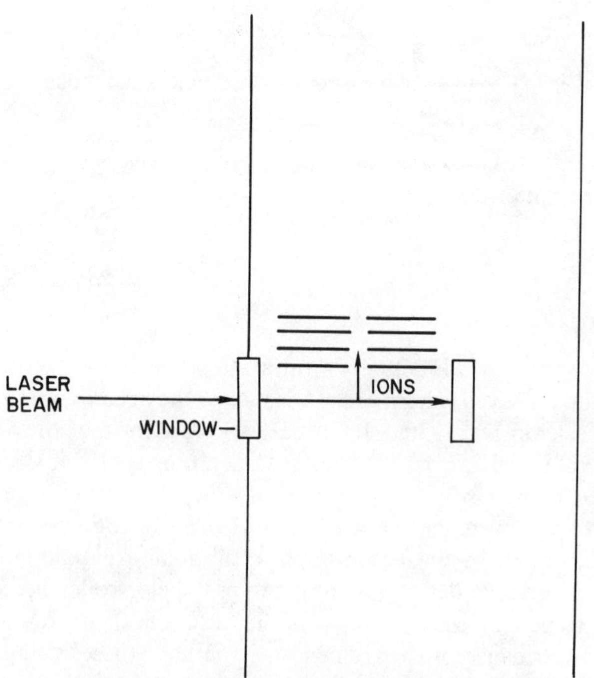

FIG. 3.7. Laser desorption ion source.

was adapted to the analysis of large organic molecules (Conzemius and Capellen, 1980). For example, using the apparatus sketched in Fig. 3.7, Kistemaker *et al.* (1981a) obtained mass spectra of complex molecules such as sucrose ($M = 342$) and digitonin ($M = 1228$). The molecule digoxin ($M = 780$) has been analyzed mass spectrometrically with this method of ionization (Kistemaker *et al.*, 1981b). An interesting aspect of the technique has been its renewed use as a source of ion beams, principally of metal ions, for studying reactions between metal ions and various species (Cody *et al.*, (1980).

J. Sources of Negative Ions

All the methods mentioned above, with the exception of photoionization, have been used to obtain beams of negative ions. In addition to reversing the polarities of all voltages and the direction of the magnetic field (if one is used), it is necessary to use some guile in generating negative ions [cf. Massey (1969–1974, 1976)]. This is because, generally, negative ions are fairly unstable and the ground states of the negative ions are above the ground states of the corresponding neutral molecules. It thus becomes necessary to stabilize a negative ion before it decomposes or loses an electron. Moreover, because the electron attachment cross sections have fairly sharp maxima at low energies (Massey, 1976), it becomes advantageous to use low-energy electrons; to generate these slow electrons, high-energy electrons are sometimes used to bombard a metal plate, ejecting lower-energy electrons, which then attach to the molecules (Paulson, 1972; Futrell and Tiernan, 1972). In terms of obtaining mass spectra, there seems to be an advantage to using negative ions since the fragmentation patterns are often simpler than those obtained from positive-ion mass spectrometry (Large and Knof, 1976).

3.3. Major Types of Mass Spectrometers

This discussion will consider two very different types of mass analyzers: (1) static, and (2) dynamic. By static analyzer is meant an analyzer whose performance does not include a time-dependent parameter, while by dynamic analyzer is meant one whose performance includes a time-dependent parameter. For example, quadrupole mass filters are dynamic analyzers since their performance depends on an rf voltage ($V \cos \omega t$) being applied to the analyzer elements. The first two analyzers discussed below are static, while the last three are dynamic.

A. Magnetic Analyzers

A charged particle of mass m and charge e moving in static magnetic and electric fields obeys the equation of motion:

$$m\mathbf{a} = -e\,\nabla V + (e/c)\mathbf{v} \times \mathbf{B}, \tag{3.9}$$

where V is the potential, B the magnetic induction, v the velocity, and a the acceleration. Equation (3.9) is the basis of the magnetic mass analyzers. There are many types of magnetic analyzers with specially shaped magnetic fields and with crossed electric and magnetic fields. It is not the aim of this review to discuss all these instruments, since full treatments are available in the books by Barnard (1953), Inghram and Hayden (1954), and Beynon (1960). Rather, an attempt will be made to present a particular analyzer (60° sector field) and to discuss its performance. In the next section the combination of an electric velocity selector and a magnetic analyzer will be described. The first mass spectrometer (Dempster, 1918) was a 180° direction-focusing instrument, while the first mass spectrograph (Aston, 1919) was a velocity-focusing instrument.

Let us assume now that ions formed in the ion source and having a mass m and charge e have been accelerated to a potential v. The kinetic energy of the ions is $(mv^2)/2$ and is equal to the energy gained electrically by falling through a potential V:

$$\tfrac{1}{2}mv^2 = eV. \tag{3.10}$$

The ions now enter the magnetic field at a right angle (at the entrance slit in Fig. 3.8a) and experience a force in a direction orthogonal to the direction of motion and to the direction of the magnetic field, as shown in Fig. 3.8b. This force is given by

$$F = Hev, \tag{3.11}$$

where H is the magnetic field. For ions to emerge at the exit slit, their centrifugal force (mv^2/r) must balance this force:

$$Hev = mv^2/r. \tag{3.12}$$

When combined with Eq. (3.10), the result is the familiar mass spectrometer equation

$$m/e = H^2e^2/2V. \tag{3.13}$$

When H is expressed in gauss, V in volts, r in centimeters, and (m/e) in atomic mass units (3.13) is reduced to

$$m/e = 4.82 \times 10^{-5}\, r^2H^2/V. \tag{3.14}$$

Now, Eq. (3.12) may be rewritten as

$$r = (mv)/He, \tag{3.15}$$

where (mv) is the momentum of the ion. Instruments of this type are sometimes referred to as *momentum* analyzers, since ions of the same momentum (but, perhaps, different combinations of m and v) can appear at the same r.

The discussion above assumes ideal conditions: magnetic fields have sharp edges, ions are monoenergetic, and the initial spatial width of the ion beam is nearly zero. Of course, such conditions are not obtainable in practice, and how these parameters deviate from ideality determines the performance char-

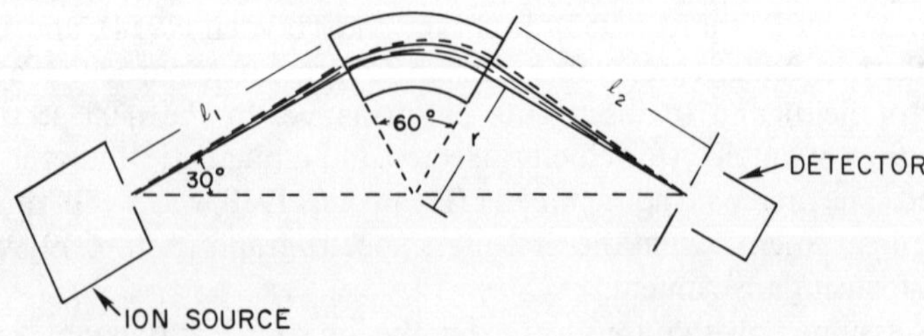

FIG. 3.8. 60° sector field magnetic mass spectrometer.

acteristics of the mass analyzers (resolution and transmission). Compromises can be made to achieve usable performance. For example, magnets can be shaped to give fairly sharp fields and the ion kinetic energy can be controlled by the use of ion sources that have low energy spread such as photon or electron impact sources (for high-resolution work it becomes necessary to add a velocity selector). The beamwidth can be controlled by specially designed slits that optimize sharpness and homogeneity of field lines (Barnard, 1953). A fairly common analyzer that was initially designed by Nier (1940, 1949) is the 60° sector field analyzer, which is sketched in Fig. 3.8a. In this mass analyzer the entrance slit, the apex of the sector field, and the exit slit are collinear; generally the analyzer is symmetrical (i.e., the entrance and exit slits are equidistant from the magnet), although this symmetry is not necessary, and, in fact, some analyzers have been built with asymmetric focal points (Barnard, 1953). The symmetrical 60° analyzer has first-order focusing properties, while the asymmetric 60° sector analyzer has second-order focusing. The gains from asymmetry are outweighed by the difficulty of assembly. The resolving power of the instrument (Beynon, 1960) is given by

$$\Delta m/m = (s_1 + s_2 + gr)/r, \tag{3.16}$$

where s_1 and s_2 are the slit widths and g is an aberration constant characteristic of an instrument. Resolution of as much as 1/1800 can be achieved with this type of mass spectrometer (the accelerting voltage is ~ 5 kV and the magnetic field is ~ 10 kG). The advantages are that (1) it is fairly easy to use, (2) transmission is low but is approximately constant over a wide mass range, and (3) it has fairly high resolution. The disadvantages are that (1) the ions have to be accelerated to high kinetic energy, necessitating work at high voltages, (2) the high magnetic fields, high voltages, and high-precision machining make it an expensive machine, and (3) fragmentation patterns are affected by stray or fringe magnetic fields (Beynon *et al.*, 1975).

B. Double-Focusing Mass Spectrometers

As the name implies, these instruments focus the ions twice: first (generally) with an electrostatic analyzer and second with a magnetic analyzer. Equation (3.15) indicates that the ion velocity spread can have an important effect on the mass resolution; or, to restate the point, if v is absolutely fixed ($\Delta v = 0$), the momentum analyzer will become a mass analyzer with infinite resolution. Early in the history of mass spectrometry it was realized that mass resolution would be immensely improved by velocity selection of the ions. One early design (Bartky and Dempster, 1929) proposed the use of an analyzer with crossed magnetic and electric fields. A somewhat simpler arrangement was to separate the magnetic and electric fields. Thus Dempster (1936) designed

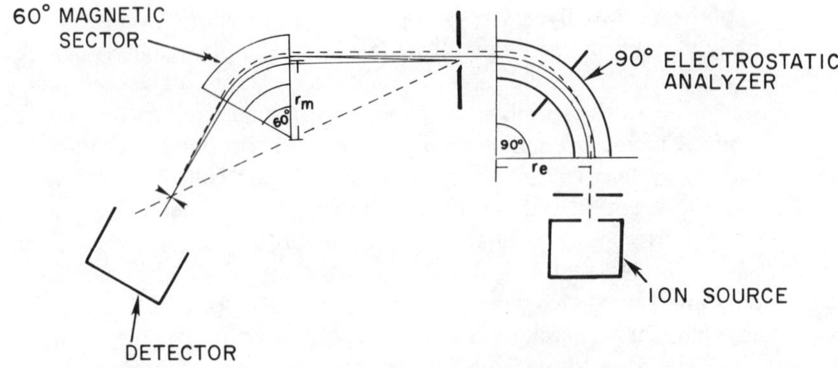

FIG. 3.9. Double-focusing mass spectrometer; $r_e/r_m = 1.238$.

a double-focusing instrument consisting of a 90° electrostatic analyzer followed by a 180° magnetic analyzer. Bainbridge and Jordan (1936) also described a mass spectrograph consisting of a 127°17′ electrostatic analyzer followed by a 60° sector field; this mass spectrograph had a resolution of 1/7000. An instrument that has been used frequently is the Mattauch–Herzog double-focusing mass spectrograph, which consists of a 31°50′ electrostatic analyzer followed by a 90° magnetic analyzer; resolution of about 1 part in 10^7 has been obtained in this way (Hintenberger, 1962). A double-focusing mass spectrometer that has been used commercially was first built by Nier *et al.* (1949) and consisted of a 90° electrostatic analyzer followed by a 60° magnetic sector analyzer. A sketch of this instrument is shown in Fig. 3.9. An interesting aspect of this mass spectrometer is the asymmetric magnetic field which gives second-order direction focusing.

The advantages of this type of mass spectrometer are (1) tremendous resolution over a wide mass range, and (2) fairly constant mass transmission. The disadvantages of these instruments are that (1) they are very bulky and need large laboratory space, (2) their operation requires a specialist who is familiar with high-resolution fragmentation patterns, and (3) they are very expensive.

C. Quadrupole, Monopole, and 3-D Quad Mass Filters

The quadrupole mass analyzer was first described by Paul and co-workers (Paul and Steinwedel, 1953; Paul and Raether, 1955) and has since become a workhorse in mass spectrometry. This instrument, to be more precise, is not an analyzer in the same sense as the magnetic mass analyzer; rather it may be likened to a filter with variable bandpass. A sketch of a quadrupole

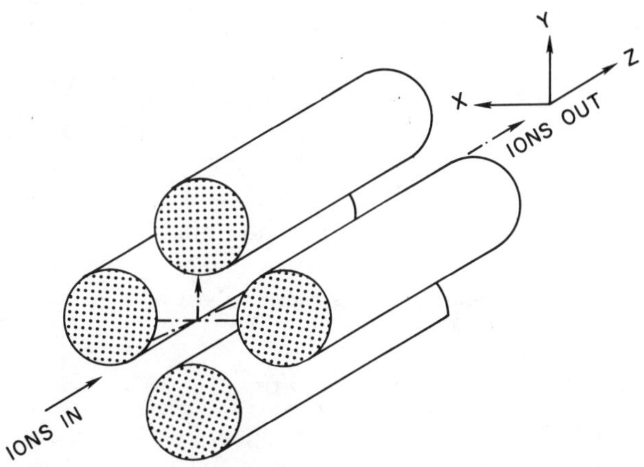

FIG. 3.10. Quadrupole mass filter.

mass filter is shown in Fig. 3.10. The concept behind the instrument is fairly simple, although the details of its operation turn out to be complex [see Blauth (1966) and Dawson and Whetten (1969b). A dc voltage and an rf voltage are applied to the rods, each opposite pair being connected together. The rods have, ideally, hyperbolic shape, although circular rods are much more common. Ions are injected in or near the center of the rods in the z direction and they travel at constant velocity in that direction. As stated above, both dc (U) and ac ($V \cos \omega t$) potentials are applied in the x and y directions, i.e.,

$$\Phi(x, y, t) = (U + V \cos \omega t)(x^2 - y^2)/r_0^2. \qquad (3.17)$$

Reference is made to the paper by Todd and Lawson (1975) for a derivation of the equations of motion of the ions, which are

$$d^2x/dt^2 + (e/m)(2/r_0^2)(U + V \cos \omega t)x = 0, \qquad (3.18)$$

$$d^2y/dt^2 - (e/m)(2/r_0^2)(U + V \cos \omega t)y = 0. \qquad (3.19)$$

$d^2z/dt^2 = 0$ since the ions have constant velocity in the z direction. These equations of motion are similar to the Mathieu equations:

$$d^2x/d\xi^2 + (a - 2q \cos 2\xi)x = 0 \qquad (3.20)$$

$$d^2y/d\xi^2 - (a + 2q \cos 2\xi)y = 0 \qquad (3.21)$$

and become the Mathieu if the constants a, q, and ξ are

$$2\xi = \omega t, \qquad a = 8eU/mr_0^2\omega^2, \qquad q = 4eV/mr_0^2\omega^2. \qquad (3.22)$$

Solutions of Eqs. (3.20) and (3.21) take the form of summations of the type

$$x(\xi) = \alpha_1 \exp(\mu\xi) \sum[d \exp(2is\xi)] + \alpha_2 \exp(-\mu\xi) \sum[d \exp(-2is\xi)]. \quad (3.23)$$

The exponent μ determines whether the trajectory will be stable ($x < r_0$) or unstable ($x > r_0$). Tables of these values are available (Maeda *et al.*, 1969; Maeda and Fukuda, 1970) and of help in designing quadrupole mass filters. The stability diagram for a mass filter is shown in Fig. 3.11. Ultimate resolution is obtained at $a = 0.237$ and $q = 0.706$. To transmit a mass at such a resolution requires [by substituting these values of a and q into Eq. (3.22) above and combining]:

$$m/e = 5.66V/(\omega^2 r_0^2). \quad (3.24)$$

Thus a mass scan can be obtained by changing V or ω. There are limitations on the angular acceptance of the quadrupole mass filter and on the size of the injection orifice [see, for example, Rafal'son (1965) and Hennequin and Inglebert (1978)].

There are variations of the quadrupole mass filter, and one of these, the monopole, was developed by von Zahn (1963). A sketch of this mass filter is shown in Fig. 3.12. The equations of motion for the monopole are the same as for the quadrupole (given above), and the stability diagram is similar. Ions

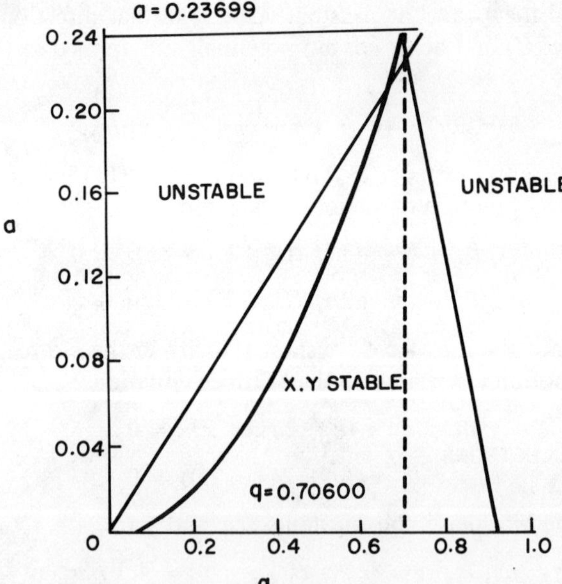

FIG. 3.11. Stability diagram for quadrupole mass filter.

must be injected a little off-axis to achieve optimum transmission and resolution (Lever, 1966). Another variation of the quadrupole mass filter is the three-dimensional quadrupole (3-D quad). Equation (3.17) described the potential equation for a two-dimensional field in the x and y directions; no field was applied in the z direction since ions were propelled in that direction at constant velocity. By extending the treatment to three dimensions, the potential equation becomes (Fischer, 1959)

$$\Phi(x, y, z, t) = (u - v \cos \omega t)(x^2 + y^2 - 2z^2)/2r_0^2. \tag{3.25}$$

A sketch of a 3-D quad is shown in Fig. 3.12b. In this instrument the end electrodes are three-dimensional hyperbolic surfaces that are electrically connected, while the center electrode is a hyperbolic surface that surrounds these two electrodes. Electrons are pulsed through one of tle end electrodes. Ions formed in the center of the 3-D quad have stable paths (i.e., x, y, and $z < r_0$) depending on ω, r_0, U, and V as in the conventional quadrupole. The effect of this is that ions of a given mass can be stored for a long time.

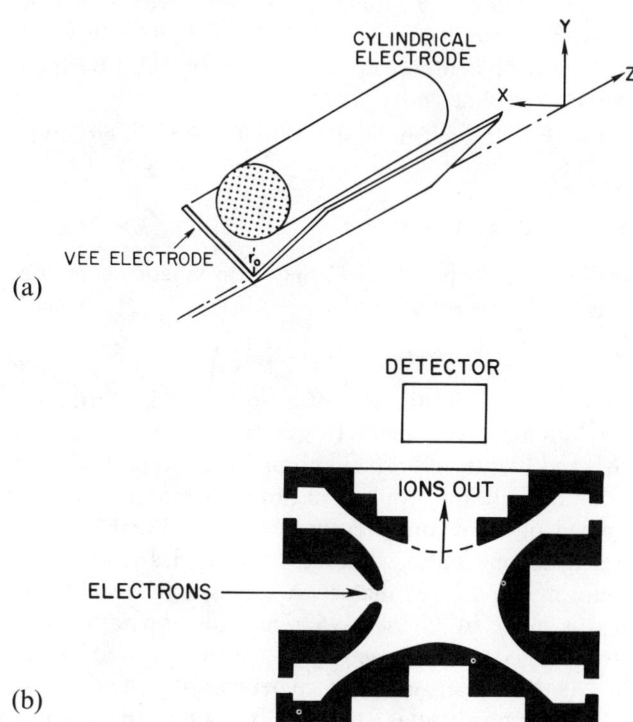

FIG. 3.12. (a) Monopole mass filter and (b) three-dimensional quadrupole ion trap.

Indeed, with such ion storage devices, various spectroscopic properties of ions have been studied (Major and Dehmelt, 1968; Church, 1969). Dawson and Whetten (1968) described a 3-D quad for use as a residual gas analyzer; their design was greatly simplified later when they used hand-formed steel mesh electrodes (Dawson *et al.*, 1969), which were used to measure residual pressures of $\sim 10^{-12}$ torr. This unusual variation of the quadrupole mass filter has also been used extensively by Todd and co-workers [see, for example, Bonner *et al.* (1973) and Todd and Lawson (1975)] to study the kinetics of many ion–neutral reactions (they have called this apparatus Quistor, an acronym derived from quadrupole ion storage).

It is appropriate to conclude the discussion of the quadrupole mass filter by mentioning that even though it is simpler to operate than magnetic analyzers and is considerably smaller, it does have some disadvantages, such as mass discrimination effects and resonances in mass peaks (Whetten and Dawson, 1969; Dawson and Whetten, 1969a). It is also worth noting that while the theory of the quadrupole mass filter has been studied extensively, the operation of these devices seems to demand less exactness than the theory requires. For example, a quadrupole mass filter with *flat* electrodes has been used with a resolution of $\sim 1/15$ (Pearce and Halsall, 1978). A quadrupole without a dc component on the rods has also been used with fairly high resolution (Holme *et al.*, 1978).

The advantages of the quadrupole mass filter are small size, high transmission, low cost, and operation at low dc voltages (usually ~ 5 V dc).

D. Time-of-Flight Mass Analyzers

When ions fall through a potential V, they gain kinetic energy according to Eq. (3.10), which may be rearranged:

$$m/e = 2V/v^2. \tag{3.26}$$

Thus, if V is constant, a measurement of v would yield information about m/e. Many early attempts were made to use this concept for mass analysis [see Kiser (1965) and Blauth (1966)], but all of these had problems stemming from the fact that if the beam is pulsed in order to establish a time marker, the velocity spread of the beam (presumably Maxwellian) tends to merge the fast species from one pulse with the slow species from the previous pulse, thus confusing the derived masses. A successful attempt to overcome this handicap was made by Glenn (1952), and his apparatus is shown in in Fig. 3.13a. Ions are formed in some way and are accelerated by a dc potential on grid G_1. As the ions cross the space between G_1 and G_2, a sawtooth repeller potential is applied to G_1, the idea being that the slower ions get larger acceleration than the faster ions. The ions now enter the drift tube and, because of the ramp voltage applied between G_1 and G_2, they arrive at G_3

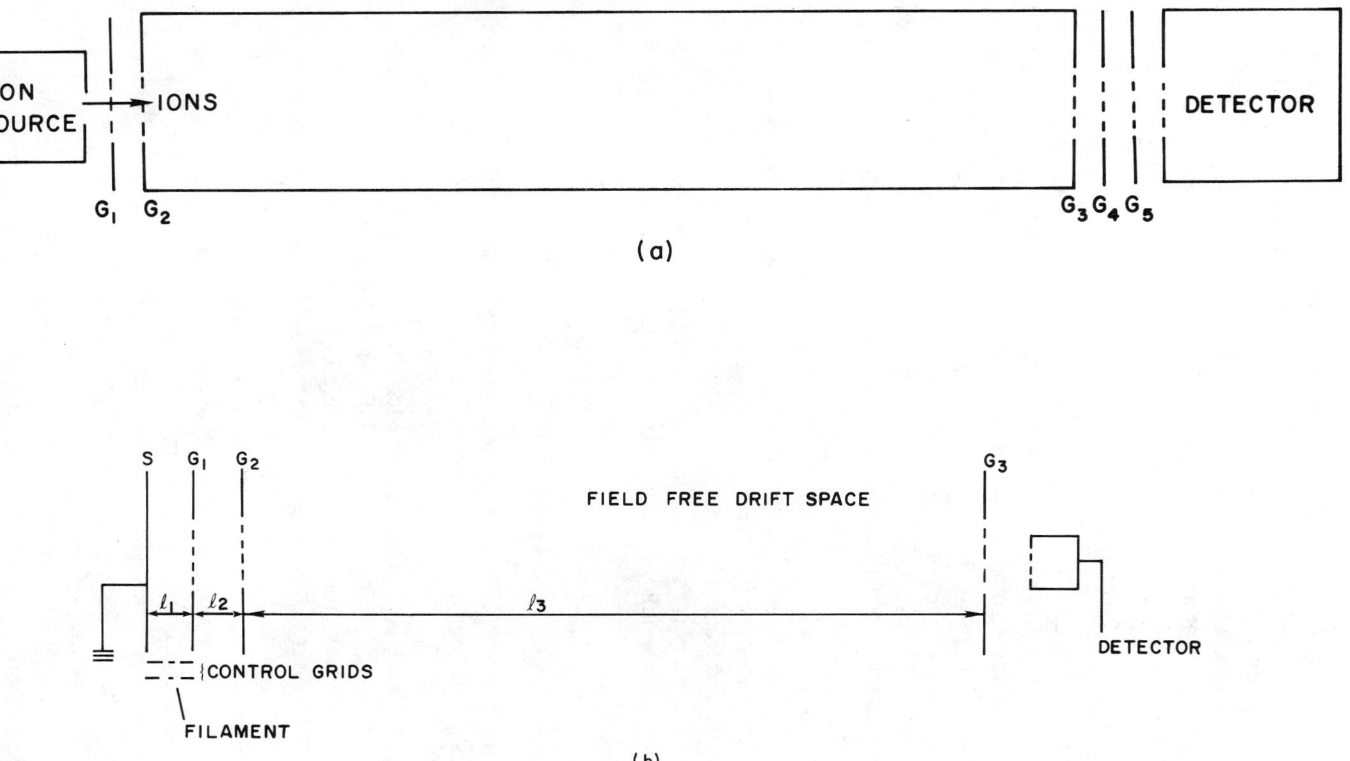

FIG. 3.13. (a) Glenn mass spectrometer and (b) time-of-flight mass spectrometer. $l_1 = 0.2$–0.4 cm; $l_2 = 1$–2 cm; and $l_3 = 40$ cm.

in bunches of different masses, but the same velocity. Grid G_5 has a repeller voltage so that none of the ions reach the detector. A gate pulse is applied to G_4 so that only the bunch of ions having a given mass can pass through G_5 and on to the detector. This mass analyzer was designed to be used as an isotope separator and had fairly good resolution. It did not achieve wide use because of the complexities of the pulse and ramp sequences needed for the operation.

Wiley and McLaren (1955) built what became the first successful commercial time-of-flight mass analyzer, the Bendix TOF mass analyzer, which is sketched in Fig. 3.13b. In this design, ionizing electrons are pulsed into the source; while this is going on, G_1 and S are at the same potential. As soon as ionization has stopped, S is pulsed with a positive potential so that the ions are kicked into the region between G_1 and G_2, and from there they are accelerated by G_2 to the full potential. The drift space, which was initially 40 cm but later extended to 1 m, provides the separation according to mass. This method provides very good mass resolution because the energy spread of the ions is limited, because the total accelerating voltage (~ 3 kV) occurs between G_1 and G_2, and because the initial ions are formed in a very narrow region. An advantage of TOF mass spectrometers has been the speed with which mass spectra can be obtained (of the order of milliseconds), allowing their use for studying reaction kinetics. Another advantage is that the instruments are less bulky (and less expensive) than the magnetic mass spectrometers.

E. Ion Cyclotron Resonance

This fairly new entry into mass spectrometry actually had an earlier incarnation as the omegatron (Hipple *et al.*, 1949; Sommer *et al.*, 1951; Wabschall *et al.*, 1963), an instrument that was promising in theory but difficult to operate [for a historical survey see McIver (1978a)]. A sketch of an omegatron is shown in Fig. 3.14a. Ions are formed in the center of the ion box by electron impact; the ion box is placed in a high magnetic field (Hipple *et al.* used 4700 G). Surrounding the ionization region are positively biased guard rings, which confine the ions to the center of the box. An rf voltage is applied to the rings at a frequency that is varied manually. At some resonant frequency (the ion's cyclotron frequency) ions of a given m/e undergo a spiral flight with increasing amplitude until they strike the collector. Since the frequency can be measured very accurately, the resolution is, in theory, very high. The problems with this instrument were due to the scattering by neutral background gas of ions on their journey to the collector and the electrical fields from the guard rings, which tended to distort the flight paths of the ions. Both of these effects tended to reduce the sensitivity and the resolution of the instrument. The attempt to increase the resolution and sensitivity led to today's ICR instruments [see Beauchamp *et al.* (1967); Baldeschwieler and Woodgate (1971); and McIver (1978a)]. Much of the impetus for the development of the instrumentation came from investigators interested in measuring the kinetics and mechanisms of ion–neutral reactions (Henis, 1972). A later variation of the ICR, the Fourier transform ICR (FT-ICR), established the technique in high-resolution mass spectrometry.

When an ion is injected into a magnetic field, it moves in a direction orthogonal to its velocity direction and to the direction of the magnetic field according to Eq. (3.9). Since the force is always perpendicular to the velocity,

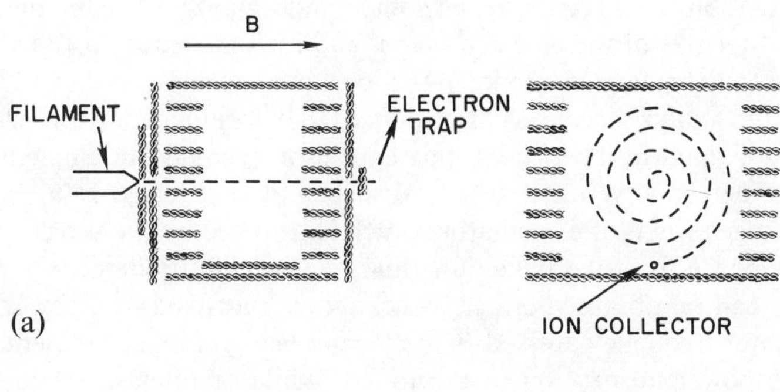

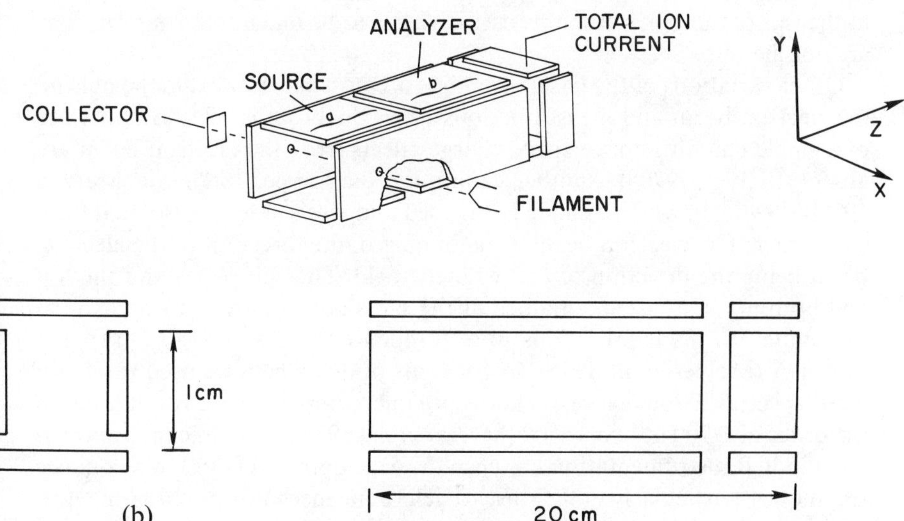

FIG. 3.14. (a) Omegatron and (b) ion cyclotron resonance cell.

the movement becomes circular with an angular or cyclotron frequency (v/r) given by the scalar equations

$$mv^2/r = evB/c, \qquad \text{or} \qquad \omega_c = v/r = (e/m)(B/c), \tag{3.27}$$

where ω_c is the resonance frequency and the other terms are as defined before. When an alternating electric field of frequency ω_c is applied normal to the magnetic field, the ions will absorb energy from the electric field and will be accelerated to larger velocities and larger orbits. A sketch of an ICR cell is shown in Fig. 3.14b. The cell consists of three sections: the source, the analyzer, and the collector. Ions are formed in the first section by electron impact. The top and bottom plates have a static dc voltage that confines the orbiting ions to a region in the source and analyzer. The magnetic field is in the direction of the electron beam, and for that reason a repeller field is applied to the side plates to keep the ions away. Since the top and bottom plates of the analyzer sections are isolated, they form a capacitor; when the plates are excited by an rf field, this capacitor becomes an element in the resonance detector. When power is absorbed, it is reflected as a change in the rf voltage level of the oscillator, which is detected by the use of modulation and phase-sensitive detection (marginal oscillator detector). A mass spectrum can be obtained either by scanning B at fixed ω or by scanning the oscillator frequency at fixed B, the former being more convenient. Measuring the power absorption in the tuned oscillator offers a very sensitive measurement of ion intensities; for example, 10 Ar^+ ions can lead to a measurable signal (Henis, 1972). Of course, a separate detector can be placed at the exit of the cell, but in this case care has to be taken that spurious ions are not measured.

Other variations of the basic technique are possible. For example, pulsing the electron beam and measuring ions when the beam is off allows the use of a single chamber, since space charge effects from the electron beam are absent (McIver, 1970a). Another variation is the trapped ion mode (McIver, 1970b, 1978b), in which a single cell is used and all six sides are isolated from each other. The electron beam is again pulsed, the direction of the electron beam being the direction of the magnetic field. The end plates and the top and bottom plates are maintained at the same potential with respect to the side plate. In this manner ions were trapped for ~3 s at ~80% trapping efficiency (McIver *et al.*, 1975). Instruments of this type were used to obtain mass spectra of low-vapor-pressure organic compounds at resolutions of the order of 1/700 at $m/e \sim 500$ (McIver *et al.*, 1975). A significant improvement in ICR instrumentation has been the development of double-resonance techniques, particularly in their use to determine mechanisms of ion–neutral reactions (Anders *et al.*, 1966; Henis, 1972). In this variation of the ICR technique (Fig. 3.146) the two trapping plates are connected to different oscillators. One oscillates at the frequency of the reactant (source) ion ω_{c1}, and the other oscillates at the frequency of the product (analyzed) ion ω_{c2}. If the product ion is indeed coming from the reaction of the primary ion with the neutral gas, then scanning ω_{c1} and observing ω_{c2} will show a change in the latter. This simplified picture shows why the technique is so powerful in studying the mechanisms of ion–neutral reactions. Because the ion velocities are fairly low (corresponding to near-thermal energies), the method has been used to measure a large number of rate constants for ion–neutral reactions (Henis, 1972; Bowers and Su, 1973).

Another important innovation in ICR work has been the development of FT-ICR. This technique applies the Fourier transform methodology developed for IR and NMR work to ICR, and it seems to have been first suggested by Comisarow and Marshall (1974). The technique is described fully by McIver (1980), so that only a sketch will be given below. The ions are formed by a pulsed electron beam in a single-chamber ICR machine and are stored for some time (milliseconds to seconds). The rf field is then swept at a frequency that varies linearly with time [see Eq. (3.27)] and the ion current or the resonance current is measured. What is obtained is a spectrum that looks like a damped oscillator modulated at a high frequency. When a Fourier transform (time-to-frequency conversion) of this signal is made, a high-resolution mass spectrum ($\sim 1/10^6$) is obtained. Quantitative treatments of this topic have been given by Comisarow and Marshall (1976), Comisarow (1978), and Marshall *et al.* (1979). A related development in high-resolution ICR has been the rapid-scan ICR, which has been used to obtain mass spectra in the range 20–1000 amu at resolutions $>10^4$ [see Hunter and McIver (1977, 1982).

Finally, it should be mentioned that ICR instruments have the advantages of being small, relatively inexpensive, and very sensitive. Because of the unique detection system ICR has $\sim 100\%$ collection efficiency of the ions (compared to $\sim 0.1\%$ for standard magnetic analyzers).

3.4. Detectors

A. Photographic Plates

This is the oldest method of measuring a mass spectrum and was used by Thomson and his predecessors to detect the particles. Aston (1919) used it to determine accurate atomic masses from his mass spectrograph. Basically, in this method a photographic plate is placed at the exit of a mass spectrograph and the mass-analyzed beam of ions impinge on it. The ions collide with the plate at high energies and interact with the emulsion (silver halides and related compounds) in a complex manner, eventually leaving an image of the beam. The technique has the advantage of being an integrating detector (which sometimes is a disadvantage), in that it accumulates readings for a long time. Another advantage is that it records a full mass spectrum at one time. There are many disadvantages, however, and these will be mentioned briefly [a more detailed discussion being given by Inghram and Hayden (1954)]:

(1) There are many types of photographic films and each of them has a different reaction to ion impact, so that standardization and calibration are very important in trying to elicit absolute abundances.

(2) The response of the photographic plate to ions of different masses is very complex and is hard to predict.

(3) The response of the plate to ions of different structures is not well established.

(4) Intensity of the image seems to depend on the kinetic energy of the ions.

(5) Intensity of the image does not seem to vary linearly with the product of exposure and time.

(6) The ion beams can charge the photographic plates (since they are made of plastic and glass) and the electrostatic charge thus built (sometimes as high as 1000 V) can have a defocusing effect on the ion beam, causing the latter to become distorted.

These problems have limited, but not eliminated, the use of this technique.

B. Single Collector

This electrical way of recording the mass spectrum was first used by Dempster (1918). Its aim of measuring the electric current due to the mass-analyzed ions is accomplished fairly easily provided care is taken to suppress

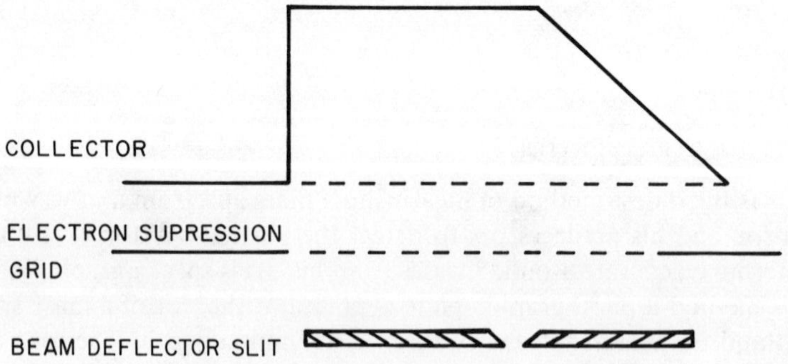

FIG. 3.15. Single collector.

secondary electrons emitted by the collector when it is bombarded by the energetic ions and provided intensities are high enough that an electrometer can measure them. Figure 3.15 shows a sketch of a single collector assembly; in this assembly there is a grid across the collector to help trap the charged particles in the collector. In addition, the electron suppression grid helps to retard any secondary electrons that escape, since it is negatively biased with respect to the collector. This bias voltage is of the order of 5 V and is too small to affect the primary ion beam (which has energies of a few keV). There are other variations of this method, such as a dual collector for measuring the ratios of two isotopes (Nier *et al.*, 1947) and suppressive ion detectors for high-pressure work, as in leak detectors (Fox and Hipple, 1948). Single collectors are still used in leak detectors, but otherwise have limited use.

C. Electron Multipliers

An electron multiplier amplifies the ion current by several orders of magnitude and there are many ways of achieving this objective. The earliest type is the Π-type multiplier developed by Allen (1947, 1950). The basic principle is that an ion impinges on a metal surface at high energies (a few kilo-electron-volts) and ejects one or more electrons, which are then accelerated to a second surface (hereafter called a dynode). Each electron that impinges on the second dynode ejects two or more electrons. The process is repeated many times (16- and 20-stage multipliers being common) so that tremendous gains are achieved. If the conversion of ions to electrons on the first dynode is C (this is sometimes called the conversion efficiency) and the electron multiplication on each succeeding dynode is D, then the gain is $C \cdot D^n$, where n is the number of stages. For example, for a 16-stage multiplier with $C = 1$ and $D = 2$, the gain is $\sim 3 \times 10^4$. The conversion efficiency depends on a number parameters: ion kinetic energy, ion structure, angle of incidence, and mass of ion. Most Allen-type multipliers are constructed of dynodes made of alloys of Be–Cu or Ag–Mg, the former being more common because it is more tolerant of abuse. There is evidence that the multiplier gain at a given impact energy increases with the molecular weight of the ion (Barnett *et al.*, 1954; van Gorkom and Glick, 1970; Fehn, 1976). In addition to mass effects, molecular structure seems to affect the efficiency [see Inghram and Hayden (1954) and Stanton *et al.* (1956)]. Since the conversion efficiency of the first dynode plays an important part in the overall gain of the multiplier (Dietz, 1965), there are many prescriptions for activating this and the other dynodes to increase both C and D (Rappaport, 1954; Sommer, 1958). In general, the gain of the multiplier increases with the ion kinetic energy until a near plateau is reached (Barnett *et al.*, 1954). Other effects that need to be considered in the use of electron multipliers are saturation or aging effects

(Barnett *et al.*, 1954) and contamination of dynode surfaces by oils and other organic compounds [coming, for example, from diffusion pump oil; see Hirashima and Miyashiro (1957)]; and when pulse counting techniques are used care must be taken that the measured ion pulse rates are not higher than can be separated by the counter. Specially prepared dynodes made of a Be–Cu layer 300 Å thick deposited on a Be–Cu surface seem to be ~25% more efficient than similar dynodes made of a Be–Cu layer deposited on a stainless steel surface (Swingler, 1978b). Likewise, specially designed dynode structures with field lines that focus the secondary electrons in a narrow area can also improve the gain (Swingler, 1978a).

A related type of an electron multiplier is the venetian blind multiplier [see Beynon (1960)]. This multiplier consists of circular plates with slats attached to them at angles of 30°–40° as sketched in Fig. 3.16b. The dynodes are assembled with alternating slat directions and each dynode has a mesh to isolate it from the field of the previous dynode. This multiplier is probably more common now than the Allen-type multiplier because of its ease of use and because it seems to suffer less from mass effects (Ryan, 1968). The angle of the slats and the angle of incidence of the ion beam play a role in determining the overall gain of the electron multiplier, and special wires along the slat openings can improve the performance of the multiplier [see Göhrlich *et al.* (1961)]. A related type of electron multiplier is a commercial instrument, the focused-mesh particle multiplier (patented structure marketed by Johnston Laboratories, Inc.), in which each dynode consists of raised electron emissive surfaces and holes for the passage of the electrons to the next dynode. These multipliers are quite rugged, have large gains and long-term stability (Murad, 1974, unpublished data), and have fast rise times; all of these properties make them ideal for particle counting and for timing studies.

A third major type of electron multiplier that has played an important role in the time-of-flight mass spectrometer is the magnetic strip electron multiplier. It is helpful to recall that when a charged particle moves in a crossed electric and magnetic field its path describes a cycloidal motion, a fact that became the basis for the first magnetic multipliers (Smith, 1951). Here the dynodes were made of flat strips of Be–Cu held in a magnetic field and had an electric potential, increasingly positive, applied to them. The magnetic and electric fields were normal to each other and were also normal to the direction of motion of the secondary electrons. The strips were 1/8 in. wide and were fairly close together. The first such multipliers, built by Smith (1951), had a gain of $\sim 10^5$ and had total transit times of $\sim 5 \times 10^{-10}$ s, making them ideal for use with fast scanning devices. This latter property led Goodrich and Wiley (1961) to develop this multiplier further for use with

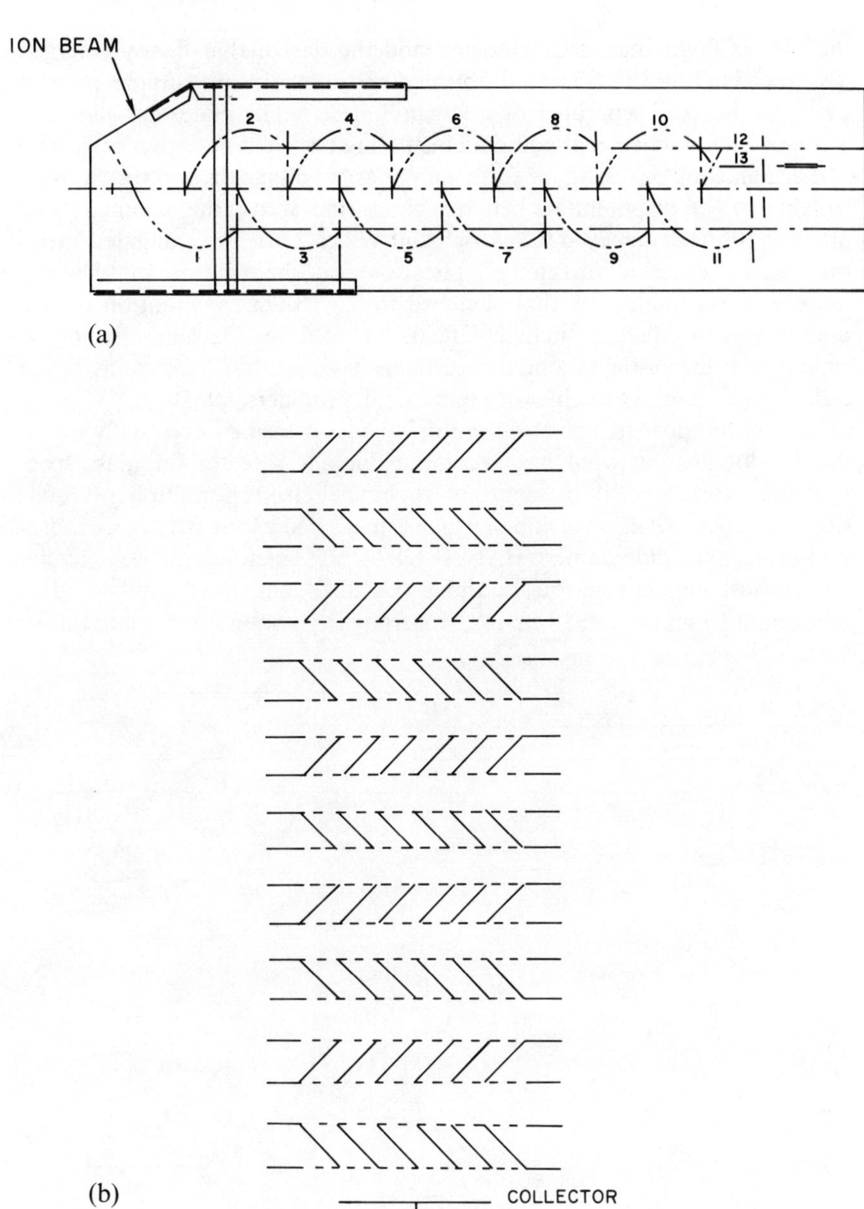

FIG. 3.16. (a) Allen Π-type electron multiplier and (b) venetian blind electron multiplier.

the time-of-flight mass spectrometer, and the design that finally emerged is sketched in Fig. 3.17a. The multiplier consists of two plane surfaces parallel to each other and separated by a few millimeters. The plates are generally made of a conductive coating on an insulating base (glass) so that each strip had a high enough resistance to sustain a large voltage drop across it. By a suitable choice of potentials between plates and across them, gains of the order of 10^7 were achieved (Goodrich and Wiley, 1961). Several gated variations were also tested for timing applications, but the structure that became more or less standard is that sketched in Fig. 3.17a. A variation of this multiplier which uses no magnetic fields but achieves the same type of cycloidal focusing of the secondary electrons has been built and gains of the order of 10^8 have been achieved (Spindt and Shoulders, 1965).

The continuous-strip electron multiplier just described eventually led to the development of what has become a popular detector for mass spectrometric work, namely the continuous-channel electron multiplier (Goodrich and Wiley, 1962), a version of which is marketed by the Bendix Corporation under the trade name CHANNELTRON. Generally, the commercial continuous-channel electron multiplier (CCEM) consists of a hollow glass tube about 1 mm i.d. and 10 cm long coated with a conductive surface on the

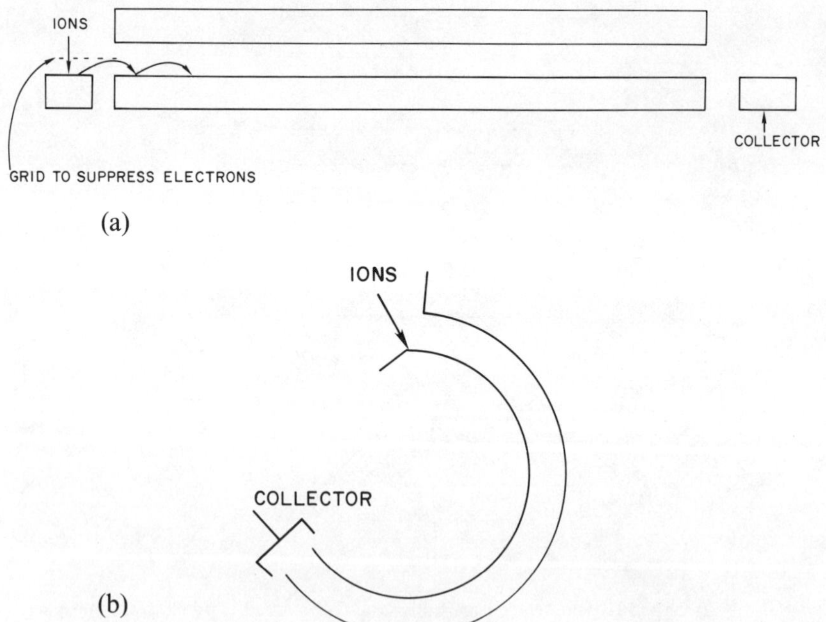

FIG. 3.17. (a) Magnetic strip electron multiplier and (b) continuous-channel electron multiplier.

inside so that the total resistance is quite large ($\sim 10^9$ ohms). This tube has the shape of a circle and describes an arc of about 270° (Burrous *et al.*, 1967). The entrance of the tube is sometimes fluted and the ions impinge on the surface at an angle of $\sim 10°$. Many variations in sizes and shapes are available, depending on the application, and the multiplier seems to tolerate abuse. At constant ion kinetic energies the gain for different masses seems to be not very discordant once a plateau is reached (Burrous *et al.*, 1967), and the absolute efficiency seems to be quite high [see Iglesias and McGarity (1971), for data on proton efficiency]. Slightly different types for special applications can be hand-made individually without much difficulty (Becker *et al.*, 1972). These devices have been successfully used to detect low-energy (10–1000-eV) electrons and conversion efficiencies of about 0.8 have been achieved (Bordoni, 1971). These detectors have also been used to measure vacuum ultraviolet radiation in the range 2–2000 Å (Schmidt, 1969; Becker *et al.*, 1972).

Yet another type of electron multiplier, which combines some of the characteristics of the other types, is the transmission dynode multiplier (Reynolds, 1966), which is used in image intensifiers. In this type of multiplier all the dynodes except the first consist of thin films of porous material such as potassium chloride. The first dynode is made of some material that has a high conversion efficiency (Be–Cu for particles or a photocathode for light measurements). The multiplication occurs because electrons from one dynode are accelerated to high energies before they impinge on the next dynode. These electrons penetrate the dynode and liberate electrons on the reverse side. While the conversion can be as high as 40, the statistics are high enough to make these multipliers noisy (Smith *et al.*, 1966). Some attempts have been made to construct hybrid multipliers in which one dynode is a transmission dynode (Dietz *et al.*, 1967), an arrangement that is much more usable at count rates as high as 2×10^6 pulses per second. More recent advances in the field of image intensifiers have used thin channel arrays (many straight, short, continuous-channel electron multipliers fused together) to achieve enormous gains in intensity, so that ion intensities of less than one per second are easily observed [see, for example, Griffin *et al.* (1974)]. Developments in the field of high-contrast image intensifiers [e.g., Baumgartner and Zimmerman (1972) and Emerson and Holmshaw (1972)] promise to make this method a powerful tool for the observation and study of low-abundance ions. One other method of multiplication, namely the scintillation detector, will be mentioned. Here the ion beam impinges at high energy on a phosphor, causing the phosphor to emit light, which is then measured by a photoelectric sensor [see, for example, Young (1955); Daly (1960, and Daly *et al.* (1971)]. This method is sensitive but the phosphor can deteriorate rapidly, requiring frequent changes and calibrations.

The brief summary given above of the uses and kinds of electron multipliers serves as an introduction to a field in which there is much active research. One final comment on the topic has to do with translating the output of the multiplier into a kinds of absolute measure, and here there are two options: (1) to measure the output as current or as voltage drop across a resistor, or (2) to count the electron pulses by standard nuclear counting techniques [a full treatment of the latter is given by Price (1964)]. For the first option, the multiplier gain must be measured with a single collector and the possibility of mass effects in the conversion efficiency of the first dynode must be evaluated. For the second, the conversion efficiency can also be important, particularly if the counting apparatus has special pulse height requirements.

D. RF Absorption in ICR

This is listed separately because in most of the ICR experiments a separate detector is not used. Instead, the resonant oscillator circuit is used to measure the ion intensities because of its great sensitivity, as was discussed in Subsection 3.3.E.

3.5. Uses of Mass Spectrometry

The topics that are discussed below are somewhat arbitrary in their division and often overlap with one another; for example, the discussion of geochemical applications of mass spectrometry (meteorites, etc.) overlaps with atmospheric and planetary composition. Nevertheless, because of the breadth of work in these areas, breaks along rough subject matter are convenient.

A. Isotope Analysis, Geochemistry, and Isotope Separation

From its inception mass spectrometry was used to measure the isotopic abundances of the elements (Dempster, 1918; Aston, 1919), and once the isotopic abundances were established, mass spectrometric research in this area shifted toward determining atomic masses to very high accuracy. Much of the current information about the identities and abundances of the minor isotopes has come from mass spectrometric studies, since the determination of relative abundances to an accuracy of about 1 part in 1000 is not very difficult. Higher accuracies become progressively more difficult [for a discussion of some of the minor isotopes, see McMullen and Thode (1963) and Hintenberger (1966)]. For example, White *et al.* (1955) studied the abundance of tantalum isotopes and found ^{180}Ta to be $\sim 0.01\%$ of ^{181}Ta and, furthermore, placed a limit of $< 10^{-4}\%$ on other Ta isotopes.

The isotope of a particular nuclide may be an important indicator of radioactive decay, of the age of the sample being studied, and of any processes leading to fractionation in the sample. To illustrate these points it may be mentioned that when sedimentary rocks are analyzed for their constituents it is found that they contain ^{40}Ar in higher amounts than the atmospheric abundance and this turns out to be due to the decay of ^{40}K (^{40}K has a natural abundance of $\sim 0.01\%$, a half-life of $\sim 1.3 \times 10^9$ years, and decays to ^{40}Ar by K-electron capture followed by γ emission). The ratio $^{40}Ar/^{40}K$ can then give information about the age of the sample, since radioactive decay is a unimolecular process. As an example, consider the radioactive decay process

$$A \rightarrow B + \gamma. \tag{3.28}$$

The rate equation is $dA/dt = -\lambda t$, where λ is the decay constant (the half-life of the atom, τ, is equal to $0.693/\lambda$) and t the time. The amount of B formed after a time t is $A_0 - A_0 \exp(-\lambda_A t)$, where A_0 is the initial concentration of A. This simple scheme was, in fact, used by Nier (1939) to determine the age of a number of rocks. He measured the abundances of ^{206}Pb and ^{207}Pb, which are end products of the decay of ^{238}U and ^{235}U, respectively. In addition, by measuring the abundances of ^{238}U and ^{235}U and knowing the half-lives of these isotopes, he related the time t to the ratio of the isotopes:

$$\frac{[^{207}Pb]}{[^{206}Pb]} = \frac{[^{235}U]\,[\exp(\lambda_{^{235}U}t) - 1]}{[^{238}U]\,[\exp(\lambda_{^{238}U}t) - 1]}. \tag{3.29}$$

From this he derived a value of 2.2×10^9 yr. Later, similar studies were performed on meteorites and these led to ages of 4.5×10^9 years (Collins *et al.*, 1953; Kulp, 1955). Other isotope pairs such as Rb–Sr and Re–Os have been used to determine the ages of meteorites [for a review of the early work see Hintenberger (1962); for later work see McCulloch and Wasserberg (1978)]. Another pair of isotopes that has been used to study the age of meteorites is $^{143}Nd/^{144}Nd$. Very careful mass spectrometric measurements of this ratio led to an age of $4.56 \pm 0.08 \times 10^9$ years for the Juvinas meteorite (O'Nions *et al.*, 1979). Related studies include the measurements of abundances of the elements in tektites, those small glassy objects which are found in well-defined areas on the surface of the earth. Much of the analysis of the composition of tektites was performed on mass spectrometers, and many books and articles have been written speculating on their origin. Most observers agree now on their extraterrestrial origin [see Vand (1965)], although the possibility of a terrestrial origin has not been eliminated [for contrasting views see Taylor and McLennan (1979) and O'Keefe (1980)]. In addition to these studies, much work has been done on trying to assess the variation in isotopic distribution of some of the elements in meteorites, terrestrial rocks, and planetary samples (Clayton, 1978; Bochsler, 1983). The situation is somewhat complicated by the possibility of fractionation among the isotopes. An example is the wide variation in $^{15}N/^{14}N$ observed in the solar system as established by means of mass spectrometric analysis, a variation that has broad implications regarding the age of the solar system [for a review see Geiss and Bochsler (1982)]. Other isotopic variations are observed in meteorites, and from analysis of the Mg/Al ratio in the Allende meteorite information about an extinct isotope, ^{26}Al, has been derived [see Bochsler (1983)]. The types of measurements mentioned above are simple in principle, but are quite difficult to carry out and require a great deal of effort and patience (Kung and Clayton, 1978).

Information about the half-life can also be obtained from careful measurements of isotopic abundances. For example, Inghram *et al.* (1951) determined the half-life of ^{240}Pu to be 6580 ± 40 years by measuring the abundances of ^{239}Pu, ^{240}Pu, ^{235}U, and ^{236}U and using the known half-life of ^{239}Pu.

The determination of masses to very high accuracy is important in understanding the binding forces in atoms. Thus the determination of the atomic masses of H and D to be $1.008144 \pm 2 \times 10^{-6}$ and $2.0147406 \pm 6 \times 10^{-6}$ (Quisenberry *et al.*, 1956) led to a determination of the binding energy in D. A comprehensive picture of the binding energy as a function of mass has emerged from this type of work (Collins *et al.*, 1954).

Fairly early in the growth of mass spectrometry, it was realized that it could be used to separate isotopes of the elements, although this research did not really get under way until the beginning of World War II [for a historical survey, see review by Karmohapatro (1976)]. The early attempts were hampered by low ion intensities, a situation that changed as more effort went into understanding ion and electron optics. Probably the credit for the first use of a mass spectrometer to obtain a sample of a particular isotope goes to Smyth *et al.* (1934), who prepared small (micrograms) samples of ^{6}Li, ^{7}Li, ^{39}K, and ^{41}K. The electromagnetic isotope separators (called calutrons), which have been used to obtain mass-analyzed beams approaching an ampere, are 180° magnetic analyzers of 48 in. radius of curvature. These instruments are used to produce a large number of isotopes of many elements, particularly metals (Keim, 1955; Allen *et al.*, 1955).

B. Analytical Chemistry

This application of mass spectrometry has been alluded to a number of times above. Quite from the beginning, it was thought by Dempster and Aston that the mass spectrometer could be used as a powerful analytical instrument, and indeed its adoption as such became almost universal with the introduction of commercial mass spectrometers that could perform routine analysis [for a description of the early instrumentation, see Dibeler (1963)]. The early and successful efforts to use mass spectrometry for analysis used electron impact ionization; because of the complexity of the resulting fragmentation patterns, much effort was devoted to cataloguing these patterns under standardized conditions for many compounds [see, for example, Cornu and Massot (1975)]. The efforts at systematizing the fragmentation patterns lead to increased understanding of the physics of ionization, and this, in turn, lead to the development of progressively more sophisticated analytical techniques [see McLafferty (1966a) and Beynon and Morgan (1978)]. Appreciation of the effect of molecular structures on molecular decomposition and on the formation of ions containing particular functional groups led to ever more complicated structures being determined with the mass spectrometer. For example, the use of a high-resolution mass spectrometer equipped with a field ionization source made it possible for Ligon (1979) to analyze a sample of polyphenylene oxide having an average molecular weight of ~ 2000; in this case ions of $(C_6H_4O)_n^+$ with m/e as high as ~ 3000 were observed. A further advance in the use of mass spectrometry for analysis occurred when mass spectrometers were successfully coupled to liquid chromatography (LC) and gas chromatrography (GC) directly, so that fragmentation patterns of a *separated* component could be observed directly (Ligon, 1979).

This type of an application has been particularly useful in forensic and biomedical research. For example, Facchetti *et al.* (1980) were able to measure dioxin contamination in the blood of women exposed to dioxin following an accident in Seveso(Italy) by using the combination of gas chromatographic separation followed by mass analysis. This combination of instrumental techniques (GC/MS) or LC/MS) has also had some use in the mass spectrometric analysis of hormones and biomedical compounds. When these techniques are coupled with modern computers, so that a library containing $>10^5$ mass spectra is directly accessible for comparison with an unknown mass fragmentation pattern, the result can be impressive. Several such instruments are currently available commercially [a discussion of some of the commercial instruments available is given by Middleditch (1979)].

The development of FT-ICR as an instrument for routine analytical use has made it possible to obtain high-resolution mass spectra fairly easily. For example, in a recent study (Allemann *et al.*, 1983) resolution ($m/\Delta m$) of the order of 10^8 was observed at $m/e = 18$ (H_2O^+) and at $m/e = 1466$ and 1485 (M^+ and $M{-}F^+$ for the compound $C_{30}F_{56}H_3$).

The coupling of a gas chromatograph and an FT-ICR mass spectrometer has been suggested as a way of obtaining a large dynamic range and a high-resolution spectrum of each of the components of a mixture (Ledford *et al.*, 1980), and indeed the use of ICR as a GC detector has been studied (Nguyen *et al.*, 1981). In another recent study (Beuhler and Friedman, 1982) water cluster ions with $m/e < 59{,}000$ were analyzed with a quadrupole mass filter. Devienne *et al.* (1983) have used a double-focusing mass spectrometer to analyze clusters of uranium with as many as 37 uranium atoms ($m/e \sim 8800$ (amu).

A development to which reference has already been made is ^{252}Cf fission fragment spectroscopy. This technique and the related use of other fission material have been very useful in the analysis of biochemicals. For example, Håkansson *et al.* (1982) used 90-MeV ^{127}I (formed in an accelerator and having +20 charges) to bombard a sample of bovine insulin; the ions thus formed were analyzed with a time-of-flight mass spectrometer equipped with a multichannel array detector. By the use of multichannel scaling techniques these authors obtained a mass spectrum in the range 2000–7000 amu and observed a peak at $m/e = 5730 \pm 10$ corresponding to the parent ion of insulin [insulin is a protein and has a complex structure, which is summarized by Klostermeyer and Humbel (1966); its molecular weight is an average because of isotope contributions and because of the presence of water of hydration). In addition, a peak at $m/e \sim 12{,}000$ was observed and was attributed to the dimer of insulin. This type of research with particular application to biomedical research has become a specialty of its own, and *Biomedical Mass Spectrometry* and *Organic Mass Spectrometry* are journals devoted to this research.

Another recent innovation in the field of analytical mass spectrometry has been the development of MS/MS techniques. Here, a mass spectrometer is used to analyze a sample and, following mass analysis, a particular fragment, or a group of fragments, is injected into a second mass spectrometer for high-resolution analysis. The procedure is complex and powerful [see McLaufferty (1981)], since by suitable engineering of the region between the two mass spectrometers structural information about the original ion can be obtained. This can be illustrated by an example given by McLafferty (1981): the ionization of 5-methyl-3-hexanone [$CH_3CH_2COCH_2CH(CH_3)_2$] by electron impact. Among the ions generated by the electron impact of this ketone is a fragment at $m/e = 57$, which can be attributed to $C_4H_9^+$ ($m/e = 57.070$) and $C_2H_5CO^+$ ($m/e = 57.034$), corresponding to the scission at the C_3–C_4 position and subsequent ionization of the fragments. Having formed the fragment at $m/e = 57$ in the first mass spectrometer, the ions enter a region where they undergo collision-induced decomposition followed by mass analysis with a second mass spectrometer. The collision-induced decomposition patterns for $C_4H_9^+$ and $C_2H_5CO^+$ are different, and by comparing this structure with a known pattern (obtained by the fragmentation of $C_4H_9^+$ from C_4H_{10}, for example) a decision can be made as to which ion is present. The example given is a simple one and the answer could also have been obtained by other means. However, when the parent molecule is quite large (e.g., a peptide) this technique can be very helpful in structure elucidation.

The analysis of liquid organic compounds with electrohydrodynamic ionization also seems to have some promise (Simons *et al.*, 1974). In these experiments a liquid in a capillary is ionized by a strong electrostatic field and the ions thus produced are characteristic of the liquid; in the study just cited amino acids were analyzed. Large organic molecules have also been analyzed using negative ion–chemical ionization, as, for example, in the mass analysis of the pentafluorobenzoyl derivative of Δ^9-tetrahydrocannabinol, where quantities of the order of 10^{-18} mole were used for analysis. A review of mass spectrometric research with particular emphasis on biomedical and biochemical analysis has recently been published by Burlingame *et al.* (1982). By combining mass spectral patterns obtained by different techniques, information about the structure of large molecules or parts of large molecules (such as amino acids) can be obtained (Schulten, 1979; Nakanishi and Occolowitz, 1979). The interpretation of high-resolution mass spectra ($m/\Delta m \sim 150{,}000$) requires some experience, but once that is gained this approach can be very useful in structural work (McLafferty, 1966b).

C. Analysis of Solids

Here we come to a topic which, in the early days of mass spectrometry, was of great interest in industrial studies, particularly in metal processing applications. The lines between this branch of mass spectrometry and other branches were blurred, however, as the biochemicals that can be mass analyzed became bigger, and as it became necessary to find a way to analyze solid organic compounds. In its early application, the analysis of solids was performed using spark sources or high-temperature Knudsen cells, which will be mentioned in more detail below. More recently, other, more sophisticated tools have been developed for the analysis of solids with less violence than is present in spark sources.

The spark source was one of the first ion sources used in mass spectrometry and it continues to be used for the analysis of solid samples for their elemental composition. It has a number of disadvantages, among which are the inconvenience of breaking vacuum for the insertion of the photographic plate, the difficulty of using the method with material that is not conductive, and the problem of trying to analyze unstable samples. Other disadvantages were discussed in Subsection 3.3.H. The difficulty related to the use of photographic plates is overcome if new methods of electro-optical (continuous-channel electron multiplier arrays followed by a phosphorescent) detection are used (Donohue *et al.*, 1980).

One of the earliest attempts to bypass the limitations of the spark source was made by Barrington *et al.* (1966), who developed the ion microprobe mass spectrometer. In this instrument a beam of 10-keV ions bombard a surface and ions sputtered off the surface are mass-analyzed. Thus, Barrington *et al.* (1966) were able to analyze the composition of thin films and to study the variation in composition with depth. Because of the focusing of the primary beam the technique is quite sensitive and requires small samples (surface area of 0.1 mm^2), and, in fact, Barrington *et al.* demonstrated its utility by analyzing a piece of the Holbrook meteorite. This study indicated that $^{7}Li/^{6}Li$ varied widely along the surface of the meteorite. In a somewhat related method Castaing and Slodzian (1966) bombarded a surface with a beam of mass-selected ions and observed the image of the sputtered ions on a fluorescence screen, thereby obtaining an image of the surface of the plate and of the changes taking place as bombardment continued. In a later study Dillon *et al.* (1968) bombarded a polymer surface with N_2^+ at 2 keV and observed ions characteristic of the surface. These studies became the progenitors of a new technique for the analysis of solids, SIMS (acronym for secondary ion mass spectrometry), in which a beam of ions at an energy of 2–10 keV is used to bombard a surface and the ions (positive and negative) sputtered off that surface are mass-analyzed (usually magnetic sector or double-focusing mass spectrometers are used). When Ar^+ impinges on an aluminum surface in an oxygen atmosphere (pressure = 10^{-6} to 10^{-4} torr), the ions Al_2^+, Al^{2+}, O^-, AlO^-, and AlO_2^- are observed (Castaing and Hennequin, 1971). The instrumentation has been simplified by the use of quadrupole mass filters for mass analysis of the secondary ions (Huber *et al.*, 1972). SIMS has been very useful in studying surfaces, their composition, thicknesses of layers, and contamination of the surfaces. One of the first uses of SIMS was to study the surface of a Cu–2% Be plate (which is widely used in electron multipliers) and to measure the contaminants on the surface (Huber *et al.*, 1972); when 2.4-keV Ar^+ bombarded this surface the following ions were observed: O^-, OH^-, C^-, C_2H^-, $C_2H_2^-$, Cl^-, Cu^+, Be^+, Na^+, K^+, Al^+, Cr^+, and $(C_nH_m)^+$. After bakeout for 10 h at 350°C most of these ions were considerably reduced, but not eliminated; the only exception was Cu^+, which disappeared. The latter observation was explained as being due to the diffusion of Be to the surface, causing Be to become the target material. In a recent study SIMS was used to investigate the sputtering mechanism and the crystal structure of CsI when the latter is bombarded by 4.7-keV Xe^+ ions (Barlak *et al.*, 1982). In this work clusters of CsI having the formula $Cs(CsI)_n^+$, where $n = 1–70$ ($m/e > 18{,}000$), were observed; furthermore, certain structures corresponding to well-defined values of n ($n = 13, 22, 31, 37, 52,$ and 62) seemed to have abnormally low abundances, leading the authors to conclude that these clusters correspond to intrinsically more stable structures, which are harder to desorb. Other studies have been performed to determine ion implantation depths (Leta *et al.*, 1980) and depth profiles (Huber *et al.*, 1974), and to determine the composition of dental enamel (Larsson *et al.*, 1978).

A related method for probing surfaces is FAB (acronym for fast atom bombardment). When an ion undergoes charge exchange,

$$A^+ + B \rightarrow A + B^+, \tag{3.30}$$

the reaction occurs when the internuclear separation between A^+ and B is fairly large, with the result that A retains much of its energy. If the reaction is symmetric ($A^+ + A \rightarrow A^+ + A$), there is no internal excitation in the product ion, and the neutral product carries nearly all the forward momentum. Fast atom bombardment uses energetic neutrals (atoms) formed by charge exchange reactions such as (3.30) above. These fast atoms then bombard a surface and desorb ions from it. While SIMS has been used mostly in studying the composition and structure of metallic surfaces, FAB has assumed a similar role in the analysis of biochemical and biomedical materials. For example, in a recent study Barber *et al.* (1981) generated a beam of Ar^+ in a discharge ion source and then neutralized it by passing it through a cell containing Ar gas at high pressures (10^{-3} to 10^{-4} torr). The primary Ar^+ had kinetic energies that were tunable between 1 and 8 keV. The intensity of the fast neutral atoms can be varied, but in the work just cited a flux of 10^{10} to 10^{11} atoms cm^{-2} s^{-1} was used. Under these conditions Barber *et al.* were successful in obtaining mass spectra of peptides (e.g., human gastrin, whose molecular weight is 2096 amu) and of vitamin B_{12}. Similarly, Gibson and Biemann (1982) recently determined the primary structure of macromomycin and a number of other proteins with FAB.

D. Composition Measurements in the Atmosphere

This topic overlaps with the composition measurements on meteorites, which were discussed in Subsection 3.5.A; in this section other aspects of this problem will be covered, as well as general studies of the composition of the earth's atmosphere and of other planets. In these experiments the data on composition are transmitted by telemetry.

The first mass spectrometric measurements of the composition of the earth's atmosphere seem to have been made by Johnson *et al.* (1958), who flew a Bennett-type mass spectrometer and measured the nighttime ion composition at 115 km. They observed positive ions at $m/e = 14$, 16, 18, 28, 30, and 32 and a negative ion at $m/e = 46$. These measurements were explained in terms of the then-prevailing understanding of atmospheric composition, which postulated the ions to be N^+, O^+, N_2^+, NO^+, O_2^+, and some H_2O^+. Later measurements by Istomin and Pokhunkov (1963), also using a Bennett-type mass spectrometer, gave similar results with the addition of ions at $m/e = 24$, 40, and 56 at an altitude of 105 km; the latter ions were attributed to Mg^+, Ca^+, and Fe^+. In both of these studies the resolution was not very high, and a number of questions remained on how to interpret the observations, although the metallic ions were attributed to the ablation of metals from meteors. The next advance in atmospheric composition measurements came when Nier *et al.* (1964) flew a small double-focusing mass spectrometer and a 90° sector mass spectrometer at altitudes between 90 and 209 km. They used an electron impact ion source to measure the neutral composition and obtained profiles for N_2, O_2, and O. The reliability of the data on O was questioned in view of surface reactions and accommodation of O atoms.

These studies, which confirmed a simple picture of the thermosphere and ionosphere [for definitions of notations and terms and for a discussion of the subject, see the treatise by Banks and Kockarts (1973)], were jolted somewhat when Narcisi and Bailey (1965) published the results of an experiment in which they flew a quadrupole mass filter pumped by a liquid nitrogen-chilled trap in the altitude region 64–105 km. They confirmed the metal ion layer by obtaining the triplet at $m/e = 24$, 25, and 26 corresponding in relative abundance to those of the Mg^+ isotopes. In addition, they obtained the first indication of the existence of hydronium ion clusters $H^+ \cdot (H_2O)_n$. Later studies (Narcisi, 1966) improved on the resolution and the sensitivity, obtaining altitude profiles for $m/e = 23$ (Na^+) and correctly assigning the ion at $m/e = 28$ to Si^+.

Later work with higher sensitivity and resolution (Narcisi, 1968; Narcisi and Roth, 1970; Goldberg and Aikin, 1971; Krankowsky *et al.*, 1972; Narcisi, 1973; Zhlood'ko *et al.*, 1975; Zbinden *et al.*, 1975; and Herrmann *et al.*, 1978) agreed on the main features of the positive-ion composition of the lower D and E layers of the ionosphere (roughly 80–130 km), and the picture that emerges is this: The major ions at 100–130 km are NO^+ and O_2^+ (the densities being $\sim 4 \times 10^3$ and 800 cm^{-3}, respectively, at $\sim$130 km); at lower altitudes metallic ions arising from meteor ablation become important at $\sim$95 km [Fe^+ reaching densities as high as 1×10^4 cm^{-3} (Swider, 1984)]; at lower altitudes (<80 km) NO^+ and O^+ begin to decrease and hydronium ion clusters, $H^+ \cdot (H_2O)_n$, begin to become very important.

Much effort has been spent in trying to understand the processes by which these ions are formed, and some of the mass identifications have turned out to be incorrect. Understanding of the processes that give rise to these ions has gone hand in hand with measurements of rate constants for ion–molecule reactions, a subject that will be discussed in Subsection 3.5.F. An example is the case of the ion at $m/e = 48$, which was attributed to Ti^+ (Zbinden *et al.*, 1975). Later analysis, using newly measured rate constants (Swider *et al.*, 1979), showed this ion to be due to SO^+. Some problems remain in this area, particularly in the identification of high-mass clusters and in the identification of metallic compounds, if any, in ionic form. Large clusters, such as $H^+ \cdot (H_2O)_n$, can be broken up in collisions with the entrance orifice or with the ambient gas, and it is possible that n is much larger than the observed maximum [see Narcisi and Roth (1970)]. The metallic species have been the subject of many studies, but some problems remain [see discussions by Swider (1969) and (Murad (1978)], particularly since the identities of neutral intermediates can affect the ion concentrations (Murad and Swider, 1979). Positive ions such as Fe^+ have also been measured mass spectrometrically at much higher altitudes (~300 km) aboard satellites (Grebowsky and Brinton, 1978). High-energy ions such as H^+, He^{2+}, and O^{6+} from the solar wind have been analyzed mass spectrometrically aboard an ISEE-C satellite (Coplan *et al.*, 1978; Kunz *et al.*, 1983).

In addition to the positive ions, there are negative ions in the lower D region, and here there are many problems because of the difficulty of the measurements and because contamination can be quite serious. For example, in cases where instruments were cleaned with fluorocarbons, it was found that a major ion was Cl^-. The main negative ions seem to be hydrates of CO_3 and NO_3, $CO_3^- \cdot (H_2O)_n$ and $NO_3^- \cdot (H_2O)_n$ (Narcisi, 1973, and references cited therein).

Composition of the neutral atmosphere has also been determined with the mass spectrometer, and the major constituents N_2, O_2, O, and Ar have been measured at altitudes of 100–200 km (Hedin and Nier, 1966; Gross and von Zahn, 1971; Kayser and Potter, 1978; Trinks *et al.*, 1978). Minor constituents such as CO_2, NO, N, and H_2O have also been measured in this altitude region (Offermann and von Zahn, 1971; Offermann *et al.*, 1972). There are questions about the H_2O data because of the difficulty of avoiding contamination and because of the possibility that water can be desorbed from the walls when other particles collide with a metal surface. In addition to these experiments, determinations of positive- and negative-ion composition in the stratosphere have been performed with balloon-borne mass spectrometers (Arnold *et al.*, 1981; Arijs *et al.*, 1982). The situation here is much more complex because the ions represent a very small fraction of the ambient (perhaps 1 part in 10^{10}) and because the high ambient pressure necessitates limiting the intake of sample through an orifice, possibly giving rise to ions that are produced in the expansion of the gas.

Finally, it is worth mentioning that mass spectrometers aboard the Viking Mars Lander have given information about the composition of the soil and about the atmosphere of Mars [see Biemann *et al.* (1976a,b)].

E. High-Temperature Mass Spectrometry and Thermochemistry

Mass spectrometry has probably affected thermochemistry and chemical thermodynamics more profoundly than any other field. Whereas before its introduction dissociation energies were obtainable accurately only for a few well-behaved molecules, the use of mass spectrometers made it possible to have a universal method for the determination of thermochemical properties (heats of formation and heats of reaction). A few extensive reviews of the subject have been published (Inghram and Drowart, 1960; Drowart and Goldfinger, 1967; Grimley, 1967) and reference is made to these for a detailed treatment.

The determination of thermochemical properties of gaseous species with the mass spectrometer began when two groups almost simultaneously (Chupka and Inghram, 1953a,b; Honig, 1953) analyzed the molecular species evaporating from a carbon surface. They observed C, C_2, and C_3 and, from the temperature dependence of the intensities of these ions, derived heats of sublimation of these species. At that time a controversy had been raging about the heat of sublimation of carbon for almost 50 years (this quantity is important in that the heat of formation of any gaseous carbon-containing compound depends on the heat of formation of gaseous C atoms). The controversy had to do with a choice for this heat of a low value (~ 140 kcal/mole) or a high value (~ 170 kcal/mole). The preliminary results just mentioned confirmed the high value. A fuller discussion of this topic is given by Gaydon (1968). Questions about these mass spectrometric results were raised, particularly about whether the measurements yielded the heat of sublimation or the activation energy of evaporation. To answer these questions Chupka and Inghram (1955) conducted new experiments in a Knudsen cell, with a material heated in the cell; gaseous species effuse from the cell the cell, ensuring that any effusing molecule had undergone many collisions with the wall material and was in thermodynamic equilibrium. By measuring the ion intensity as a function of temperature, Chupka and Inghram calculated the heats of sublimation of C, C_2, and C_3 to be 170, 190, and 200 kcal/mole, respectively. This study immediately, and finally settled the controversy over the heat of sublimation of carbon.

Before proceeding further, it is worthwhile to review the pertinent thermodynamic laws so that the work in this field can be discussed adequately and its importance appreciated. Consider a hypothetical equilibrium

$$A(s) = A(g). \tag{3.31}$$

The equilibrium constant k_{eq} for this reaction is simply P_A, where P is the pressure [assuming A(s) has an activity of 1]. The second law of thermodynamics is [for a detailed treatment see Lewis *et al.* (1961)]:

$$\Delta F = \Delta H - T\,\Delta S \tag{3.32}$$

and

$$\Delta F = -RT \ln k_{eq}, \tag{3.33}$$

where ΔF is the reaction free energy, ΔH the heat (enthalpy) of reaction, ΔS the entropy of reaction, T the temperature, and R the gas constant. By rearranging we obtain

$$\ln k_{eq} = \Delta S/R - \Delta H/RT, \tag{3.34}$$

which is the well-known van't Hoff equation. We now see two ways of calculating ΔH:

(1) Second-law treatment: Measure k_{eq} as a function of temperature and plot $\ln k_{eq}$ as a function of $1/T$. In this case the plot should be a striaght line with a slope of $\Delta H/R$ and an intercept of $\Delta S/R$.

(2) Third-law treatment: Calculate ΔS, or a function related to it, from molecular parameters (vibrational frequency and moment of inertia, if diatomic or larger, and energy levels and statistical weights of ground and low-lying electronic states), using statistical-mechanical procedures [for a description see Mayer and Mayer (1940)]. Then each measurement of k_{eq} would yield a heat of reaction.

In practice, a number of details make mass spectrometric measurement of thermodynamic properties a little more difficult than it seems. In the hypothetical example given above, (3.31), the equilibrium constant k_{eq} has the dimension of pressure ($k_{eq} = P_A$), which means that the ion intensity has to be converted to pressure, as shown in Eq. (3.3). This equation will now be modified slightly to

$$I_A^+ \cdot T = P_A \cdot \Gamma \cdot \sigma \cdot (\mathrm{EE} - \mathrm{IP}), \tag{3.35}$$

where I_A^+ is the ion current, T the gas temperture, P_A the pressure, Γ the instrument factor (incorporating transmission correction, detector efficiency, electron density, and path length), σ the electron impact ionization cross section, EE the electron energy, and IP the ionization potential of the species in question. Generally, Γ is obtained by calibrating the instrument with a solid (e.g., silver or gold) whose vapor pressure and electron impact ionization cross section are known. The temperature T enters in the expression from the ideal gas law and essentially corrects for the velocities, which are different at different temperatures. The expression (EE − IP) comes about because over a narrow range above threshold, the electron impact ionization cross section increases linearly with energy. Using this technique, Chupka and Inghram measured P_C over graphite and determined the heat of sublimation of C to be 171 ± 10 kcal/mole. Later measurements confirmed these results (Wachi and Gilmartin, 1972); the currently accepted value of 171.29 ± 0.11 kcal/mole (Chase *et al.*, 1982) is based on a spectroscopic determination of the dissociation energy of carbon monoxide $D_0^0(\mathrm{CO})$.

In order to bypass the need to measure absolute pressures, sometimes gaseous isomolecular equilibria are studied. For example, consider an equilibrium that was studied a few years ago (Murad and Hildenbrand, 1975):

$$\mathrm{BO(g) + Zr(g) = B(g) + ZrO(g)}. \tag{3.36}$$

In the above work, $D_0^0(\mathrm{BO})$ was known and $\Delta H = D_0^0(\mathrm{ZrO}) - D_0^0(\mathrm{BO})$. Thus a measurement of ΔH would yield $D_0^0(\mathrm{ZrO})$ directly. The intensities of the molecular ions were measured at a constant increment above threshold, i.e., at constant (EE − IP). $k_{eq} = P_B \cdot P_{ZrO}/P_{BO} \cdot P_{Zr}$. When the intensity from Eq. (3.35) is substituted, we obtain

$$k_{eq} = \{[\mathrm{B}^+][\mathrm{ZrO}^+]/[\mathrm{BO}^+][\mathrm{Zr}^+]\} \cdot (\sigma_{BO} \cdot \sigma_{Zr}/\sigma_B \cdot \sigma_{ZrO}) \cdot \Gamma_{eq}, \tag{3.37}$$

where Γ_{eq} is the ratio of the instrumental sensitivities. For the magnetic mass spectrometer the transmission is nearly constant with mass and the detector efficiency ratios are ~ 1. Thus only the correction due to σ is left. These can be estimated, and there is evidence that for exchange equilibria such as (3.36) the correction is ~ 1. It should be noted that since ΔH varies with $\ln k_{eq}$, an uncertainty of a factor of 2 in the ratio of σ's appears as $RT \ln 2$ in ΔH, corresponding to an uncertainty of ± 2.8 kcal/mole at 2000 K. Thus k_{eq} can be calculated directly from the intensities. These measurements were in agreement with those obtained from a gas–solid equilibrium

$$\mathrm{Zr(s) + ZrO_2(s) = 2ZrO(g)}, \tag{3.38}$$

which has a dimension of pressure. The heat of formation of ZrO(g), and hence the dissociation energy of ZrO$(D_0^0(\mathrm{ZrO}) = \Delta H_f(\mathrm{Zr}) + \Delta H_f(\mathrm{O}) - \Delta H_f(\mathrm{ZrO})]$ derived from equilibria (3.36) and (3.38) using second- and third-law treatments, agreed very well with each other.

In this manner, hundreds of dissociation energies have been obtained [see Huber and Herzberg (1979)]. The method, while powerful, is not perfect, and problems can arise. One of the most troublesome is the failure to establish thermodynamic equilibrium, and a good criterion for that is the consistency of heats derived from the third-law treatment. As mentioned above, when the molecular constants are available it is possible to calculate the entropy term in Eq. (3.34), and that combined with the equilibrium measurements leads to a heat of reaction at each temperature. If thermodynamic equilibrium has not been established, there is usually a trend in the heats with temperature. Thus it becomes advantageous to cover as wide a temperature range as possible. An example of such a problem can be given based on the author's experience (Hildenbrand and Murad, 1969). In this particular case it was desired to measure the thermochemical properties of SiO(g), and an isomolecular equilibrium was chosen,

$$\mathrm{Ge(g) + SiO(g) = GeO(g) + Si(g)}, \tag{3.39}$$

because D_0^0(GeO) was well established. Because GeO_2(s), which was the source of GeO(g), had a much higher vapor pressure than Si, it was placed in a lower chamber of the cell and a diaphragm with a pinhole separated this chamber from an upper chamber that contained Si(s). This arrangement permitted a pressure differential such that the lower chamber had considerably higher pressure than the upper and GeO(g) passed over Si(s). Ion intensities were measured in the temperature range 1426–1560 K. The dissociation energy of SiO derived from these measurements was $\sim$6 kcal/mole lower than earlier mass spectrometric measurements. Soon after the work was published it became apparent that this value of D_0^0(SiO) was too low. The problem was the failure to establish thermodynamic equilibrium, and since the temperature range was narrow, a trend in third-law heats was not apparent. Later measurements (Hildenbrand, 1972) confirmed this and reestablished $D_0^0(\mathrm{SiO}) = 188.6 \pm 2.8$ kcal/mole. This illustrates the care that must be taken to make sure that a thermodynamic equilibrium has been established. When the intensities are high and it is possible to obtain reliable second-law heats, then agreement between the two heats is good evidence for the establishment of a thermodynamic equilibrium.

Another problem in this type of work is the presence of impurities in a sample. An example is the measurement of the dissociation energy of MgO (Drowart *et al.*, 1964), which was complicated by the presence in the sample of a small impurity of ^{40}Ca ($^{24}\mathrm{Mg}^{16}\mathrm{O} = {}^{40}\mathrm{Ca}$). A third problem in these measurements has been alluded to already, namely the electron impact ionization crosssections. An example of this effect of this factor is provided by the dissociation energy of AlO. In this case the mass spectrometric results gave $D_0^0(\mathrm{AlO}) = 118 \pm 3$ kcal/mole (Hildenbrand, 1973), while a chemiluminescence study gave 118.3 ± 2 kcal/mole (Gole and Zare, 1972). When cross sections were taken into account (Drowart, 1973), the dissociation energy of AlO derived from mass spectrometric measurements was raised to 121.8 ± 3 kal/mole. More recent laser-induced fluoroscence measurements (Dagdigian *et al.*, 1975) have yielded 120.7 ± 1.3 kcal/mole for D_0^0(AlO).

The many equilibria such as (3.39) which have been measured have been used to build a network of interrelated dissociation energies. Much of the work so far has concentrated on the gaseous monoxides, monohalides, and some intermetallic species. A few measurements have been made on carbides, cyanides, and hydrides. More complex vapor species, such as carbonates and nitrates, have not yet been investigated in a systematic way. For the gaseous monoxides, a network that relates all the dissociation energies has been assembled (Pedley and Marshall, 1983).

F. Ion–Molecule Reactions

From the beginning, workers in mass spectrometry observed ion species that could arise only from the reaction between ions and neutrals. In fact, H_3^+ was first reported by Dempster (1916); this ion is now known to arise from the reaction

$$H_2^+ + H_2 \rightarrow H_3^+ + H. \tag{3.40}$$

Since then, and particularly following World War II, this subject has evolved into a rather crowded specialty and with many applications (as, for example, in the case of chemical ionization sources, which were discussed in Subsection 3.2.C). A comprehensive historical survey is given by Franklin (1972) and by Lias and Ausloos (1975) and a summary of some of the publications that stand out in the development of this field is given by Franklin (1979).

Initially, ion–molecule reactions were considered a nuisance since they arose because of the poor vacuum systems of the day and because of the high pressures necessary to observe ion signals. As vacuum technology improved and as detectors became more and more sensitive, it became possible to eliminate these unwanted ions. At that point, investigators concerned with understanding basic reaction kinetics became interested in these strange species, and this led to the development of this field. Parenthetically, it is worth noting that the experimental study of a reaction such as (3.40) or

$$H^+ + D_2 \rightarrow HD^+ + D \tag{3.41}$$

is easier than study of the corresponding neutral reactions because it is easier to generate a pure reactant beam and to work at pressures low enough to ensure that secondary collisions are not taking place. In the late 1940s research on ion–molecule reactions proceeded along two lines: (1) mass spectrometry and (2) radiation chemistry. The first topic, mass spectrometry, will be discussed below. Radiation chemistry in relation to ion–molecule reactions will not be discussed, except to mention that when a sample is irradiated with nuclear particles (for example, γ-rays) products are formed that can only come from reactions of ions with neutrals. Readers interested in the subject are referred to the monograph by Lias and Ausloos (1975) for a full treatment of the topic.

In the initial phase, ion–molecule reactions were studied in the mass spectrometer by simply raising the pressure in the ion source and observing the mass spectrum. Ions that were observed at high pressure and whose intensity depend on the square root of the pressure were attributed to bimolecular ion–neutral reactions. The earliest such study was performed on the reaction

$$H_2O^+ + H_2O \rightarrow H_3O^+ + OH, \tag{3.42}$$

whose occurrence was established by the dependence of $[H_3O^+]$ on $[H_2O]^2$ (Mann *et al.*, 1940). The basis of chemical ionization mass spectrometry, CH_5^+, is formed by reaction (3.6), which was first reported by Tal'roze and Lyubimova (1952). For some time afterward a great deal of work was done on ion–molecule reactions in the ion source of the mass spectrometer, as mentioned above. These studies, which are generally called single-source experiments, were used to derive kinetic data (thermal rate constants) and reaction mechanisms. It will be instructive to consider how a rate constant is derived, using reaction (3.42) as an example. The rate equations are

$$-d[H_2O^+]/dt = k_{42}[H_2O^+][H_2O] \tag{3.43}$$

and

$$d[H_3O^+]/dt = k_{42}[H_2O^+][H_2O], \tag{3.44}$$

which lead to

$$[H_2O^+]/[H_2O^+]_0 = \exp(-k_{42}[H_2O]t) \tag{3.45}$$

and

$$[H_3O^+]/[H_2O^+]_0 = 1 - \exp(-k_{42}[H_2O]t), \tag{3.46}$$

where the subscript 0 denotes initial concentrations and t is the reaction time. At low conversion, which is the normal operating procedure, $[H_2O^+] \approx [H_2O^+]_0$ and $\{1 - \exp(-k_{42}[H_2O]t)\} \approx k_{42}[H_2O]t$. The reaction time is the time the ion spends in the ion source, and that depends on the path length and on the repeller field, which expels the ions from the source (see Fig. 3.2). Thus a plot of $[H_3O^+]/[H_2O^+]$ versus pressure at constant repeller field should yield a line whose slope is k_{42} at that energy. Many (perhaps thousands) of rate constants were obtained in this fashion. Other variations on this method are possible, and these include a pulsing technique that was first introduced by Tal'roze and Frankevich (1960). In this case both the repeller and the filament are pulsed sequentially in such a way that while electrons are entering the source the repeller field is turned off and the reaction proceeds at the ambient temperature (thermal energy). After the electron beam is turned off, the repeller is pulsed so that the ions are expelled. In this way Tal'roze and Frankevich measured k_6 and k_{42} to be 1.16×10^{-9} and 0.85×10^{-9} cm^3 molecule^{-1} s^{-1}, respectively.

The single-source technique was used to measure the rate constants and to follow the mechanisms of many reactions, and a full survey can be found in discussions by Franklin (1972) and Henchman (1972). Perhaps it is appropriate to include in this section the use of photoionization as a technique for studying ion–molecule reactions. In this case ions are formed by photoionization, and generally the ions are formed in their ground states. Because of the energy resolution that is available (by use of the monochromator) ions in particular vibrational levels can be prepared and their reactions studied. In this way, reaction (3.6) was studied by Poschenrieder and Warneck (1966). Other, similar experiments have been performed, and these have been summarized by Chupka (1972). One of the problems with single-source experiments is that it is sometimes hard to establish which ion causes which reaction. In principle, lowering the electron energy to the ionization threshold would identify the precursor. In practice, the electron beam has an energy distribution and it may be hard to preclude the formation of excited primary ions by the high-energy tail of the electrons; in addition, if the desired ion is a fragment ion, the adiabatic transition that would generate it in its ground state may not be accessible. Another problem is that there is an uncertainty in the reaction energy because the primary ions gain their full energy by falling through a potential between the repeller and the exit slit of the ion source. The energy that is used is an average energy, assuming the ions are formed in the middle of the ion source. This problem is solved by using pulsing techniques.

It was partially to answer some of these equations that Lindholm (1953) built what has come to be called a tandem mass spectrometer. In Lindholm's work one mass spectrometer was coupled to another mass spectrometer at right angles; thus a mass-selected ion beam from the first selector entered a collision chamber and the product ions were extracted at right angles. As understanding of the kinematics of ion–molecule reactions increased, it became obvious that this arrangement had inherent problems, in that if the products of the reaction had momentum in the forward direction, they were discriminated against. It was this problem that led Giese and Maier (1961, 1963a,b) to build a tandem mass spectrometer in which the reactant and product beams were collinear. The results were startling and confirmed the suspicion that the previous tandem instruments had discriminated against product ions with appreciable forward momentum. This work was followed by a number of other studies in which similar, as well as more sophisticated, tandem instruments were built for the study of ion–molecule reactions. A particularly important development was the assembly of a tandem mass spectrometer that could be used to determine the angular distribution of the products of ion–neutral reactions (Herman *et al.*, 1967; Gentry *et al.*, 1967). This type of experiment is now done by a number of groups and reviews of the subject are available (Futrell and Tiernan, 1972; Koski, 1975; Gentry, 1979).

A serious disadvantage of the use of tandem mass spectrometers to measure reaction cross sections is that they are limited to energies (in the laboratory system of coordinates) >0.5 eV. Comparison with single-source experiments is not easy because there the energy range is from thermal to a few electron volts. In addition, some of the theories and some of the applications (e.g., chemical reactions in the upper atmosphere) require the cross sections at thermal energies. Largely to answer these needs, other approaches began to develop. One of these new methods utilizes a merged beam, where an ion beam and a neutral beam travel parallel to each other at high absolute energies, but at low (thermal and up) relative velocities [for a review see Neynaber (1969); more recent work is discussed briefly by Gentry (1979)]. The fast neutral reactant beam is generated by charge exchange. Ionized species are formed and are mass-analyzed, and following mass analysis they enter a collision chamber where they undergo charge exchange reactions; the neutral atoms keep most of the forward momentum (described in Subsection 3.5.C in connection with FAB). Beside the fast neutral beam now comes a beam of mass-analyzed ions traveling at approximately the same energy. The two beams traverse a long path length, where they have a chance to interact at low energies. The reactants and the products then enter a third mass spectrometer, where they are analyzed and measured. This type of experiment has yielded a great deal of useful and interesting data; in fact, it is not limited to ion–neutral reactions, and a number of neutral–neutral reactions have been studied in this way. One disadvantage of the technique appears to be that enough excited states can be present in the neutral beam to affect the reaction. A case in point is the reaction

$$Na^+ + O_2 \rightarrow NaO^+ + O, \tag{3.47}$$

which was studied in a merged-beam experiment at thermal energies (Rol and Entemann, 1968). This result was at variance with crossed-beam and flowing afterglow experiments (Henderson *et al.*, 1967; Farragher *et al.*, 1969), which failed to detect NaO^+ in any measurable quantities. Later thermochemical measurement of $D_0^0(NaO)$ and $D_0^0(Na^+\text{-}O)$ established that the reaction is endothermic by almost 5 eV (Hildenbrand and Murad, 1970); hence the reaction can only proceed if one of the reactants is in an excited state.

In response to the then-critical need for rate constants at thermal energies for ion–neutral reactions, Ferguson *et al.* (1964) [see also Fehsenfeld (1966)] developed the flowing afterglow technique for measuring the rate constants of ion–neutral reactions. In this method a gas (usually helium) at a pressure of $\sim 1/2$ torr continuously flows through a tube at nearly thermal velocities

($\sim 10^4$ cm s^{-1}). At the entrance of the tube it is ionized by electron bombardment. Downstream, a gas is added, and since IP(He) is greater than that of any other gas, charge exchange (e.g., $He^+ + A \rightarrow He + A^+$) and dissociative charge transfer (e.g., $He^+ + A_2 \rightarrow He + A^+ + A$, if diatomic) take place. The ions thus formed are thermalized by collision with the buffer gas (helium) and are measured by a quadrupole mass filter located at the end of the flow tube. After the primary ions (A^+ in this case) have been measured, a second gas at a known pressure and flow rate is introduced downstream from the first injection port. The decrease in the primary ion beam is measured, and from that the reaction cross section or the rate constant is calculated [for a discussion of rate constants and cross sections see Johnson (1982)]. By utilizing this method, many rate constants (perhaps thousands) at thermal energies were obtained [see Ferguson (1972)]. The pressure of helium and the primary gas is adjusted to give the required ion. Later, the apparatus was modified and the product ions were measured. The plasma that is set up in the flow tube generates not only positive ions but also negative ions and metastable neutrals, and reactions of these species have been studied as well. A summary of the rate constants that have been measured in this manner is given by Albritton (1978). The interaction energy available in flowing afterglow experiments is limited to near thermal; in order to overcome this limitation a flow–drift tube was developed (Heimerl *et al.*, 1969). In this case the ions drift in the flow tube under the influence of a weak electric field before they enter the region where the neutral gas is injected. A quadrupole mass filter then analyzes the products of the reaction. In this manner interaction energies varying between thermal (~ 0.030 eV) and ~ 2 eV have been achieved (McFarland *et al.*, 1973; Kaneko, 1980).

While the flowing afterglow was a powerful tool in the study of thermal ion–neutral reactions at thermal energies, it had some disadvantages: the ions formed by collision with the ionized helium were not always predictable; the ions produced were a mixture of ions (positive, negative, neutral); and it was not easy to generate complex ions. These and other limitations led to a breakthrough of tremendous importance, namely the introduction of a mass-analyzed ion beam into the flow tube. SIFT (an acronym for selected ion flow tube) was introduced by Adams and Smith (1976) and has since become a major source of ion–neutral rate constants at thermal energies. In this method the primary ions are formed in an ion source and are mass-analyzed in a quadrupole mass filter. They are then injected upstream in a flow tube, as in the flowing afterglow method, and are thermalized by collision with the buffer gas (usually helium. Downstream a neutral gas is injected and farther downstream the reactant and product ions are extracted and are mass-analyzed in a second quadrupole mass filter. This innovation has been very important in developing the morphology of a particular species through a complex chain, as, for example, the processes leading from C^+ to CH_5^+ (Adams and Smith, 1978). A summary of these experiments is given by Smith and Adams (1979). In the short time since it was introduced, SIFT has acquired a dominant role in the field and its versatility seems to be unbounded; an example is its use to measure rate constants for the mutual neutralization of positive and negative ions (Smith *et al.*, 1978). An important development that has enhanced SIFT even more has been its adaptation to study of the internal energy content of product ions (Bierbaum *et al.*, 1977). Here infrared emission from products of ion–molecule reactions is measured directly, thus permitting a better characterization of the collision mechanism. A summary of this work has been published by Bierbaum *et al.* (1984).

While advances were being made in the use of the flowing afterglow to measure rate constants and reaction mechanisms, work on the use of ICR to achieve similar goals was being pursued by other investigators. Some of this work has been mentioned in the discussion of ICR (Subsection 3.3.E). The use of double-resonance techniques made it possible to follow the paths that led to the formation of a particular ion. In addition, the method has been perfected so that quantitative rate data can be obtained. Most of the investigators active in the use of ICR for the determination of rate constants have written reviews (Henis, 1972; Bowers and Su, 1973; Beauchamp, 1975; McIver, 1975; Nibbering, 1978), and the book by Lehman and Bursey (1976) discusses many of the mechanistic aspects of ion–molecule reactions studied by ICR techniques. Use of ICR to determine the energetics and the thermochemical properties of ions by the measurement of equilibrium constants of ion–molecule reactions will be discussed in the next section.

The above discussion is a very abbreviated summary of work being done in a complex field. Work on reactions of negative ions with molecules has not been mentioned explicitly, although it should be understood that all the methods mentioned above have been used to study ion–neutral reactions (Paulson, 1972; McIver, 1975; Tiernan, 1975; Bartmess and McIver, 1979). In addition, ion–molecule reactions can often lead to the emission of light, and this work has not been mentioned; much work on the infrared chemiluminescence has been done by Leone and his colleagues (Zwier *et al.*, 1980), and work on the visible and near-ultraviolet emission of products formed in ion–neutral reactions has been done by other investigators, among whom are Leventhal and his students (e.g., Bearman *et al.* (1977)], Marx and her colleagues [e.g., Gérard *et al.* (1978)], and Tiernan and his colleagues [e.g., Jones *et al.* (1980)]. Another active area of research that has not been covered in this section is the reaction and production of organometallic ions by ion–molecule reactions. Principal among the researchers in this area have been Beauchamp and his students [e.g., Armentrout and Beauchamp (1981)] and Freiser and his students (Byrd *et al.*, 1982). All these experiments use mass spectrometers of one kind or another. Another point that should be made is that theoretical treatments of collision processes played a synergistic part in the development and improvement of experimental techniques for the study of ion–molecule reactions. Among the workers in this field have been Stevenson [see Gioumousis and Stevenson (1958)], Kaufman [for a summary see Kaufman (1979)], Bowers and his students [for a summary see Su and Bowers (1979)], Bates [see Bates (1962)], and Dalgarno [see McDaniel *et al.* (1970)]. A very comprehensive treatment of ion–neutral collisions can be found in the formidable work of Massey (1969–1974, particularly, Vols 3 and 4).

G. Ionization Potentials and Ion Thermochemistry

Fairly early in the development of mass spectrometry, attempts were made to use it to measure ionization potentials. Before then, ionization potentials were obtained from Rydberg series extrapolations, which can yield very accurate ionization potentials for atoms and for simple diatomic molecules. As the complexity of the molecule increases, the spectrum becomes more complex and it becomes harder to discern the series of excitation leading to ionization. The threshold for

$$A + e \rightarrow A^+ + 2e \tag{3.48}$$

can be measured by observing the ion intensity of A^+ as a function of decreasing electron energy. In addition, by measuring the threshold for dissociative ionization

$$A_2 + e \rightarrow A^+ + A + 2e, \tag{3.49}$$

one can derive a dissociation energy for A_2 is the ionization potential of A is known. A great deal of work was done on processes such as (3.48) and (3.49) with the idea of obtaining accurate thermochemical data for the ions. These early results were summarized in a monumental work (Field and Franklin, 1957), which was revised later (1970). Many attempts were made to obtain ionization potentials with accuracies comparable to those of spectroscopic data; these experiments involved the use of specially designed electron velocity selectors to generate a beam of electrons with a narrow energy distribution and as Gaussian as possible. A major contributor in this area has been Kerwin, who with his students perfected the 127° electrostatic analyzer [see, for example, Marmet and Kerwin (1960) and Kerwin *et al.* (1963)]. High-resolution appearance potential curves were obtained with this velocity selector and in some cases the resolution was enough to observe individual vibrational levels in the ions, as in the case of N_2^+, where the vibrational spacings $0 \rightarrow 1$, $1 \rightarrow 2$, and $2 \rightarrow 3$ were measured at 0.270, 0.265, and 0.275 eV, all to an accuracy of ± 0.01 eV. Similar results were obtained by Lossing and his colleagues, who developed a two-stage double hemispheric selector [see Maeda *et al.* (1968)] through which they obtained an electron beam with a full width at half-maximum (FWHM) of 0.060 eV. With the latter analyzer, Maeda *et al.* were able to measure appearance potential curves that showed breaks due to $^2P_{1/2}$ states of the rare-gas ions. Other work on electron velocity selectors has been done [for example, Leventhal and North (1971)], but their complexity and the threshold laws for ionization by electron impact led to a decline in their use. Of course, sometimes one has no alternative to using electron impact to measure ionization potentials, and in this case care must be taken in finding the threshold. A case in point is the measurement of IP(SiO). Electron impact data (Hildenbrand and Murad, 1969), which gave 11.6 ± 0.2 eV, were confirmed by later photoelectron results, which gave the more accurate value of 11.61 ± 0.02 eV (Colbourn *et al.*, 1978).

The ionization cross section of a molecule, σ, depends on the number of particles leaving the ionization collision, being a delta function for electron capture, a step function for photoionization, and a linear function for electron impact single ionization [see Morrison (1957)]. This means that because of the energy spread in the electron beam and because an adiabatic transition may not be accessible, the threshold may not be very obvious, and the ionization efficiency curve may have a long tail. These considerations eventually made photoionization very attractive for obtaining ionization and appearance potentials, since in this case the cross section is a step function convoluted with a Gaussian energy distribution for the photon beam (Morrison, 1957; Hurzeller *et al.*, 1958). In fact, for some time (until the full development of photoelectron spectroscopy) this was the method of choice for obtaining accurate ionization and appearance potentials. In this area the work of Inghram (who initiated the use of photoionization for obtaining ionization and appearance potentials) and his students, Deibler and his colleagues, Chupka, and Berkowitz stands out. Since it is impossible in this brief review to discuss the work in detail, interested readers are referred to the books by Marr (1967) and Berkowitz (1979) and to the compilation of ionization and appearance potentials by Rosenstock *et al.* (1977), where various aspects of this subject are discussed in detail. One example, namely the ionization potentials of aliphatic free radicals, will be mentioned here. These were measured by photon impact (Elder *et al.*, 1962) and the ionization potentials were lower than had been obtained previously by electron impact. In addition, the thresholds (each of which should have been a step function) showed some curvature, leading the authors to conclude that these transitions were not adiabatic and that the observed appearance potentials were upper limits to the ionization potentials. Since then other measurements of these ionization potentials have been made using electron impact and photoelectron spectroscopy (PES). The PES measurements are in conflict with each other in that one concludes that the measured appearance potentials of the aliphatic free radicals are not adiabatic (Morris *et al.*, 1983, private communication), while the other reaches the opposite conclusion (Houle and Beauchamp, (1979). These measurements are summarized in Table 3.3. Photoionization experiments have yielded structural information about the molecular states of ions, often comparable in resolution with spectroscopic data [see, for example, Dehmer and Chupka (1975), Eland *et al.* (1980), and Duncan *et al.* (1981)].

Another way to obtain thermochemical data for ions has been to use the ICR to measure a thermodynamic equilibrium involving an ion–molecule reaction. Consider a hypothetical equilibrium

$$A^+ + B = C^+ + D. \tag{3.50}$$

In an ICR the reactant gas B can be maintained at a known pressure and the ion intensities A^+ and C^+ can be measured by using double-resonance techniques. From these measurements one can calculate the equilibrium constant and thence the heat of reaction [from Eq. (3.35)], which can be used to derive the heat of formation of an ion if the heats of formation of the other species are known. By choosing a suitable reactant B and by changing the cell temperature over a narrow range it is usually possible to form a

TABLE 3.3

IONIZATION POTENTIALS OF ALIPHATIC FREE RADICALS

Species	Photon impact[a] (eV)	Electron impact[b] (eV)	Photoelectron spectroscopy (eV)
CH_3	9.82 ± 0.04	9.8 –11.2[c]	9.84[d,e]
C_2H_5	≤ 8.4	8.67–8.78[c]	8.39[e]
n-C_3H_7	≤ 8.1	8.69[f]	8.17[g]
i-C_3H_7	≤ 7.5	7.9[h]	7.36[e]

[a] Elder *et al.* (1962).
[b] Electron impact data before the measurements of Elder *et al.* (1962).
[c] See Elder *et al.* (1962) for compilation.
[d] Dyke *et al.* (1972).
[e] Houle and Beauchamp (1979).
[f] Lossing and Desousa (1959).
[g] Beauchamp (1983), private communication.
[h] Farmer and Lossing (1955).

product ion C^+ and then to calculate its heat of formation. If the heat of formation of the neutral, $\Delta H_f(C)$, is known, then the measurement can be used to derive an ionization potential for C. The proton affinities of many molecules have been obtained by using ICR techniques [see, for example, Aue and Bowers (1979), and Walder and Franklin (1980)]. Heats of formation of other species, particularly organic species, have been similarly obtained. Major contributors in this area have been Ausloos and Lias [see, for example, Lias (1979)], who have analyzed the data and measured the heats of formation of many positive ions. The uncertainties in the derived heats of formation are often ≤ 1 kcal/mole, making the information more precise than that available from other sources. The thermodynamic properties of negative ions have been treated in a similar way, and the extension of concepts of liquid-phase chemistry has yielded valuable insight into the structure and behavior of ions. An example is the work of Bartmess and McIver (1979), who tabulated acidity scales for a large number of species. This work is intertwined with other thermochemical information about molecules, such as dissociation energies and electron affinities. Another way to obtain thermochemical information about ions has been to measure the threshold of endothermic ion–neutral reactions, and an early example of such experiments is the work of Giese and Maier (1963a), who measured

$$X^+ + CO \rightarrow C^+ + O + X, \tag{3.51}$$

where X is a rare gas (He, Ne, or Ar). By measuring the thresholds for the cross sections for X = Ne and Ar (whose reactions are endothermic), they were able to derive $D_0^0(CO) = 11.11$ eV, in agreement with the thermochemical values, which were based on the heat of sublimation of carbon measured by Chupka and Inghram (1955). Similar experiments have been done on many such reactions. For example, $D_0^0(Al^+ - O)$ was obtained by measuring the threshold for the reaction

$$Al^+ + O_2 \rightarrow AlO^+ + O. \tag{3.52}$$

These studies (Rutherford and Vroom, 1976; Armentrout *et al.*, 1982; Murad, 1982) lead to $D_0^0(Al^+ - O) = 1.69 \pm 0.1$ eV, in agreement with the thermochemical data of Hildenbrand (1973), who measured $D_0^0(AlO)$ and IP(AlO). Similarly, $D_0^0(Ca^+ - O)$ and $D_0^0(Sr^+ - O)$ have been measured (Murad, 1983).

The electron affinities of various neutral species have been measured in a variety of ways by using mass spectrometry. A major method has been to measure the threshold for the photodetachment from negative ions. The results of many such measurements as well as the results obtained from thermochemical equilibria with ICR are discussed by Janousek and Brauman (1979).

H. Miscellaneous Comments

This review has attempted to present a reasonably comprehensive picture of areas of research related to the general field of mass spectrometry. Some areas were not discussed at all for lack of space. Examples are ion optics and sampling techniques, both of which play important roles in mass spectrometry. Some specialized topics that were not discussed belong more properly elsewhere. Examples are the spectroscopic properties of ions [see, for example, Carrington (1979), Danon *et al.* (1982), and Cosby and Helm (1982)] and the photochemical decomposition of ions [see Dunbar (1979)].

Acknowledgments

I would like to thank Dr. P. Bochsler for helpful comments and Mrs. Theresa Walker for her skill in transforming rough sketches into legible drawings.

References

Aberth, W. H., Spindt, C. A., Scolnick, M. E., Sperry, R. R., and Anbar, M. (1974). *In* "Advances in Mass Spectrometry" (A. R. West, ed.), Vol. 6, pp. 437–443. Appl. Sci. Publ., London.

Adams, N. G., and Smith, D. (1976). *Int. J. Mass Spectrosc. Ion Phys.* **21,** 349–359.

Adams, N. G., and Smith, D. (1978). *Chem. Phys. Lett.* **54,** 530–534.

Albritton, D. L. (1978). *At. Data Nucl. Data Tables* **22,** 1–101.

Allemann, M., Kellerhals, H., and Wanczek, K. P. (1983). *Int. J. Mass Spectrosc. Ion Phys.* **46,** 139–142.

Allen, J. S. (1947). *Rev. Sci. Instrum.* **18,** 739–749.

Allen, J. S. (1950). *Proc. IRE.*, **38,** 346–358.

Allen, W. D., Dawton, R. H., Smith, M. L., and Thonemann, P. C. (1955). *Nature* **175,** 101–103.

Anders, L., Beauchamp, J. L., Dunbar, R., and Baldeschwieler, J. (1966). *J. Chem. Phys.* **45,** 1062–1063.

Arijs, E., Nevejans, D., and Ingels, J. (1982). *J. Atm. Terr. Phys.* **44,** 43–53.

Armentrout, P. B., and Beauchamp, J. L. (1981). *J. Am. Chem. Soc.* **103,** 784–791.

Armentrout, P. B., Halle, L. F., and Beauchamp, J. L. (1982). *J. Chem. Phys.* **76,** 2449–2457.

Arnold, F., Henschen, G., and Ferguson, E. E. (1981). *Planet. Space Sci.* **29,** 185–193.

Aston, F. W. (1919). *Philos. Mag.* **38,** 707–714.

Aston, F. W. (1920). *Philos. Mag.* **39,** 611–625.

Aue, D. H., and Bowers, M. T. (1979). *In* "Gas Phase Ion Chemistry" (Michael T. Bowers, ed.), Vol. 2., pp. 2–52. Academic Press, New York.

Bainbridge, K. T., and Jordan, E. G. (1936). *Phys. Rev.* **49,** 421.

Baldeschwieler, J. D., and Woodgate, S. S. (1971). *Accts. Chem. Res.* **4,** 114–120.

Banks, P. M., and Kockarts, G. (1973). "Aeronomy," Academic Press, New York.

Barber, M., Bordoli, R. S., Sedgwick, R. D., and Taylor, A. N. (1981). *Nature* **293,** 270–275.

Barlak, T. M., Wyatt, J. R., Colton, R. J., De Corpo, J. J., and Campana, J. E. (1982). *J. Am. Chem. Soc.* **104,** 1212–1215.

Barnard, G. P. (1953). "Modern Mass Spectrometry." Inst. Phys., London.

Barnett, C. F., Evans, G. E., and Stier, P. M. (1954). *Rev. Sci. Instrum.* **25,** 1112–1115.

Barrington, A. E., Herzog, R. F. K., and Poschenrieder, W. P. (1966). *Prog. Nucl. Energy, Ser. 9,* **7,** 243–273.

Bartky, W., and Dempster, A. J. (1929). *Phys. Rev.* **33,** 1019–1022.

Bartmess, J. E., and McIver, R. T., Jr. *In* "Gas Phase Ion Chemistry" (Michael T. Bowers, ed.), Vol. 2, pp. 88–123. Academic Press, New York.

Bates, D. R. (1962). *In* "Atomic and Molecular Processes" (D. R. Bates, ed.), pp. 550–621. Academic Press, New York.

Baumgartner, W., and Zimmerman, U. (1972). *Adv. Electron. Electron Phys.* **33A,** 125–132.

Bearman, G. H., Harris, H. H., and Leventhal, J. J. (1977). *J. Chem. Phys.* **66,** 4111–4115.

Beauchamp, J. L. (1975). *In* "Interactions between Ions and Molecules" (P. Ausloos, ed.), pp. 413–444. Plenum, New York.

Beauchamp, J. L., Anders, L. R., and Baldeschwieler, J. D. (1967). *J. Atm. Chem. Soc.* **89,** 4569–4577.

Becker, H., Dietz, E., and Gerhardy, U. (1972). *Rev. Sci. Instrum.* **43,** 1587–1589.

Beckey, H. D. (1962). *Z. Naturforschung* **17a,** 1103–1111.

Beckey, H. D. (1969). *Ang. Chem., Int. Ed.* (*English*) **8,** 623–639.

Beckey, H. D. (1978). "Principles of Field Ionization and Field Desorption Mass Spectrometry," p. 270. Pergamon, Oxford.

Berkowitz, J. (1979). "Photoabsorption, Photoionization, and Photoelectron Spectroscopy," Academic Press, New York.

Berkowitz, J., and Chupka, W. A. (1964). *J. Chem. Phys.* **40,** 287–295.

Bernstein, R. B. (1982). *J. Phys. Chem.* **86,** 1178–1183.

Beuhler, R. J., and Friedman, L. (1982). *J. Chem. Phys.* **77,** 2549–2557.

Beynon, J. H. (1960). "Mass Spectrometry and Its Applications to Organic Chemistry." Elsevier, Amsterdam.

Beynon, J. E., and Morgan, R. P. (1978). *Int. J. Mass. Spectrosc. Ion Phys.* **27,** 1–30.

Beynon, J. H., Fontaine, A. E., Turner, D. W., and Williams, A. E. (1967). *J. Sci. Instrum.* **44,** 283–284.

Beynon, J. H., Ast, T., Keough, T., and Cooks, R. G. (1975). *Int. J. Mass Spectrosc. Ion Phys.* **16,** 343–347.

Biemann, K., Oro, J., Orgel, L. E., Nier, A. O., Anderson, D. M., Simmonds, P. G., Flory, D., Diaz, A. V., Rushneck, D. R., and Biller, J. A. (1976a). *Science* **194,** 72–76.

Biemann, K., Owen, T., Rushneck, D. R., LaFleur, A. L., and Howarth, D. W. (1976b). *Science* **194,** 76–78.

Bierbaum, V. M., Ellison, G. B., Futrell, J. H., and Leone, S. R. (1977). *J. Chem. Phys.* **67,** 2375–2376.

Bierbaum, V. M., Ellison, G. B., and Leone, S. R. (1984). *In* "Gas Phase Ion Chemistry" (Michael T. Bowers, ed.), Vol. 3, pp. 1–39. Academic Press, New York.

Bingham, R. A., and Salter, P. L. (1976). *Int. J. Mass Spectrosc. Ion Phys.* **21,** 133–144.

Blauth, E. W. (1966). "Dynamic Mass Spectrometers." Elsevier, Amsterdam.

Blewett, J. P., and Jones, E. J. (1936). *Phys. Rev.* **50,** 464–468.

Bochsler, P. (1983). *Europhysics News* **14**(2), 1–3.

Bonner, R. F., Lawson, G., and Todd, F. J. (1973). *Int. J. Mass Spectrosc. Ion Phys.* **10,** 197–203.

Bordoni, F. (1971). *Nucl. Instrum. Meth.* **97,** 405–408.

Bowers, M. T., and Su, T. (1973). *Adv. Electron. Electron Phys.* **34,** 223–279.

Brion, C. E. (1965). *Anal. Chem.* **37,** 1706–1709.

Burke, P., Jennings, K. R., Morgan, R. P., and Gilchrist, C. A. (1982). *Anal. Chem.* **54,** 1304–1308.

Burlingame, A. L., Dell, A., and Russell, D. H. (1982). *Anal. Chem.* **54,** 363–409.

Burrous, C. N., Lieber, A. J., and Zaviantseff, V. T. (1967). *Rev. Sci. Instrum.* **38,** 1477–1481.

Byrd, G. D., Burnier, R. C., and Freiser, B. S. (1982). *J. Am. Chem. Soc.* **104,** 3565–3569.

Carlson, E. G., Andre, M. L., and O'Neal, M. J. (1963). *In* "Advances in Mass Spectrometry" (R. M. Elliott, ed.), Vol. 2, pp. 377–392. Pergamon, London.

Carrington, A. (1979). *Proc. R. Soc. London Ser. A* **367,** 433–449.

Carroll, D. I., Dzidic, I., Stillwell, R. N., Horning, M. G., and Horning, E. C. (1973). *Abstr. Annu. Meet. Am. Soc. Mass Spectrom., 21st*, pp. 370–373.

Carroll, D. I., Dzidic, I., Horning, E. C., and Stillwell, R. N. (1981). *Appl. Spectrosc. Rev.* **17,** 337–406.

Castaing, R., and Hennequin, J. F. (1971). *In* "Advances in Mass Spectrometry" (A. Quayle, ed.), Vol. 5., pp. 419–426. Inst. Petroleum, London.

Castaing, R., and Slodzian, G. (1966). *In* "Advances in Mass Spectrometry" (W. L. Mead, ed.), Vol. 3., pp. 91–98.

Chait, B. T., Agosta, W. C., and Field, F. H. (1981). *Int. J. Mass. Spectrosc. Ion Phys.* **39,** 339–366.

Chase, M. W., Jr., Cornutt, J. L., Downey, J. R., Jr., McDonald, R. A., Syverud, A. N., and Valenzuela, E. A. (1982). *J. Phys. Chem. Ref. Data* **11,** 695–940.

Chupka, W. A. (1972). *In* "Ion–Molecule Reactions" (J. L. Franklin, ed.), pp. 33–76. Plenum, New York.

Chupka, W. A., and Inghram, M. G. (1953a). *J. Chem. Phys.* **21,** 1313.

Chupka, W. A., and Inghram, M. G. (1953b). *J. Chem. Phys.* **21,** 371–372.

Chupka, W. A., and Inghram, M. G. (1955). *J. Phys. Chem.* **59,** 100–104.

Church, D. A. (1969). *J. Appl. Phys.* **40,** 3127–3134.

Clayton, R. N. (1978). *Annu. Rev. Nucl. Part. Sci.* **28,** 501–522.

Cody, R. B., Burnier, R. C., Breents, W. D., Jr., Carlin, T. J., McCrery, D. A., Lengel, R. K., and Freiser, B. S. (1980). *Int. J. Mass. Spectrosc. Ion Phys.* **33,** 37–43.

Colbourn, E. A., Dyke, J. M., Lee, E. P. F., Morris, A., and Trickle, I. R. (1978). *Mol. Phys.* **35,** 873–882.

Collins, C. B., Russell, R. D., and Farquhar, R. M. (1953). *Can. J. Phys.* **31,** 402–418.

Collins, T. L., Nier, A. O., and Johnson, W. H., Jr. (1954). *Phys. Rev.* **86,** 408–412.

Comisarow, M. B. (1978). *J. Chem. Phys.* **69,** 4097–4104.

Comisarow, M. B., and Marshall, A. G. (1974). *Chem. Phys. Lett.* **25,** 282–283.

Comisarow, M. B., and Marshall, A. G. (1976). *J. Chem. Phys.* **64,** 110–119.

Conzemius, R. J., and Capellen, J. M. (1980). *Int. J. Mass. Spectrosc. Ion Phys.* **34,** 197–271.

Coplan, M. A., Ogilvie, K. W., Bochsler, P. A., and Geiss, J. (1978). *IEEE Trans. Geosci. Electron.* **GE-16,** 185–191.

Cornu, A., and Massot, R. (1975). "Compilation of Mass Spectral Data," 2nd ed. Heyden, London.

Cosby, P. C., and Helm, H. (1982). *J. Chem. Phys.* **76,** 4720–4724.

Craig, R. D., and Errock, G. A. (1959). *In* "Advances in Mass Spectrometry" (J. D. Waldron, ed.), Vol. 1., pp. 66–85. Pergamon, London.

Craig, R. D., Bateman, R. H., Green, B. N., and Hillington, D. S. (1979). *Philos. Trans. R. Soc. London Ser. A* **293,** 135–155.

Crawford, C. K. (1968). *J. Vac. Sci. Technol.* **5,** 131–140.

Dagdigian, P. J., Cruse, H. W., and Zare, R. N. (1975). *J. Chem. Phys.* **62,** 1824–1833.

Daly, N. R. (1960). *Rev. Sci. Instrum.* **31,** 264–267.

Daly, N. R., McCormick, A., and Powell, R. E. (1971). *In* "Advances in Mass Spectrometry" (A. Quayle, ed.), Vol. 5., pp. 300–304. Inst. Petroleum, London.
Danon, J., Mauclaire, G., Govers, T. R., and Marx, R. (1982). *J. Chem. Phys.* **76,** 1255–1262.
Dawson, P. H., and Whetten, N. R. (1968). *J. Vac. Sci. Technol.* **5,** 1–10, 11–18.
Dawson, P. H., and Whetten, N. R. (1969a). *Int. J. Mass Spectrosc. Ion Phys.* **3,** 1–12.
Dawson, P. H., and Whetten, N. R. (1969b). *Adv. Electron. Electron Phys.* **27,** 60–185.
Dawson, P. H., Heldman, J. W., and Whetten, N. R. (1969). *Rev. Sci. Instrum.* **40,** 1444–1450.
Dehmer, P. M., and Chupka, W. A. (1975). *J. Chem. Phys.* **62,** 4525–4534.
Dempster, A. J. (1916). *Philos. Mag.* **31,** 438–443.
Dempster, A. J. (1918). *Phys. Rev.* **11,** 316–325.
Dempster, A. J. (1936a). *Rev. Sci. Instrum.* **7,** 46–49.
Dempster, A. J. (1936b). *Phys. Rev.* **49,** 416.
Devienne, F. M., Repoux, M., and Roustan, J-C. (1983). *Int. J. Mass. Spectrosc. Ion Phys.* **46,** 143–146.
Dibeler, V. H. (1963). *In* "Mass Spectrometry" (C. A. McDowell, ed.), pp. 334–374. McGraw-Hill, New York.
Dibeler, V. H., Krauss, M., Reese, R. M., and Harlee, F. N. (1965). *J. Chem. Phys.* **42,** 3791–3796.
Dietz, L. A. (1965). *Rev. Sci. Instrum.* **36,** 1763–1770.
Dietz, L. A., Hanrahan, L. R., and Hance, A. G. (1967). *Rev. Sci. Instrum.* **38,** 176–183.
Dillon, A. F., Lehrle, R. S., Robb, J. C., and Thomas, D. W. (1968). *In* "Advances in Mass Spectrometry" (E. Kendrick, ed.), Vol. 4, pp. 477–490. Inst. Petroleum, London.
Ditchburn, R. W., and Arnot, F. L. (1929). *Proc. R. Soc. London, Ser. A* **123,** 516–536.
Donohue, D. L., Carter, J. A., and Mamantov, G. (1980). *Int. J. Mass Spectrosc. Ion Phys.* **33,** 45–55.
Drowart, J. (1973). "High Temperature Studies in Chemistry," *Faraday Symp. Chem. Soc.* No. 8, 165–167.
Drowart, J., and Goldfinger, P. (1967). *Angew. Chem., Int. Ed.* **6,** 581–596.
Drowart, J., Exsteen, G., and Verhaegen, G. (1964). *Trans. Faraday Soc.* **60,** 1920–1933.
Duckworth, H. E. (1958). *In* "Mass Spectroscopy," pp. 1–10. Cambridge Univ. Press, Cambridge.
Dunbar, R. C. (1979). *In* "Gas Phase Ion Chemistry" (Michael T. Bowers, ed.), Vol. 2, pp. 182–220. Academic Press, New York.
Duncan, M. A., Dietz, T. G., and Smalley, R. E. (1981). *J. Chem. Phys.* **75,** 2118–2125.
Dyke, J., Jonathan, N., Lee, E., and Morris, A. (1972). *J. Chem. Soc. Faraday Trans. II* **72,** 1385–1396.
Eland, J. H. D., Berkowitz, J., and Monahan, J. E. (1980). *J. Chem. Phys.* **72,** 253–259.
Elder, F. A., Giese, C. F., Steiner, B., and Inghram, M. G. (1962). *J. Chem. Phys.* **36,** 3293–3296.
El-Kareh, A. B., and El-Kareh, J. C. J. (1970). "Electron Beams, Lenses, and Optics." Academic Press, New York.
Elliott, R. M. (1963). *In* "Mass Spectrometry" (C. A. McDowell, ed.), pp. 69–103. McGraw-Hill, New York.
Emberson, D. L., and Holmshaw, R. T. (1972). *Adv. Electron. Electron Phys.* **33A,** 133–144.
Facchetti, S., Fornari, A., and Montagna, M. (1980). *In* "Advances in Mass Spectrometry" (A. Quayle, ed.), Vol. 8, pp. 1405–1414. Inst. Petroleum, London.
Farmer, J. B., and Lossing, F. P. (1955). *Can. J. Chem.* **33,** 861–869.
Farragher, A. L., Peden, J. A., and Fite, W. L. (1969). *J. Chem. Phys.* **50,** 287–293.
Fehn, U. (1976). *Int. J. Mass Spectrosc. Ion Phys.* **21,** 1–14.

Fehsenfeld, F. C., Schmeltekopf, A. L., Goldan, P. D., Schiff, H. I., and Ferguson, E. E. (1966). *J. Chem. Phys.* **44,** 4087–4094.

Ferguson, E. E. (1972). *In* "Ion–Molecule Reactions" (J. L. Franklin, ed.), pp. 363–393. Plenum, New York.

Ferguson, E. E., Fehsenfeld, F. C., Dunkin, D. B., Schmeltekopf, A. L., and Schiff, H. I. (1964). *Planet. Space Sci.* **12,** 1169–1171.

Field, F. H. (1972a). *MTP Int. Rev. Sci.*; *Phys. Chem., Ser. One,* **5,** 133–181.

Field, F. H. (1972b). *In* "Ion–Molecule Reactions" (J. L. Franklin, ed.), pp. 261–314. Plenum, New York.

Field, F. H., and Franklin, J. L. (1957). "Electron Impact Phenomena and the Properties of Gaseous Ions," 1st ed. Academic Press, New York.

Fischer, E. (1959). *Z. Phys.* **156,** 1–26.

Fite, W. L., Rutherford, J. A., Snow, W. R., and Van Lint, V. A. J. (1962). *Discuss. Faraday Soc.* **33,** 264–272.

Fox, R. E., and Hipple, J. A. (1948). *Rev. Sci. Instrum.* **19,** 62–468.

Franklin, J. L. (1972). *In* "Ion–Molecule Reactions" (J. L. Franklin, ed.), pp. 9–32. Plenum, New York.

Franklin, J. L., ed. (1979). "Ion–Molecule Reactions: Part 1. Kinetics and Dynamics." Dowden, Hutchinson and Ross, Stroudsburg, Pennsylvania.

Franzen, W., and Porter, J. H. (1975). *Adv. Electron. Electron Phys.* **39,** 73–119.

Friichtenicht, J. F. (1974). *Rev. Sci. Instrum.* **45,** 51–56.

Futrell, J. H., and Tiernan, T. O. (1972). *In* "Ion–Molecule Reactions" (J. L. Franklin, ed.), pp. 485–551. Plenum, New York.

Gaydon, A. G. (1968). "Dissociation Energies and Spectra of Diatomic Molecules," 3rd ed. Chapman and Hall, London.

Gehrcke, E., and Reichenheim, O. (1906). *Ber. Dtsch. Phys. Ges.* **8,** 559–566.

Geiss, J., and Bochsler, P. (1982). *Geochim. Cosmochim. Acta* **46,** 529–548.

Gentry, W. R. (1979). *In* "Gas Phase Ion Chemistry" (Michael T. Bowers, ed.), Vol. 2, pp. 221–297. Academic Press, New York.

Gentry, W. R., Gislason, E. A., Mahan, B. H., and Tsao, C. W. (1967). *Discuss. Faraday Soc.* **44,** 137–145.

Gérard, M., Govers, T. R., and Marx, R. (1978). *Chem. Phys.* **30,** 75–83.

Gibson, B. W., and Biemann, K. (1982). Presented at *Annu. Conf. Mass Spectrom. Allied Topics, Honolulu, 1982*, pp. 232–233.

Giese, C. F., and Maier, W. B., II (1961). *J. Chem. Phys.* **35,** 1913–1914.

Giese, C. F., and Maier, W. B., II (1963a). *J. Chem. Phys.* **39,** 197–200.

Giese, C. F., and Maier, W. B., II (1963b). *J. Chem. Phys.* **39,** 739–748.

Gioumousis, G., and Stevenson, D. P. (1958). *J. Chem. Phys.* **29,** 294–299.

Glenn, W. E., Jr. (1952). "A Time of Flight Mass Spectrograph," *Tech. Rep. Univ. of Calif. Radiat. Lab.* UCRL-1628.

Göhrlich, P., Krohs, A., and Pohl, H-J. (1961). *Brit. J. Appl. Phys.* **12,** 525–526.

Goldberg, R. A., and Aikin, A. C. (1971). *J. Geophys. Res.* **76,** 8352–8364.

Goldberg, R. A., and Aikin, A. C. (1973). *Science* **180,** 294–296.

Gole, J. L., and Zare, R. N. (1972). *J. Chem. Phys.* **57,** 5331–5335.

Goodrich, G. W., and Wiley, W. C. (1961). *Rev. Sci. Instrum.* **32,** 846–849.

Grebowsky, J. M., and Brinton, H. C. (1978). *Geophys. Res. Lett.* **5,** 791–794.

Griffin, C. E., Boettger, H. G., and Norris, D. D. (1974). *Int. J. Mass Spectrosc. Ion Phys.* **15,** 437–449.

Grimley, R. T. (1967). *In* "The Characterization of High Temperature Vapors" (J. L. Margrave, ed.), pp. 195–243. Wiley, New York.

Grivet, P. (1972). "Electron Optics," 2nd English ed. Pergamon, New York.
Gross, J., and von Zahn, U. (1971). *Space Res.* **11,** 875–885.
Håkansson, P., Kamensky, I., Sunquist, B., Fohlman, J., Peterson, P., McNeal, C. J. and MacFarlane, R. D. (1982). *J. Am. Chem. Soc.* **104,** 2948–2949.
Hannay, N. B. (1954). *Rev. Sci. Instrum.* **25,** 644–648.
Hanson, G. R. (1975). *J. Chem. Phys.* **62,** 1161–1180.
Hartmann, K. N., Lias, S., Ausloos, P., Rosenstock, H. M., Schroyer, S. D., Schmidt, C. C., Martinson, D., and Milne, G. W. A. (1979). "A Compendium of Gas Phase Basicity and Proton Affinity Measurements," **NBSIR-79-1777.** Government Printing Office, Washington, D.C.
Hedin, A. E., and Nier, A. O. (1966). *J. Geophys. Res.* **71,** 4121–4131.
Heimerl, J., Johnsen, R., and Biondi, M. A. (1969). *J. Chem. Phys.* **51,** 5041–5048.
Henchman M. J. (1972). *In* "Ion–Molecule Reactions" (J. L. Franklin, ed.), pp. 101–260. Plenum, New York.
Henderson, W. R., Mentall, J. E., and Fite, W. L. (1967). *J. Chem. Phys.* **46,** 3447–3449.
Henis, J. M. S. (1968). *J. Am. Chem. Soc.* **90,** 844–851.
Henis, J. M. S. (1972). *In* "Ion–Molecule Reactions" (J. L. Franklin, ed.), pp. 395–456. Plenum, New York.
Hennequin, J. F., and Inglebert, R. L. (1978). *Int. J. Mass Spectrosc. Ion Phys.* **26,** 131–135.
Herman, Z., Kerstetter, J., Rose, T., and Wolfgang, R. (1967). *Discuss. Faraday Soc.* **44,** 123–136.
Herrmann, U., Eberhardt, P., Hidalgo, M. A., Kopp, E., and Smith, L. G. (1978). *Space Res.* **18,** 249–252.
Hildenbrand, D. L. (1972). *High Temp. Sci.* **4,** 244–247.
Hildenbrand, D. L. (1973). *Chem. Phys. Lett.* **20,** 127–129.
Hildenbrand, D. L., and Murad, E. (1969). *J. Chem. Phys.* **51,** 807–811.
Hildenbrand, D. L., and Murad, E. (1970). *J. Chem. Phys.* **53,** 3403–3408.
Hintenberger, H. (1962). *Annu. Rev. Nucl. Sci.* **12,** 435–506.
Hintenberger, H. (1966). *In* "Advances in Mass Spectrometry" (W. L. Mead, ed.), Vol. 3, pp. 517–546. Inst. Petroleum, London.
Hipple, J. A., Sommer, H., and Thomas, H. A. (1949). *Phys. Rev.* **76,** 1877.
Hirashima, M., and Miyashiro, S. (1957). *J. Phys. Soc. Jpn.* **12,** 770–777.
Hogg, A. M., and Kebarle, P. (1965). *J. Chem. Phys.* **43,** 449–456.
Holme, A. E., Sayyid, S., and Leck, J. H. (1978). *Int. J. Mass Spectrosc. Ion Phys.* **26,** 191–204.
Honig, R. E. (1953). *J. Chem. Phys.* **22,** 126–131.
Hood, A., and O'Neal, M. J. (1959). *In* "Advances in Mass Spectrometry" (J. D. Waldron, ed.), Vol. 1, pp. 175–192. Pergamon, Oxford, England.
Houle, F. A., and Beauchamp, J. L. (1979). *J. Am. Chem. Soc.* **101,** 4067–4074.
Huber, K. P., and Herzberg, G. (1979). "Molecular Spectra and Molecular Structure: IV. Constants of Diatomic Molecules." Van Nostrand, New York.
Huber, W. K., Selhofer, H., and Benninghoven, A. (1972). *J. Vac. Sci. Technol.* **9,** 482–486.
Huber, W. K., Löbach, E., and Rettinghaus, G. (1974). *In* "Advances in Mass Spectrometry" (A. R. West, ed.), Vol. 6, 683–689. Inst. Petroleum, London.
Hunt, D. F. (1982). *Int. J. Mass Spectrosc. Ion Phys.* **45,** 111–123.
Hunt, D. F., and Crow, F. W. (1978). *Anal. Chem.* **50,** 1781–1784.
Hunter, R. L., and McIver, R. T., Jr. (1977). *Chem. Phys. Lett.*, **49,** 577–582.
Hunter, R. L., and McIver, R. T., Jr. (1982). *In* "Lecture Notes in Chemistry," No. 31, pp. 464–483. Springer-Verlag, Berlin and New York.
Hurzeller, H., Inghram, M. G., and Morrison, J. D. (1957). *J. Chem. Phys.* **27,** 313–314.
Hurzeller, H., Inghram, M. G., and Morrison, J. D. (1958). *J. Chem. Phys.* **28,** 76–82.

Husmann, O. K. (1966). *J. Appl. Phys.* **37,** 4662–4670.

Iglesias, G. E., and McGarity, J. O. (1971). *Rev. Sci. Instrum.* **42,** 1728–1729.

Inghram, M. G. (1948). *In* "Advances in Electronics," Vol. 1 (L. Marton, ed.), pp. 219–268. Academic Press, New York.

Inghram, M. G., and Chupka, W. A. (1953). *Rev. Sci. Instrum.* **24,** 518–520.

Inghram, M. G., and Drowart, J. (1960). *In* "High Temperature Technology," pp. 219–229. McGraw-Hill, New York.

Inghram, M. G., and Gomer, R. (1954). *J. Chem. Phys.* **22,** 1279–1280.

Inghram, M. G., and Hayden, R. J. (1954). "Mass Spectroscopy." Nucl. Sci. Series, Report No. 14, Nat. Acad. Sci.–Nat. Res. Council, Washington, D.C.

Inghram, M. G., Hess, D. C., Jr., and Fields, P. R. (1951). *Phys. Rev.* **83,** 1250.

Istomin, V. G., and Pokhunkov, A. Z. (1963). *Space Res.* **3,** 117–131.

Janousek, B. K., and Brauman, J. I. (1979). *In* "Gas Phase Ion Chemistry" (Michael T. Bowers, ed.), Vol. 2, 53–87. Academic Press, New York.

Jason, A. J. (1967). *Phys. Rev.* **156,** 266–285.

Johnson, C. Y., Heppner, J. P., Holmes, J. C., and Meadows, E. B. (1958). *Ann. Géophys.* **14,** 475–482.

Johnson, R. E. (1982). "Introduction to Atomic and Molecular Collisions." Plenum, New York.

Jones, E. G., Tiernan, T. O., Fee, D. C., and Hughes, B. M. (1980). *J. Chem. Phys.* **73,** 1200–1211.

Kaminsky, M. (1965). "Atomic and Ionic Impact Phenomena on Metal Surfaces." Springer-Verlag, Berlin.

Kaneko, Y. (1980). *In* "Electronic and Atomic Collisions" (N. Oda and K. Takayanagi, eds.), pp. 109–124. North-Holland Publ., Amsterdam.

Karmohapatro, S. B. (1976). *Adv. Electron. Electron Phys.* **42,** 113–177.

Kaufman, J. J. (1979). *In* "Kinetics of Ion–Molecule Reactions" (P. Ausloos, ed.), pp. 1–30. Plenum, New York.

Kayser, D. C., and Potter, W. E. (1978). *J. Geophys. Res.* **A83,** 1147–1153.

Kebarle, P., and Hogg, A. M. (1965). *J. Chem. Phys.* **42,** 668–674.

Keim, C. P. (1955). *Nature* **175,** 98–101.

Kelner, L., Markey, S. P., Fales, H. M., Crawford, C. K., and Cole, P. A. (1983). *Int. J. Mass Spectrosc. Ion Phys.* **46,** 3–6.

Kerwin, L. (1956). *Adv. Electron. Electron Phys.* **8,** 187–253.

Kerwin, L., Marmet, P., and Clarke, E. M. (1963). *In* "Advances in Mass Spectrometry"(R. M. Elliott, ed.), Vol. 2, pp. 522–526. Pergamon, London.

Kiser, R. W. (1965). "Introduction to Mass Spectrometry and Its Applications." Prentice-Hall, New York.

Kistemaker, P. G., van der Peyl, G. J. A., and Haverkamp, J. (1981a). *In* "Soft Ionization Biological Mass Spectrometer" (H. R. Morris, ed.), pp. 120–136. Heyden, London.

Kistemaker, P. G., Lens, M. M. J., van der Peyl, G. J. A., and Boerboom, A. J. H. (1981b). *In* "Advances in Mass Spectrometry" (A. Quayle, ed.), Vol. 7, pp. 928–934. Heyden, London.

Klemperer, O., and Barnett, M. E. (1971). "Electron Optics," 3rd ed. Cambridge Univ. Press, Cambridge.

Klostermeyer, H., and Humbel, R. E. (1966). *Angew. Chemie, Int. Ed.* **5,** 807–822.

Koontz, S. L., and Denton, M. B. (1981). *Int. J. Mass Spectrosc. Ion Phys.* **37,** 227–239.

Koski, W. (1975). *Adv. Chem. Phys.* **23,** 185–246.

Krankowsky, D., Arnold, F., Wieder, H., and Kissel, J. (1972). *Int. J. Mass Spectrosc. Ion Phys.* **8,** 379–390.

Kulp, J. L. (1955). *Geol. Soc. Am. Special Paper* **62,** 609–630.

Kung, C. C., and Clayton, R. N. (1978). *Earth Planet. Sci. Lett.* **38,** 421–425.

Kunz, S., Bochsler, P., Geiss, J., Ogilvie, K. W., and Coplan, M. A. (1983). *Solar Phys.* **88,** 359–376.

Langmuir, I., and Kingdon, K. H. (1925). *Proc. R. Soc. London, Ser. A* **107,** 61–79.

Large, R., and Knof, H. (1976). *Org. Mass Spectrom.* **11,** 582–598.

Larsson, S. J., Lodding, A., Odelius, H., and Flim, G. J. (1978). *In* "Advances in Mass Spectrometry" (N. R. Daly, ed.), Vol. 7, 797–803. Heyden, London.

Ledford, E. B., Ghaderi, S., Wilkins, C. L., and Gross, M. L. (1980). *In* "Advances in Mass Spectrometry" (A. Quayle, ed.), Vol. 8, pp. 1707–1724. Heyden, London.

Lehman, T. A., and Bursey, M. M. (1976). "Ion Cyclotron Resonance Spectrometry." Wiley, New York.

Leta, D. P., Morrison, G. H., Harris, G. L., and Lee, C. A. (1980). *Int. J. Mass Spectrosc. Ion Phys.* **34,** 147–157.

Leventhal, J. J., and North, G. R. (1971). *Rev. Sci. Instrum.* **42,** 120–123.

Lever, R. F. (1966). *IBM J. Res. Dev.* **10,** 26–40.

Levsen, K. (1980). *In* "Advances in Mass Spectrometry" (A. Quayle, ed.), Vol. 8A, pp. 897–917. Heyden, London.

Levsen, K., and Beckey, H. D. (1974). *Int. J. Mass Spectrosc. Ion Phys.* **15,** 336–346.

Lewis, G. N., Randall, M., Pitzer, K. S., and Brewer, L. (1961). "Thermodynamics," 2nd ed. McGraw-Hill, New York.

Lias, S. G. (1979). *In* "Kinetics of Ion Molecule Reactions" (P. Ausloos, ed.), pp. 223–254. Plenum, New York.

Lias, S. G., and Ausloos, P. (1975). "Ion–Molecule Reactions: Their Role in Radiation Chemistry." Am. Chem. Soc., Washington, D.C.

Ligon, W. V., Jr. (1979). *Science* **205,** 151–159.

Lindholm, E. (1953). *Proc. Phys. Soc.* **A66,** 1068–1070.

Lossing, F. P., and Desousa, J. B. (1959). *J. Am. Chem. Soc.* **81,** 281–285.

Lossing, F. P., and Tanaka, I. (1956). *J. Chem. Phys.* **25,** 1031–1032.

Lubman, D. M., Naaman, R., and Zare, R. N. (1980). *J. Chem. Phys.* **72,** 3034–3040.

McCulloch, M. T., and Wasserburg, G. J. (1978). *Science* **200,** 1003–1011.

McDaniel, E. W., Cermak, V., Dalgarno, A., Ferguson, E. E., and Friedman, L. (1970). "Ion–Molecule Reactions." Wiley, New York.

Macfarlane, R. D., and Torgerson, D. F. (1976). *Science* **191,** 920–925.

McFarland, M., Albritton, D. L., Fehsenfeld, F. C., Ferguson, E. E., and Schmeltekopf, A. L. (1973). *J. Chem. Phys.* **59,** 6620–6629.

McIver, R. T., Jr. (1970a). *Rev. Sci. Instrum.* **41,** 126–127.

McIver, R. T., Jr. (1970b). *Rev. Sci. Instrum.* **41,** 555–558.

McIver, R. T., Jr. (1978a). *In* "Lecture Notes in Chemistry," No. 7 (H. Hartmann and K. P. Wanczek, eds.), pp. 97–135. Springer-Verlag, Berlin.

McIver, R. T., Jr. (1978b). *Rev. Sci. Instrum.* **49,** 111–118.

McIver, R. T. (1980). *Am. Lab.* **12** (11), 18–30.

McIver, R. T., Jr., Ledford, E. B., Jr., and Miller, J. S. (1975). *Anal. Chem.* **47,** 692–697.

McLafferty, F. W. (1966a). *Anal. Chem.* **38,** 350R–370R.

McLafferty, F. W. (1966b). "Interpretation of Mass Spectra. An Introduction." Benjamin, New York.

McLafferty, F. W. (1981). *Science* **214,** 280–286.

McMullen, C. C., and Thode, H. G. (1963). *In* "Mass Spectrometry" (C. A. McDowell, ed.), pp. 375–441. McGraw-Hill, New York.

Maeda, K., and Fukuda, A. (1970). *Mass Spectrosc.* (*Jpn.*) **18,** 1097–1148.

Maeda, K., Semeluk, G. P., and Lossing, F. P. (1968). *Int. J. Mass Spectrosc. Ion Phys.* **1,** 395–407 (1968).

Maeda, K., Fukuda, A., and Sakimura, M. (1969). *Mass Spectrosc.* (*Jpn.*) **17,** 530–574.
Major, F. G., and Dehmelt, H. C. (1968). *Phys. Rev.* **170,** 91–107.
Mann, M. M., Hustrulid, A., and Tate, J. T. (1940). *Phys. Rev.* **58,** 340–347.
Marmet, P., and Kerwin, L. (1960). *Can. J. Phys.* **38,** 787–796.
Marr, G. V. (1967). "Photoionization Processes in Gases." Academic Press, New York.
Marshall, A. G., and Comisarow, M. B. (1978). *In* "Transform Techniques in Chemistry" (P. R. Griffiths, ed.), 39–68. Plenum, New York.
Marshall, A. G., Comisarow, M. B., and Parisod, G. (1979). *J. Chem. Phys.* **71,** 4434–4444.
Massey, H. (1976). "Negative Ions." Cambridge Univ. Press, London.
Massey, H. S. W. (1969–1974). "Electronic and Ionic Impact Phenomena," 2nd ed., 5 Vols. Oxford Univ. Press, Oxford.
Mather, R. E., and Todd, J. F. J. (1979). *Int. J. Mass Spectrosc. Ion Phys.* **30,** 1–37.
Mattauch, J., and Herzog, R. (1934). *Z. Phys.* **89,** 786–795.
Mayer, J. E., and Mayer, M. G. (1940). "Statistical Mechanics." Wiley, New York.
Metta, D., Diamond, H., Barnes, R. F., Milsted, J., Gray, J., Jr., Henderson, P. J., and Stevens, C. M. (1965). *J. Inorg. Nucl. Chem.* **27,** 33–39.
Middleditch, B. S., ed. (1979). "Practical Mass Spectrometry: A Contemporary Introduction." Plenum, New York.
Moon, P. B., and Oliphant, M. L. E. (1932). *Proc. R. Soc. London, Ser. A* **137,** 463–480.
Morgan, R. P., Gilchrist, C. A., Jennings, K. R., and Gregor, I. K. (1983). *Int. J. Mass Spectrosc. Ion Phys.* **46,** 309–312.
Morris, A., Jonathan, N., and Dyke, J. (1983). Private communication.
Morrison, J. D. (1957). *J. Appl. Phys.* **28,** 1409–1413.
Müller, E. W. (1951). *Z. Phys.* **131,** 136–142.
Munson, B. (1971). *Anal. Chem.* **43,** A23–A43.
Munson, M. S. B., and Field, F. H. (1966). *J. Amer. Chem. Soc.* **88,** 2621–2630.
Murad, E. (1978). *J. Geophys. Res.* **83,** 5525–5530.
Murad, E. (1982). *J. Chem. Phys.* **77,** 2057–2060.
Murad, E. (1983). *J. Chem. Phys.* **78,** 6611–6613.
Murad, E. (1978). Unpublished results.
Murad, E. (1980). Unpublished results.
Murad, E., and Hildenbrand, D. L. (1975). *J. Chem. Phys.* **63,** 1133–1139.
Murad, E., and Inghram, M. G. (1964). *J. Chem. Phys.* **4,** 3263–3275.
Murad, E., and Swider, W. (1979). *Geophys. Res. Lett.* **6,** 929–932.
Nakanishi, K., and Occolowitz, J. L. (1979). *Proc. R. Soc. London Ser. A* **293,** 3–11.
Narcisi, R. S. (1966). *Ann. Geophys.* **22,** 224–234.
Narcisi, R. S. (1968). *Space Res.* **8,** 360–369.
Narcisi, R. S. (1973). *In* "Physics and Chemistry of Upper Atmospheres" (B. M. McCormac, ed.), pp. 171–183.
Narcisi, R. S., and Bailey, A. D. (1965). *J. Geophys. Res.* **70,** 3687–3700.
Narcisi, R. S., and Roth, W. (1970). *Adv. Electron. Electron Phys.* **29,** 79–113.
Neynaber, R. H. (1969). *Adv. Atom. Mol. Phys.* **5,** 57–108.
Nguyen, M. T., Wronka, J., Starry, S., and Ridge, D. P. (1981). *Int. J. Mass Spectrosc. Ion Phys.* **40,** 195–210.
Nibbering, N. M. N. (1978). *In* "Kinetics of Ion Molecule Reactions" (P. Ausloos, ed.), pp. 165–198. Plenum, New York.
Nier, A. O. (1939). *Phys. Rev.* **55,** 153–163.
Nier, A. O. (1940). *Rev. Sci. Instrum.* **11,** 212–216.
Nier, A. O., Ney, E. P., and Inghram, M. G. (1947). *Rev. Sci. Instrum.* **18,** 294–297.

Nier, A. O., Roberts, T. R., and Franklin, E. G. (1949). *Phys. Rev.* **75,** 346.

Nier, A. O., Hoffman, J. H., Johnson, C. Y., and Holmes, J. C. (1964). *J. Geophys. Res.* **69,** 979–989.

Offermann, D., and von Zahn, U. (1971). *J. Geophys. Res.* **76,** 2520–2522.

Offermann, D., Pelka, K., and von Zahn, U. (1972). *Int. J. Mass Spectrosc. Ion Phys.* **8,** 391–401.

O'Keefe, J. A. (1980). *Geochim. Cosmochim. Acta* **44,** 2151–2152.

O'Nions, R. K., Carter, S. R., Evensen, N. M., and Hamilton, P. J. (1979). *Annu. Rev. Earth Planet. Sci.* **7,** 11–38.

Parks, E. K., Young, C. E., and Wexler, S. (1971). *Rev. Sci. Instrum.* **42,** 1404–1407.

Paul, W., and Raether, M. (1955). *Z. Phys.* **140,** 262–273.

Paul, W., and Steinwedel, H. (1953). *Z. Naturforschong* **8a,** 448–450.

Paul, W., and Raether, M. (1955). *Z. Phys.* **140,** 262–273.

Paul, W., Reinhard, H. P., and von Zahn, U. (1958). *Z. Phys.* **152,** 143–182.

Paulson, J. F. (1972). *In* "Ion–Molecule Reactions" (J. L. Franklin, ed.), pp. 77–100. Plenum, New York.

Pearce, C. G., and Halsall, D. (1978). *Int. J. Mass Spectrosc. Ion Phys.* **27,** 31–41.

Pedley, J. B., and Marshall, E. M. (1983). *J. Phys. Chem. Ref. Data* **12,** 967–1031.

Persky, A., Greene, E. F., and Kuppermann, A. (1968). *J. Chem. Phys.* **49,** 2347–2357.

Plumlee, R. H. (1957). *Rev. Sci. Instrum.* **28,** 830–832.

Poschenrieder, W., and Warneck, P. (1966). *J. Appl. Phys.* **37,** 2812–2820.

Price, W. J. (1964). "Nuclear Radiation Detection," 2nd ed. McGraw-Hill, New York.

Quisenberry, K. S., Scolman, T. T., and Nier, A. O. (1956). *Phys. Rev.* **102,** 1071–1075.

Rafal'son, A. E. (1965). *Sov. Phys.–Tech. Phys.* (*Engl. Transl.*) **10,** 1–9.

Rappaport, P. (1954). *J. Appl. Phys.* **25,** 288–292.

Reid, N. W. (1971). *Int. J. Mass Spectrosc. Ion Phys.* **6,** 1–31.

Reynolds, G. T. (1966). *IEEE Trans. Nucl. Sci.* **NS-13,** 81–87.

Robertson, A. J. B. (1972). *MTP Int. Rev. of Sci.*: *Phys. Chem., Ser. One* **5,** 104–131.

Rol, P. K., and Entemann, E. A. (1968). *J. Chem. Phys.* **49,** 1430–1431.

Röllgen, F. W., Giessmann, U., and Schulten, H-R. (1977). *In* "Advances in Mass Spectrometry" (N. R. Daly, ed.), Vol. 7B, pp. 1419–1424. Heyden, London.

Rosenstock, H., Draxl, K., Steiner, B. W., and Herron, J. T. (1977). *J. Phys. Chem. Ref. Data* **6,** (Suppl. 1).

Rutherford, J. A., and Vroom, D. A. (1976). *J. Chem. Phys.* **65,** 4445–4449.

Ryan, K. R. (1968). *J. Sci. Instrum., Series 2* **1,** 867–868.

Saha, M. N. (1920). *Philos. Mag.* **40,** 472–488.

Saha, M. N. (1921). *Proc. R. Soc. London Ser. A* **99,** 135–153.

Schmidt, K. C. (1969). Technical Application Note 9803, Bendix Corporation, Electro-Optics Division, Ann Arbor, Mich.

Schmitt, H. W., Kiker, W. E., and Williams, C. W. (1965). *Phys. Rev.* **137,** B837–B847.

Schönheit, E. (1957). *Z. Phys.* **149,** 153–179.

Schulten, H.-R. (1979). *Int. J. Mass Spectrosc. Ion Phys.* **32,** 97–283.

Simons, D. S., Colby, B. N., and Evans, C. A., Jr. (1974). *Int. J. Mass Spectrosc. Ion Phys.* **15,** 291–302.

Smith, D., and Adams, N. G. (1979). *In* "Gas Phase Ion Chemistry" (Michael T. Bowers, ed.), Vol. 1, pp. 1–44. Academic Press, New York.

Smith, D., Church, M. J., and Miller, T. M. (1978). *J. Chem. Phys.* **68,** 1224–1229.

Smith, H., Ruedy, J. E., and Morton, G. A. (1966). *IEEE Trans. Nucl. Sci.* pp. 77–80.

Smith, L. G. (1951). *Rev. Sci. Instrum.* **22,** 166–170.

Smyth, W. R., Rambaugh, L. H., and West, S. S. (1934). *Phys. Rev.* **45,** 724–727.

Sommer, A. H. (1958). *J. Appl. Phys.* **29,** 598–599.

Sommer, H., Thomas, H. A., and Hipple, J. A. (1951). *Phys. Rev.* **82,** 697–702.

Spindt, C. A., and Shoulders, K. R. (1965). *Rev. Sci. Instrum.* **36,** 775–779.

Stanton, H. W., Chupka, W. A., and Inghram, M. G. (1956). *Rev. Sci. Instrum.* **27,** 109.

Steiner, B., Giese, C. F., and Inghram, M. G. (1961). *J. Chem. Phys.* **34,** 189–220.

Studniarz, S. A. (1972). *In* "Ion–Molecule Reactions" (J. L. Franklin, ed.), pp. 647–672. Plenum, New York.

Studniarz, S. A., and Franklin, J. L. (1968). *J. Chem. Phys.* **49,** 2652–2659.

Stuke, M. (1982). *Ber. Bunsenges. Phys. Chem.* **86,** 837–841.

Su, T., and Bowers, M. T. (1979). *In* "Gas Phase Ion Chemistry" (Michael T. Bowers, ed.), Vol. 1, pp. 83–118. Academic Press, New York.

Swider, W. (1969). *Planet. Space Sci.* **17,** 1233–1246.

Swider, W. (1984). *Planet. Space Sci.* **32,** 307–312.

Swider, W., Murad, E., and Herrmann, U. (1979). *Geophys. Res. Lett.* **6,** 560–562.

Swingler, D. L. (1978a). *Int. J. Mass Spectrosc. Ion Phys.* **27,** 367–378.

Swingler, D. L. (1978b). *Int. J. Mass Spectrosc. Ion Phys.* **27,** 359–365.

Tal'roze, V. L., and Frankevich, E. L. (1960). *Zhur. Fiz. Khim.* **34,** 2709–2718. [English translation available in Franklin (1979).]

Tal'roze, V. L., and Lyubimova, A. K. (1952). *Dokl. Akad. Nauk SSSR* **86,** 909–912. [English translation available in Franklin (1979).]

Taylor, S. R., and McLennan, S. M. (1979). *Geochim. Cosmochim. Acta* **43,** 1551–1565.

Testerman, M. K., Raible, R. W., Gilliand, B. E., Williams, J. R., and Grimes, G. B. (1965). *J. Appl. Phys.* **36,** 2939–2943.

Thomson, J. J. (1897). *Philos. Mag.* **269,** 293–316.

Thomson, J. J., and Thomson, G. P. (1928). "Conduction of Electricity through Gases," 3rd ed. Cambridge Univ. Press, Cambridge.

Tiernan, T. O. (1975). *In* "Interactions between Ions and Molecules" (P. Ausloos, ed.), pp. 353–385. Plenum, New York.

Todd, J. F. J., and Lawson, G. (1975). *MTP Int. Rev. Sci.: Phys. Chem., Ser. Two* **5**.

Trinks, H., Offermann, D., von Zahn, U., and Steinhauer, C. (1978). *J. Geophys. Res.* **A83,** 2169–2176.

Urey, H. C. (1948). *Science* **108,** 489–496.

Utterback, N. G., Tang, S. P., and Friichtenicht, J. F. (1976). *Phys. Fluids* **19,** 900–905.

Vaille, J. L., and Duong, H. T. (1979). *J. Phys.* **B12,** 1407–1423.

Vand, V. (1965). *Adv. Geophys.* **11,** 1–114.

van Gorkom, M., and Glick, R. E. (1970). *Int. J. Mass Spectrosc. Ion Phys.* **4,** 203–218.

Vasile, M. J., and Smolinsky, G. (1973). *Int. J. Mass Spectrosc. Ion Phys.* **12,** 133–146.

Villarejo, D., Herm, R. R., and Inghram, M. G. (1966). *J. Opt. Soc. Am.* **56,** 1574–1584.

von Engel, A. (1965). "Ionized Gases," 2nd ed. Oxford Univ. Press, Oxford.

von Zahn, U. (1963). *Rev. Sci. Instrum.* **34,** 1–4.

Wachi, F. M., and Gilmartin, D. E. (1972). *High Temp. Sci.* **4,** 423–431.

Walder, R., and Franklin, J. L. (1980). *Int. J. Mass Spectrosc. Ion Phys.* **36,** 85–112.

Whetten, N. R., and Dawson, P. H. (1969). *J. Vac. Sci. Technol.* **6,** 100–103.

White, F. A., Collins, T. L., and Rourke, F. M. (1955). *Phys. Rev.* **97,** 566–567.

Wien, W. (1898). *Ann. Phys. Chem.* **65,** 440–452.

Wiley, W. C., and McLaren, J. H. (1955). *Rev. Sci. Instrum.* **26,** 1150–1157.

Weast, R. C., and Astle, M. J. (Eds.) (1981). "CRC Handbook of Chemistry and Physics," 62nd ed., pp. E79–E80. CRC press, Boca Raton, Florida.

Wobschall, D., Graham, J. R., and Malone, P. D. (1963). *Phys. Rev.* **131,** 1565–1571.

Young, J. R. (1955). *J. Appl. Phys.* **26,** 1302–1306.

Zazula, P. (1968). *Ark. Fys.* **38,** 97–111.

Zbinden, P. A., Hidalgo, M. A., Eberhardt, P., and Geiss, J. (1975). *Planet. Space Sci.* **23,** 1621–1642.

Zhlood'ko, A. D., Lebedinets, V. N., and Shushkova, V. B. (1974). *Space Res.* **14,** 277–281.

Zwier, T. S., Bierbaum, V. M., Ellison, G. B., and Leone, S. R. (1980). *J. Chem. Phys.* **72,** 5426–5436.

Index

A

Aliphatic free radicals, ionization potentials, 238
Allen Π-type electron multiplier, 211, 213
Analytical chemistry, mass spectrometry applications, 218–221
  bovine insulin, 220
  ^{252}Cf fission fragment spectroscopy, 220
  coupling of gas chromatograph and Fourier transform–ion cyclotron resonance, 219–220
  electron impact, 219–221
  forensic and biomedical research, 219
  liquid organic compounds, 221
  MS/MS (mass spectrometer/mass spectrometer) technique, 220
Anisotropically etched gratings, 83–87
  etching followed by removal of SiO_2 strip, 84
  exposure and development of photoresist layer, 84
  groove defects, 87
  orienting surface with respect to (111) planes, 83
  scanning electron micrographs, single-crystal silicon, 85–86
ASTERISK, 40–41, 43
  electric field polarization diagram, 40
Astigmatism, *see* Focal properties, gratings
Atmosphere, composition measurements, 223–225
  ion-molecule reactions, rate constants, 224–225
  neutral atmosphere, 225
  positive ions of D and E layers of ionosphere, 224

B

Bacteriorhodopsin, multiplex coherent anti-Stokes Raman spectra, 31
Beam splitters, plane gratings as, 165–166
Biological molecules, application of coherent anti-Stokes Raman spectroscopy, 58–59
Biomedical research, applications of mass spectrometry, 219
Blaze condition, 74–76
BOXCARS, 34–35, 48, 54–55, 57
  block diagram of experiment, 34
  phase-matching diagram, 33–34
1,3-Butadiene, major ions formed by photon and electron impact, 190

C

Carbon oil contamination, 139
^{252}Cf fission
  fragment spectroscopy, 220
  ion source and mass spectrometer, 192
Chemical ionization, 187–189
  major ions formed, tri-*n*-butylamine, 188
  proton transfer, 188
CO
  predicted coherent anti-Stokes Raman spectra in methane/air atmospheric-pressure flame, 35–36
  square root of coherent anti-Stokes Raman spectroscopy signal in region of CO resonance, 39
Coherent anti-Stokes Raman ellipsometry, 43
  electric field polarization diagram, 37
Coherent anti-Stokes Raman spectroscopy, 1–59
  amplitude of field, 5
  applicability, 25–26, 56–59
    biological molecules, 58–59
    BOXCARS, 57
    diagnostic for molecular jets, 56–57
    profiles of $Q(0)$ through $Q(4)$ lines in fundamental transition of neutral hydrogen, 58
    spectra of hydrogen in plasma, 58
    velocimetry in methane supersonic jet, 57
  background-free techniques, 35–43
    ASTERISK, 40–41, 43
    background cancellation, 41–42

Coherent anti-Stokes Raman spectroscopy (*continued*)
coherent anti-Stokes Raman ellipsometry, 43
double-resonance coherent anti-Stokes Raman spectroscopy, 41
double-resonance spectra of cyclohexane in benzene, 42
electric field polarization diagrams, 37, 40
ellipsometry, 38–40
nonresonant contribution, 38
predicted spectra of CO in methane/air atmospheric-pressure flame, 35–36
pulse-sequenced coherent anti-Stokes spectroscopy, 43
resonant contribution, 38
resonant signal, 38
signal intensity, 41
square root of signal from methane/air flame in region of CO resonance, 39–40
temporal behavior of resonant and nonresonant contributions, 43
combustion diagnostics, 50–53
advantages, 51–52
extension to wider variety of chemical species, 53
hydrogen concentration distribution in horizontal natural gas flame, 51
principal objective, 52
radial temperature profiles, highly sooting, laminar propane diffusion flame, 52
electric-field-induced polarization, 6–10
dielectric susceptibility tensors, 8
electric dipole moment, 7
relation between polarization and induced dipole, 7
energy-level schematic, 4, 6
coherent anti-Stokes Raman spectroscopy resonant, nonresonant and two-photon absorption contributions to $\chi^{(3)}$, 14
experimental apparatus, 26–35
axial and radial spatial resolution using colinear, focused beams, 32–33
block diagrams of experiment, 26
BOXCARS, 33–34, 54–55
gas-phase spatial resolution, 33–34
Gaussian form for beam area, 32
laser systems, 27–28
light-adapted and dark-adapted bacteriorhodopsin, multiplex spectra, 31
multiplex, 29
Nd:YAG laser, 28–29
nitrogen in cylinder of internal combustion engine, multiplex spectra, 30
nitrogen-pumped dye lasers, 28
phase matching, 27, 30–31, 33–34
pulsed laser system, 28
signal power and sample length, 32
spatial overlapping of pump and Stokes beams, 27
spatial resolution in low-density gases, 32
generation of electromagnetic wave, 10–12
high-resolution spectroscopy, 46–50
cross-beam, phase-mismatched geometry with crossed polarizations, 48
limitations, 50
methane in supersonic jet, 47–48
narrowest linewidth tunable laser source, 46
oxygen, 48–49
pulsed coherent anti-Stokes Raman spectroscopy experiments, 48
rotational coherent anti-Stokes Raman spectroscopy, 48, 50
phase-matching diagram, 12
BOXCARS, 33–34
Raman effect, 2–5
energy-level schematic, 3
frequency of emitted photon, 2
frequency shifts, 2–3
inelastic light scattering, 4
Raman response in $\chi^{(3)}$, 12–17
Fourier component of dipole moment, 16
hyperpolarizability component, 13
Raman differential scattering cross section, 17
resonance, 44–46
gas phase, 45
wavelength range of tunable laser sources, 45
selection rules, 18–19
signal intensity, 19–21
anti-Stokes signal power, 20
beam diameter at focus, 20
confocal parameter, 20
signal magnitude, 21
spectral line shape, 21–25
pure hydrogen spectrum at standard temperature and pressure, 24–25

real and imaginary components of resonant third-order dielectric susceptibility, 22
square of third-order dielectric susceptibility, 23–24
symmetry properties of $\chi^{(3)}$, 17–18
equation of motion, 15–16
time-resolved spectroscopy, 53–56
collision-free spectrum of Q branch of oxygen formed in visible photodissociation of ozone, 55–56
detection of molecular photofragments, 56
spectra of ground and excited electronic state of rhodamine 6G and B, 54–55
Combustion, diagnostics, 50–53
desirable features of coherent anti-Stokes Raman spectroscopy, 51–52
extension of coherent anti-Stokes Raman spectroscopy to wider variety of chemical species, 53
hydrogen concentration distribution in horizontal gas flame, 51
objective of coherent anti-Stokes Raman spectroscopy, 52
radial temperature profiles in highly sooting, laminar propane diffusion flame, 52
Continuous-channel electron multiplier, 214–215
Conventional ruled gratings, 72–77
blaze changes across surface of spherical concave grating, 76
blaze condition, 74–76
coating, 72–73
corrected, 82–83
electron micrograph, ruling in gold, 74
properties of surface to be ruled, 72
soft materials suitable for ruling, 73
Cyclohexane, in benzene, double-resonance coherent anti-Stokes Raman spectroscopy, 42

D

DC glow discharge, 144
Detectors, mass spectrometry
electron multipliers, *see* Electron multipliers
photographic plates, 209–210
single collector, 210–211
Diamond chatter, 128
Dielectric susceptibility, 8
third-order, *see* Third-order dielectric susceptibility
Diffraction gratings, 65–146; *see also* Grating mountings
anisotropically etched gratings, 83–87
anomalies, 135–137
angle of incidence at which coupling takes place, 135
coupling of incoming photons with surface plasmon, 135
reradiation of photons, 135–136
blazed reflection grating, 71
classical diffraction, 69
cleaning, 140–144
coating, 144
removal, 145–146
conical diffraction, 69
efficiency, 71
contamination, 137–140
conventional ruled gratings, 72–77
coordinate system, 66, 69–70
efficiency, 102–146
classical and conical diffraction, plane gratings, 115–116
conventional grating, 112–113
holographic grating, 109–112
plane grating, 115–116
plane grating used at blaze, 117
efficiency map
before and after vapor degreasing, 140–141
change from intermetallic diffusion, 144–145
comparisons, 107–108, 111
concave gratings, 116–117
first order of concave, tripartite, conventional spherical grating, 105–106
large spherical holographic grating with sinusoidal groove profiles, 108–109
second order of concave, monopartite, conventional grating, 104
spherical, concave, monopartite, conventional grating, 117–119
used and unused gratings, 139–140
zeroth and first orders, concave, tripartite, conventional spherical grating, 106
electron-beam lithography, 91
focal properties, *see* Focal properties, gratings

Diffraction gratings (*continued*)
focused stray light, 123–135
accidental error of position, 124, 127
accidental variation of groove form, 124
baffles in monochromator to shadow bad spots, 130–131
comparison of gratings, 133–134
conventional grating illuminated by xenon laser, 125–126
curvature and nonparallelism of grooves, 124
deposition rates for gold, 128–130
diamond chatter, 128
effect on measurement of reflectance, 134
error of run, 124
factors affecting rulability of vacuum-deposited metal, 128
globule of gold ejected from melt during evaporation, 130
grating in conical diffraction, 126–127
local error of position caused by smearing of globule of gold, 129
measurement between orders of grating, 131– 132
nonruled areas of grating caused by voids in coating, 130–131
periodic errors of spacing, 124
pinhole photograph showing interior of spectrograph and light scattered from structural members, 123
from two gratings, 124–125
free spectral range, 71
grating convention, 66–67
grating equation, 65–67
groove profile, 71
holographic gratings, 77–82
laminar gratings, 87–88
manufactured methods, 71–91
groove profile, 71
measurement, 102–122
angles of incidence and diffraction, 103
classical mount, angle of incidence, 116
effect of different groove profiles, 113–114
electron micrograph shadow of groove profile, conventional grating, 120
groove profile, blazed holographic grating, 121–122
interference microscope, 117, 120
reflectance of mirror coated with Al + MgF_2, 114–115
replica, 120
scanning technique, 102–103
Seya–Namioka scanning monochromator, 114–115
Talystep machine, 121
target pattern, 107
multipartite gratings, 77
rate of change of wavelength, 67–68
replica gratings, 88–89
resolving power formula, 68
transmission gratings, 89–90
Dioxin, contamination of blood, 219
Discharge ion source, 193–194
Dispersion
crossed, 161–165
echelle spectrograph, 162
iron arc spectrum, 163–164
qualitative illustration, 161
zero and double, 157–158
Double-focusing mass spectrometers, 199–200
3-D quad mass filters, 203–204

E

Electric dipole moment, 7
Fourier component, 16
Electromagnetic wave, generation, 10–12
Electron-beam lithography, 91
Electronic state, coherent anti-Stokes Raman spectra, 54–55
Electron impact, 184–186
analytical chemistry, 219
disadvantage, 186
major ions formed
1,3-butadiene, 190
5-methyl-3-hexanone, 220–221
tri-*n*-butylamine, 188
number of ions detected, 185
Richardson equation, 184
space charge effects, 185
Electron multipliers, 211–216
Allen Π-type, 211, 213
continuous-channel, 214–215
magnetic strip, 212, 214

scintillation detector, 215
transmission dynode, 215
venetian blind, 212–213
Electrostatic analyzer, 127°, 236–237
Ellipsoidal grating, 96
Engine, internal combustion, multiplex coherent anti-Stokes Raman spectra of nitrogen, 30

F

Fast atom bombardment, 223
Field ionization, 190–191
Flowing afterglow technique, 233–234
Focal properties, gratings, 91–102
aberration reduction, 98–99
anamorphic property of plane gratings, 100
astigmatism reduction, 93–94
concave holographic gratings, 98–100
cylindrical gratings with circular grooves, 96–97
defocusing caused by change in dispersion, 101
ellipsoidal grating, 96
focal curve of type III spherical holographic grating, 99
focusing condition, 92
formula for optimum width, 93
horizontal focal condition, 96
horizontal foci equation, 94
length of slit image, 93
light path, 91
plane gratings, 100–102
point source
astigmatic line length, 96
locations, 99–100
Rowland circle, 93
secondary focal curves, 97–98
secondary foci equation, 94
stigmatic image conditions, 96–97
toroid, 94–95
grating, soft x-ray region, 95–96
type III gratings, 99–100
uncorrected concave gratings, 92–98
vertical focal condition, 96
Forensic research, applications of mass spectrometry, 219
Fourier transform–ion cyclotron resonance, 209
analytical chemistry, 219
coupled with gas chromatography, 219–220

G

Gas chromatography, coupled with Fourier transform–ion cyclotron resonance, 219–220
Gases, low-density, coherent anti-Stokes Raman spectroscopy with high spatial resolution, 32
Glenn mass spectrometer, 205
Gold
conventional ruling, 74
deposition rates, 128–130
Grating mountings, 146–175; *see also* Diffraction gratings
concave, 166–174
dual grating mountings, 172–174
on-blaze monochromator using cylindrical grating with nonuniformly spaced grooves, 170–171
on-blaze mountings, 167–172
on-blaze Rowland-circle-mounting monochromator, 168–170
on-blaze spectrograph using spherical concave grating, 167–168
stigmatic, coma-free scanning spectrometer, 173–174
symmetric tandem Wadsworth mounting, 172
wavelength limits for grazing incidence on-blaze monochromator, 171
zero-dispersion broadband spectroheliograph, 173
plane, 148–166
advantages of on-blaze monochromators, 149–150
as beam splitters, 165–166
change-coupled device arrays, 164
comparison of conventional reflecting echelle spectrograph and one for use at grazing incidence, 164–165
conversion of conventional monochromators to on-blaze operation, 149

Grating mountings (*continued*)
crossed dispersion, 161–165
dual grating mountings, 157–161
echelle spectrograph of Tousey *et al.*, 162
Finkelstein monochromator, 151–152
flux through monochromator, 160
grazing incidence echelle, 156
Greig and Ferguson monochromator, 150
Hettrick and Bowyer mounting, 153–154
Hunter *et al.* double-grating monochromator, 158
interferometer using grating as beam splitter, 166
iron arc spectrum, 163–164
mirror coatings, 159–161
Monk–Gillieson mounting, 152–153
monochromator for use with SR, 152
monoparallel radiation, 152–157
nonuniform groove spacing, equation of variance, 153
on-blaze mounting, 148–152
parallel radiation, 148
qualitative illustration of crossed dispersion, 161
radial grating approximation to Hettrick and Bowyer, 155–156
secondary electron conduction vidicons, 164
transmittance and higher order suppression for double-grating monochromator, 159
Werner and Visser monochromator, 150–151
zero and double dispersion, 157–158
SKYLAB solar instruments, 147
solar spectroscopy, 147
stellar spectrographs, 147
synchrotron radiation, disadvantages, 146
transmission, 174–175

H

Holographic gratings, 77–82
advantages, 81
asymmetric groove profiles, 79–81
blazed, groove profile, 121–122
collimated recombining light beams, 77
concave, 98–100
aberration reduction, 99
focal curve, type III spherical, 99–100
point source locations, 99–100
Fourier synthesis, asymmetric groove profiles, 80–81
groove spacing formula, 77
Littrow blaze wavelength, 79
modified Sheridon technique, 80–81
orientation of interference field and substrate, 77–78
photoresist, 78–79
problems, 82
Rowland circle, 80
Sheridon technique, 79–80
symmetrical groove profile, 79
Hydrogen
coherent anti-Stokes Raman spectrum at standard temperature and pressure, 24–25
concentration distribution in horizontal gas flame, 51
in plasma, coherent anti-Stokes Raman spectra, 58
Q(0) through Q(4) profiles in fundamental transition, 58

I

Insulin, bovine, mass spectrometry, 220
Interference microscope, 117, 120
Ion cyclotron resonance, 206–209
advantages, 209
Fourier transform, *see* Fourier transform–ion cyclotron resonance
ion–molecule reactions, 235
movement scalar equations, 208
problems, 206
proton affinities, 239
pulsing of beams and measuring ions, 208
RF absorption, 216
thermodynamic equilibrium measurement, 238
Ionization
dissociative, threshold, 236
molecule cross section, 237

potentials, 237–238
aliphatic free radicals, 238
Ion microprobe mass spectrometer, 222
Ion-molecule reactions, 230–236
flowing afterglow technique, 233–234
ion cyclotron resonance techniques, 235
photoionization, 232
rate constants, 224–225
rate equations, 231
selected ion flow tube, 234–235
single-source technique, 232
tandem mass spectrometer, 232–233
Ion sources, mass spectrometry, 183–197
^{252}Cf fission ion source and mass spectrometer, 192
chemical ionization, 187–189
major ions formed, tri-*n*-butylamine, 188
discharges, 193–194
electron impact, 184–186, 188, 190
field ionization, 190–191
ion lens, 194
Langmuir–Saha equation, 186
laser desorption, 195–196
negative ions, 196–197
number of ions detected, 185
photon impact, 189–190
proton transfer, 188
radioactive sources, 191–193
Richardson equation, 184
space charge effects, 185
spark sources, 195
surface ionization, 186–187
Isotope, analysis, geochemistry and separation, 216–218
age determination of rocks, 217
radioactive decay, 217
tektite composition, 217

J

Jet
methane supersonic, coherent anti-Stokes Raman spectroscopy velocimetry, 57
molecular, diagnostics, 56–57
supersonic, high-resolution coherent anti-Stokes Raman spectra of methane, 47–48

L

Lamellar gratings, 87–88
Laminar gratings, 87–88
Langmuir–Saha equation, 187
Laser
coherent anti-Stokes Raman spectroscopy systems, 27–28
desorption, 195–196
limitation on wavelength range, 45
narrowest linewidth tunable sources, 46
Nd:YAG, 28–29
nitrogen-pumped dye, 28
pulsed coherent anti-Stokes Raman spectroscopy system, 28
Lithography, electron-beam, 91
Littrow blaze wavelength, 79

M

Magnetic analyzers, 197–199
equation of motion, 197
force in magnetic field, 198
resolving power of instrument, 199
60° sector field mass spectrometer, 198
Magnetic strip electron multiplier, 212, 214
Mass spectrometry, 181–240
applications
analysis of solids, 221–223
analytical chemistry, 218–221
composition measurements in atmosphere, 223–225
high-temperature mass spectrometry and thermochemistry, 226–230
ionization potentials and ion thermochemistry, 236–239
ion-molecule reactions, 230–236
isotope analysis, geochemistry, and isotope separation, 216–218
detectors
electron multipliers, *see* Electron multipliers
photographic plates, 209–210
rf absorption in ion cyclotron resonance, 216
single collector, 210–211

Mass spectrometry (*continued*)
3-D mass filter, 203–204
double-focusing mass spectrometers, 199–200
flowing afterglow technique, 233–234
high-temperature, 226–230
failure to establish thermodynamic equilibrium, 228–229
isomolecular equilibrium, 228–229
presence of impurities in sample, 229
history, 182–183
ion cyclotron resonance, 206–209
ion microprobe mass spectrometer, 222
ion sources, *see* Ion sources, mass spectrometry
magnetic analyzers, 197–199
monopole mass filter, 202–203
MS/MS (mass spectrometer/mass spectrometer) techniques, 220
quadrupole mass filter, 200–202
tandem, 232–233
time-of-flight mass analyzers, 204–206
Metals
interdiffusion of layers, 144–145
soft materials suitable for grating ruling, 73
Methane, high-resolution coherent anti-Stokes Raman spectra, 47–48
5-Methyl-3-hexanone, ionization by electron impact, 220–221
Mirror
coatings, 159–161
reflectance, coated with Al + MgF_2, 114–115
Monochromator, *see also* Diffraction gratings; Grating mounting
conventional, conversion to on-blaze operation, 149
double-grating
Hunter *et al.*, 158, 160
transmittance and higher order suppression, 159
Finkelstein, 151–152
flux through, 160
Greig and Ferguson, 150
on-blaze
advantage, 149–150
Rowland-circle-mounting, 168–170
using cylindrical grating, 170–171
wavelength limits, 171
for use with synchrotron radiation, 152
Werner and Visser, 150–151
Monopole mass filters, 202–203
equations of motion, 203
Multipartite gratings, 77

N

Negative ions, sources, 196–197
Nitrogen
multiplex coherent anti-Stokes Raman spectroscopy spectra within cylinder of firing internal combustion engine, 30
rotational coherent anti-Stokes Raman spectrum at standard temperature and pressure, 50

O

Organic compounds, liquid, analysis by mass spectrometry, 221
Oxygen
high-resolution coherent anti-Stokes Raman spectrum, 48–49
Q branch, collision-free coherent anti-Stokes Raman spectrum, 55–56

P

Particulate matter, removal, 143
Photoelectron spectroscopy, 238
Photofragments, detection, 56
Photographic plates, 209–210
Photoionization, 189–190
Photon impact, 189–190
major ions formed, 1,3-butadience, 190
Photoresist, 78
exposure and development, 84
properties, 79
Polarization
electric field diagram
ASTERISK, 40
coherent anti-Stokes ellipsometry, 37

electric-field-induced, 6–10
dielectric susceptibility tensors, 8
electric dipole moment, 7
relation between polarization and induced dipole, 7
nonresonant and resonant contributions, 38
transferse electric, 117
Propane, laminar diffusion flame, radial temperature profiles, 52
Pulsed-sequence coherent anti-Stokes Raman spectroscopy, 43, 48
PUSCARS, *see* Pulsed-sequence coherent anti-Stokes Raman spectroscopy

Q

Quadrupole mass filters, 200–202
advantages and disadvantages, 204
3D, 203, 204
equations of motion, 201
stability diagram, 202

R

Radioactive decay, 217
Radioactive ion sources, 191–193
Raman differential scattering cross section, 17
Raman resonance, third-order dielectric susceptibility, *see* Third-order dielectric susceptibility, Raman resonance
Reflectance, mirror coated with Al + MgF_2, 114–115
Replica gratings, 88–89, 120
RF absorption, ion cyclotron resonance, 216
Rhodamine B and 6G, coherent anti-Stokes Raman spectra of ground and excited electronic states, 54–55
Richardson equation, 184
Rocks, age determination, 217
Rowland circle, 80
concave grating mountings, 167
on-blaze, 170
on-blaze monochromator, 168–170
point source, 93

S

Scintillation detector, 215
Secondary ion mass spectrometry, 222–223
Selected ion flow tube, 234–235
Seya–Namioka scanning monochromator, 114–115
Sheridon technique, blazed holographic plane gratings, 79–80
modified, 80–81
SIFT, *see* Selected ion flow tube
Silicon, single-crystal, grating etched in, 85–86
SIMS, *see* Secondary ion mass spectrometry
Single collector, 210–211
Single-source mass spectrometry, ion-molecule reactions, 232
SiO_2, removal following anisotropic etching, 84
SKYLAB, solar instruments, 147
Solar spectroscopy, 147
Solids, analysis by mass spectrometry, 221–223
Spark source, 195
analysis of solids, 221
disadvantages, 221
Spectrograph
echelle, 162
change-coupled device arrays, 165
comparison of conventional and one for use at grazing incidence, 164–165
secondary electron conduction vidicons, 164
Hettrick and Bowyer, 153–154
corrected grating, 154
radial grating approximation, 155–156
Monk–Gillieson, 152–153
on-blaze, 167–168
stellar, 147
symmetric tandem Wadsworth mounting, 172
Spectroheliograph, zero-dispersion, 173
Spectrometer, stigmatic, coma-free scanning, 173–174
Spectroscope, grazing incidence echelle, Hettrick and Bowyer, 156
Stellar spectrographs, 147
Surface ionization, 186–187
Synchrotron radiation, 152
disadvantages, 146

T

Talystep machine, 121
Tektite, composition, 217
Thermochemistry, 226–230
  calculating heat of reaction, 227
  endothermic ion-neutral reactions, 239
  equilibrium constant, 227–228
  ion, 236–239
  isomolecular equilibrium, 228–229
  presence of impurities in sample, 229
  thermodynamic equilibrium measurement, 238
  thermodynamics laws, 226–227
Third-order dielectric susceptibility
  Raman resonance, 12–17
  coherent anti-Stokes Raman spectroscopy and two-photon absorption resonant and nonresonant contributions, 14
    equation of motion in presence of driving electric field, 15–16
    Fourier component of dipole moment, 16
    hyperpolarizability components, 13
    molecular hyperpolarizability, 15
    Raman differential scattering cross section, 17
  spectral line shape, 21–25
    coherent anti-Stokes Raman spectrum, hydrogen at standard temperature and pressure, 24–25
    real and imaginary components, 22
    squared, region of Raman resonance, 23–24
  symmetry properties, 17–18
Time-of-flight mass analyzers, 204–206
Toroidal grating, 95–96
Transmission dynode multiplier, 215
Transmission gratings, 89–90, 174–175
Tri-*n*-butylamine, major ions formed by chemical ionization and electron impact, 188
Trichlorotrifluoroethane, vapor degreasing, 140, 142

V

Vacuum ultraviolet radiation, 63–65; *see also* Diffraction gratings; Grating mountings
Vapor degreasing, 140–142
Venetian blind electron multiplier, 212–213